Local Area Networking With Microcomputers

A Guide for the Business Decision-Maker

Local Area Networking with Microcomputers

A Guide for the Business Decision-Maker

Stevanne Ruth Lehrman

A Brady Book
Published by Prentice Hall Press
New York, New York 10023

A Brady Book
Published by Prentice Hall Press
A Division of Simon & Schuster, Inc.
Gulf + Western Building
One Gulf + Western Plaza
New York, New York 10023

PRENTICE HALL PRESS is a trademark of Simon & Schuster, Inc.

Manufactured in the United States of America

2   3   4   5   6   7   8   9   10

Lehrman, Stevanne.
    Local area networking with microcomputers.

    "A Brady book."
    Includes index.
    1. Business—Data processing.   2. Microcomputers.
3. Local area networks (Computer networks)
4. Computer networks.   I. Title.
HF5548.2.L392   1986   650'.028'5468   86-91466
ISBN 0-89303-640-4

To William

who has been my mentor
in all things pertaining to computers.

Contents

Illustrations

Local Area Networking with Microcomputers

A Guide for the Business Decision-Maker

Foreword

Local area networks (LANs) were created by the combination of computers and communications. The term refers to the total communications system that links computers, word processors, printers, and other equipment.

Local Area Networking with Microcomputers addresses some of the many human and technical issues involved in selecting and implementing a local area network. Its aim is to provide business managers and corporate decision-makers with the vocabulary and basic principles of local area networking systems.

Anyone wishing a fundamental knowledge of local area networking will find this book useful:

- business and computer managers who are involved in the application of LANs in their work environment

- information management personnel who are not knowledgeable about LANs

- decision-makers who need to keep up with the latest technology

- students seeking background information

The text focuses on helping the reader to determine needs, ask appropriate questions, and evaluate proposals. Readers will gain sufficient understanding of the subject to work successfully with a consultant or vendor to select a local area network for their site.

Basic familiarity with microcomputer use and with business practices is assumed. Prior technical knowledge, while helpful, is not required. No background in engineering, programming, or mathematics is needed to understand the material.

Although focused on microcomputer LANs, the information given is, with some extension, applicable to minicomputer and mainframe networks.

Conceptually, the book can be divided into three sections:

Part I serves as background to the book as a whole, introducing local area networks and their benefits. It includes a working data communications vocabulary.

Part II examines the components of a local area network, individually and in relationship to each other. Chapters cover workstations, topology, architecture, local area network protocols, and standards.

Part III looks at management issues: managing the network, security and privacy, user concerns. It also contains worksheets and guidelines for assessing your requirements and for evaluating current local area network products.

Appendices contain a glossary; a list of microcomputer local area network vendors; and blank copies of the worksheets.

Part I

1

Introduction

More than any previous society, we are living in a culture driven by information, an age in which the possession, interpretation, and dissemination of information has become critical. Every aspect of our lives has become dependent on a constant flow of information.

We wake to the news, delay showering until we've heard the morning weather forecast. We eat breakfast hidden behind a newspaper, ingesting, along with our orange juice, our daily dose of major and minor events from the farthest corners of the globe. As we drive to work, we switch from one radio station to another, seeking the latest traffic announcements identifying today's congestion and road repairs.

At work we greet colleagues with "What's new?" and spend ten or fifteen minutes discussing the latest projects before we begin the weekly department meeting; telephone a client or customer; or tackle the pile of papers on our desk.

And more than likely, those papers contain raw information: statistics, market research, financial records. Our daily work activities involve collecting, organizing, and reorganizing this information. The end product is even more information in the form of reports, books, charts, and the like that is distributed actively and/or recorded for future access. Down the hall or on the next block, someone is waiting to read or hear that information. (See Figure 1.1.)

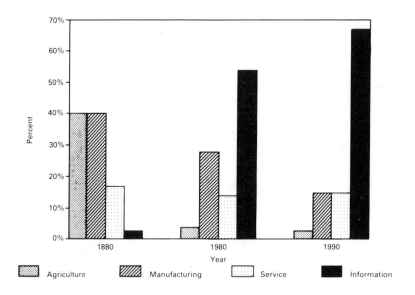

Figure 1.1 Profile of a Changing Work Force

The amount of information each one of us is exposed to is enormous and increasing daily: two years ago we needed to be aware of only a handful of data, this year the load is half again as large. (See Sidebar 1.1.)

Simply by being exposed to the daily deluge of information, we are forced to react to it. How we deal with too much information arriving too rapidly to be adequately understood or evaluated can shape our individual and/or corporate success or failure. Ignoring the problem only guarantees that when the inevitable disaster happens, you won't see what hit you.

Defining the Issues

Although organizations are increasingly aware of the necessity of managing information, (as evidenced by the multiplication of computers, microcomputers, information services, and endless articles about information centers), we have not yet learned to deal efficiently with the sheer

The Information Explosion

• A Sunday edition of *The New York Times* contains more news than an average 18th century person read or heard in a lifetime.

• Today's high school students know more biology than most doctors did at the turn of the century; know more geography than Columbus did; have read more books than Shakespeare.

• In 1983, 37,000 books were published in the United States. More than 3,000 of them were on computers.

• More than 85 percent of all the information ever put in printed form has been generated since 1950.

• Kodak Corporation claimed, in a recent study, that there are 21 trillion pages of information stored in files, desk drawers, and archives. The amount of information available for reference, but not in active use, is growing at a rate of 20 percent per year.

Sidebar 1.1 The Information Explosion

volume of data and with the rapidly decreasing time between when information is presented and when we must act on it. Few organizations can guarantee that information is available when needed. As a result, too many vital business decisions are based on incomplete, incorrect, or outdated information.

When we add computers into the situation, the problem becomes more complex:

• How do you manage the information stored in the microcomputer? How do you get the right data to the right people at the right time and in the right form?

How do you keep track of the programs in use and insure that the data is current and that everyone using the "same" data actually is?

- How do you manage access? Frequently, microcomputer use is seen as desirable, even if unnecessary. Many machines become status symbols, not productive tools. Concurrently, workers with real microcomputer needs may not have access to one. How do you insure that users have access to the resources they really need, not simply the ones that they think they need? Perhaps most difficult of all, how do you identify and restrict the people who should not have access to the system?

- How do you accommodate the effects? Microcomputers do change the way people work, as well as the way jobs are defined. Rarely are these changes fully considered beforehand. The effect of a microcomputer on the individual and on the whole organization tends to be ignored.

- How do you control costs? Microcomputer hardware costs are relatively easily defined and therefore budgeted. But software and training, which can more than double the cost of the system, are often not counted in the costs.

- How do you control acquisition? In an environment with multiple, scattered resources, automation anarchy can, and usually does, flourish. Proliferation of equipment begets further proliferation. Users find ways to disguise the purchase of computers and to develop systems on their own, neatly sidestepping control by the central data processing department.

- Who manages the microcomputers as they rapidly proliferate? Very often, managers assigned to deal with microcomputer issues have had little or no formal computer experience. Yet these managers are expected to oversee the spread of microcomputers throughout their department. To say the least, systems so developed tend to be inefficient.

You shouldn't be surprised. When you employ a new, rapidly changing technology to manage a scarcely understood resource—information—without instituting corresponding controls, the result is bound to be catastrophic.

Looking to the Local Area Network for a Solution

One proposed solution to the problem of information and microcomputer chaos is the local area network (LAN), a communications system which permits the interconnection of computers. (Chapter 2 supplies a more detailed definition of a LAN and its benefits.)

Microcomputer-based local area networks *do* have the potential to serve as constructive catalysts in the merger of computers, information, and communications. But before you can make an informed decision about the utility of a LAN in your specific organization, you need to know the issues involved.

Before we begin, it should be understood that selection and installation of a network is a complex process. Networks do not consist only of technology such as workstations, interface boards, cables, network software, operating systems, and applications programs.

Most important are the *people* who use the network. Each installed network attempts to solve a specific problem, and that problem focuses on people, not technology. No matter how promising the technology, no matter how many devices you acquire, if you do not consider the needs of the people who will use the network, you have not solved your problem.

This book addresses both the technical and human issues involved in selecting and implementing a local area network. None of these issues can be decided in isolation because all the factors interrelate. In the subsequent pages this book will help you to do the following:

• Understand the technology of local area networking.

• Evaluate your current situation:

— What equipment do you have?

— What information do you use?

— Who uses it?

• Identify what software you use to help process this information.

• Define your technical and user requirements:

— What information services should be provided?

— Which groups will these services be provided to?

— What resources will be used to provide those services?

• Determine where and when those resources will be located.

• Set your priorities.

• Evaluate existing products.

• Evaluate existing alternatives.

Installation of a local area network will impact the whole organization, not just the bottom line. By the very nature of the technology, the way jobs are done will be altered; the corporate culture will be changed. Given the complexity of information usage in even the smallest organization, and the rapidly changing technology, the decision whether or not to purchase a network, and if so, which one, can be made only after careful consideration of the management and user issues involved. Putting all the pieces together without any planning or organization might have some chance of success, but not much. Devoting an appropriate amount of your time, energy, and thought to planning before you purchase the first piece of equipment, will pay large dividends later in trouble-free, productive operation by both people and machinery.

2

Introducing Local Area Networks

A *local area network* (LAN) is a communications network designed to facilitate the interconnection of a variety of computer-based equipment within a small area. It includes both the hardware and the software connected by the network. (See Figure 2.1.)

Figure 2.1 LAN

A LAN is characterized by the following:

- A common communication medium over which all user devices can share information, programs, and equipment without regard to the physical location of the user or the resource.

- A high transmission rate intended to accommodate the needs of both people and equipment. The system normally is able to support transmission between workstations at the maximum speed at which the workstations can communicate.

- A limited geographic range: generally defined as less than 10 miles or 16 kilometers. LANs stand between two traditional computer networks: the very limited distance computer bus and the global distance of the long-haul telephone network. (See Figure 2.2.)

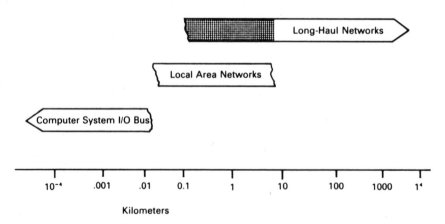

Shaded areas indicate overlap between traditional long-haul networks and emerging local networks.

Figure 2.2 Geographic Range of Communications Networks

- A low error rate. An unreliable system, that is, one which distorts or corrupts the data it conveys, is worthless. A built-in method of detecting and compensating for system errors is implied.

• User-administrated private ownership, not subject to regulation by the Federal Communications Commission. Connections over common carrier (telephone) facilities, public cable television, and public local networks generally are not considered LANs.

Who Uses the Network?

Far more than any other ability, a well-designed LAN focuses on supplying services to users. These services are defined by a person's place in the organization; the tasks performed; and the information and communication needs. As users gain experience, they tend to use the network in more complex ways. The network becomes the system as users cease to distinguish between the desktop microcomputer and the services provided by the network.

Users have many ideas about the ideal network. Above all, they demand an extremely friendly, people-oriented interface with a short learning curve so that they can get to work quickly and easily. They expect easy access to information and rapid response to their requests. They expect the system to include all the equipment they need to get their job done. This equipment includes a high capacity hard disk to meet high storage demands and specialized hardware such as plotters, laser printers, letter-quality and dot-matrix printers.

Direct communications with co-workers will have priority, replacing the telephone. Users will expect electronic mail (a computerized version of the post office) or "voice mail" (delayed delivery of a spoken message) facilities.

In short, as an information management tool, the LAN is valuable to every knowledge worker in business, science, education, government, and industry. From the corporate and managerial view, the lower equipment costs of sharing resources is the leading benefit, followed closely by increased productivity, increasing levels of communications, and more proficient management control.

Resource Sharing

By providing a facility through which a wide variety of computer equipment can be shared by many people, the local area network presents a cost-effective solution. Rarely will each person in an organization require full-time use of a hard disk or letter-quality printer. Yet everyone will need occasional access to such equipment. With a LAN, one letter-quality printer might serve five or six users. As Figure 2.3 shows, the shared resources need not be just hardware. Software and information also may be shared.

As a resource sharing tool, a LAN can:

• Permit sharing expensive hardware.

• Facilitate sharing complex programs and the information that they generate and manage.

• Aid in the integration of all aspects of information processing, particularly by transforming a group of individual, not very powerful microcomputers into a powerful distributed processing system.

Productivity

An organization has three resources: people, equipment, and information. Productivity depends on insuring that the people have timely access to the equipment and information required to perform their job. Workers are not demanding more access to computers and intelligent machines just on a whim. They know how much more productive they can be (and how much easier their job is) when they have the right tools. And increased productivity of workers translates directly into profits.

As a productivity tool, a LAN can:

• Enable wider distribution of information and the technologies needed to deal with it.

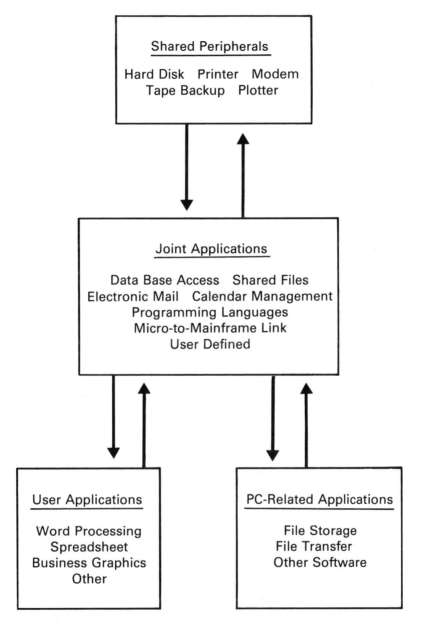

Shared Peripherals

Hard Disk   Printer   Modem
Tape Backup   Plotter

Joint Applications

Data Base Access   Shared Files
Electronic Mail   Calendar Management
Programming Languages
Micro-to-Mainframe Link
User Defined

User Applications

Word Processing
Spreadsheet
Business Graphics
Other

PC-Related Applications

File Storage
File Transfer
Other Software

Figure 2.3 Shared Network Resources

- Improve information retrieval, processing, storage, and dissemination through a distributed database. The sooner the user has the needed information, the sooner the job can be done.

- Minimize or even possibly eliminate redundant and repetitive tasks.

- Improve efficiency by facilitating the unification of systems and procedures.

- Provide graphic capabilities and other specialized applications that are not cost-effective on stand-alone micros.

Communications

Communications, with or without a computer network, is of major importance to an organization. Workers constantly need information to write orders, type letters and memos, discuss projects, listen to the latest developments, or give sales talks. The services provided by a local area network are designed to expedite this communication among workers.

As a communications resource, a LAN can:

- Facilitate communications within the organization by supplying an additional channel for coordinating the work of various groups, exchanging data, sending messages, and sharing information. In the long run, the benefits gained through the enhancement of person-to-person communication may outweigh all the technical and economic benefits of networking.

- Provide in-house, computer-to-computer communication at high speed without the complex masses of cable required in a system of directly connected machines.

- Supply a method of accessing remote resources, thereby facilitating communications with the world outside the immediate organization.

Management

The classic management problem is how to accommodate the changing needs of the organization and its people. (See Figure 2.4.) To do so, management requires appropriate tools. A well-designed network can evolve gradually as the work load grows, rather than requiring major replacements or upgrades. Equipment can be added, relocated, or removed as needed. The investment in equipment can become a variable cost.

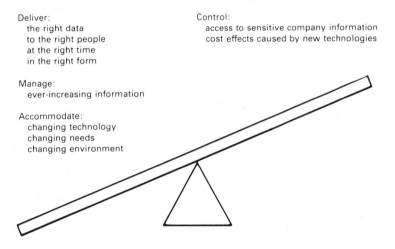

Deliver:
  the right data
  to the right people
  at the right time
  in the right form

Control:
  access to sensitive company information
  cost effects caused by new technologies

Manage:
  ever-increasing information

Accommodate:
  changing technology
  changing needs
  changing environment

Figure 2.4: The Challenge to Management

As a management tool, the LAN can:

• Increase system performance through the distribution of tasks and equipment.

• Improve the availability of computer resources. Tasks can be assigned to several machines. If one is occupied with a different task, the second can perform the work.

• Increase system reliability. Crucial processes can be duplicated and/or divided so that, on the failure of one machine, other machines can quickly take up the load.

- Minimize the adverse effects of loss of any one system.

- Help regain administrative control of equipment, especially the large number of microcomputers that have appeared on desks, but whose purchase never was officially known or approved.

Sample LANs

World Collectors is a mail order house. When they began to consider the need to improve order fulfillment and inventory control, they had two minicomputers, one for accounting and the second for inventory control. They had eight microcomputers in the order department, and four more in other departments, all of which were using the same basic information. Orders were filed in several locations: shipping, marketing, and accounting. A weekly management report consisting of purchases and orders was issued.

Consultants recommended that World install two separate networks. The first LAN would connect the microcomputers to provide an expanded database for shipping and inventory. This LAN was installed first.

A year later, the second network, linking the minicomputers, was installed. Executive workstations were introduced in the corporate offices. When both systems were working well, a bridge between the two was installed.

Mountain Associates is a progressive consulting firm. When microcomputers became popular, Mountain quickly adopted them. Two years later, there were microcomputers in every department, and managerial control of purchases was virtually nonexistent. Information management was becoming increasingly difficult.

After careful study of information usage, management installed an Ethernet-type network in several departments, specifically those with the largest number of microcomputers and the greatest need for shared information. Individual programs were replaced by networked versions on the departmental servers. An electronic mail facility was included to improve in-house communications.

Microcomputer purchases are now under control, as only micros ordered through MIS can be connected to the LAN. The newest applications packages are available only through the network, as are the letter-quality printers.

Several growth paths were designed into the original network. Connections were installed for approximately double the current number of microcomputers. Cabling was provided for eventually linking all departments into the system. Because most traffic is within a department, the current single network may be divided into several smaller networks at a later date.

3

Data Communications Vocabulary

Data refers to the raw numbers or text used by a computer. *Information* is data converted into human-usable form. A *message* is a specific piece of information.

In computerese, the smallest unit of information is the binary digit, or *bit*. The information it contains is stored and processed as electrical signals, represented by ones (1) and zeros (0). (See Figure 3.1.)

Zeros and ones convey information only when collected into longer units—*bytes*. Each byte represents one character, as represented by a group of binary digits. When we group bits into bytes, we begin the process of converting them into human-readable data.

Bits

10101110

Bits assembled into a byte

Figure 3.1 Bits and Bytes of Digital Data

The meaning of the bits and bytes is determined by how the data is coded within the computer for the computer's own use and by how the data is transmitted.

Many different codes have been developed for use in data processing. The American Standard Code for Information Interchange (ASCII) character set is the most widely used coding convention for all computers, used both for internal computer data manipulation and for communications with other devices. ASCII is employed by almost all American hardware manufacturers and by many foreign hardware manufacturers as well.

ASCII is a seven-bit code; that is, it uses seven bits to define each character. As the number of bits per character determines the maximum number of characters in the code, the basic ASCII code can represent 128 characters, covering upper- and lower-case letters, numbers, punctuation marks, and special characters known as *control characters*. Figure 3.2 lists the complete ASCII character set.

Control characters are used to give instructions. The control characters may precede, accompany, or follow a block of information. Most control characters are nonprinting: they trigger an action rather than producing a readable letter or number. Control characters may affect the following activities:

• Processes occurring within a document, such as a tab or sounding a bell.

• Processes to be performed by another device, for example, a form feed on a printer.

• Communications, such as to indicate the start and stop of a message or to acknowledge receipt of data.

ASCII Character Set

ASCII Value	Character	Translation	ASCII Value	Character	ASCII Value	Character
000	NUL	(null)	046	.	092	\
001	SOH	(start of header)	047	/	093	]
002	STX	(start of text)	048	0	094	^
003	ETX	(end of text)	049	1	095	
004	EOT	(end of transmission)	050	2	096	'
005	ENQ	(enquiry)	051	3	097	a
006	ACK	(acknowledge)	052	4	098	b
007	BEL	(bell)	053	5	099	c
008	BS	(backspace)	054	6	100	d
009	HT	(horizontal tab)	055	7	101	e
010	LF	(line feed)	056	8	102	f
011	VT	(vertical tab)	057	9	103	g
012	FF	(form feed)	058	:	104	h
013	CR	(carriage return)	059	;	105	i
014	SO	(shift out)	060	<	106	j
015	SI	(shift in)	061	=	107	k
016	DLE	(data link escape)	062	>	108	l
017	DC1	(device control 1)	063	?	109	m
018	DC2	(device control 2)	064	@	110	n
019	DC3	(device control 3)	065	A	111	o
020	DC4	(device control 4)	066	B	112	p
021	NAK	(negative acknowledgement)	067	C	113	q
022	SYN	(synchronization)	068	D	114	r
023	ETB	(end of transmission block)	069	E	115	s
024	CAN	(cancel)	070	F	116	t
025	EM	(end of medium)	071	G	117	u
026	SUB	(substitute)	072	H	118	v
027	ESC	(escape)	073	I	119	w
028	FS	(file separator)	074	J	120	x
029	GS	(group separator)	075	K	121	y
030	RS	(record separator)	076	L	122	z
031	US	(unit separator)	077	M	123	{
032	SP	(blank space)	078	N	124	—
033	!		079	O	125	}
034	"		080	P	126	=
035	#		081	Q	127	DEL
036	$		082	R		
037	%		083	S		
038	&		084	T		
039	'		085	U		
040	(		086	V		
041	)		087	W		
042	*		088	X		
043	+		089	Y		
044	,		090	Z		
045	-		091	[		

Figure 3.2 ASCII Code

Data Communications

Data communications is the active process of transporting data from one point to another. *Networks* are communications systems designed to convey information from a point of origin to a point of destination. Note that they are *communication systems*, not *computer* systems. The operative word is communication, the transfer of information from one person or device to another.

Networks come in two flavors: *local* as in local area networks, which cover a small area and have a finite, relatively small, number of users; and *global* or *long-haul*, which cover great distance and have an unlimited number of users. Telephone networks are long-haul networks. (See Figure 2.2 in previous chapter.)

Two basic principles govern the operation of a communications system: first, the system exists to transfer information from one point to another. All services supported by the network are designed to facilitate this exchange of information. Second, the receiver must understand the message. Without understanding, no communication takes place.

To be useful, the data communications network (or any communications system) must be able to accept input data; structure the data so that it can be sent quickly and accurately; transmit the data to a specific destination; and once the data has arrived, reconvert it to a form understandable by the destination.

Ingredients of a Communications Network

The components required by a communications system or network and their role in the process can be described as follows:

- The *sender*, which generates information that

- the *encoder* converts into a *message*, that is, information in a form which can be moved by

- the *transmission medium*, which provides the path on which the message is carried to

- the *decoder*, which reconverts the message into information for

- the *receiver*, which is the destination of the original information and which will use that information.

All components must be present for the network to operate. See Figure 3.3 for a diagram of a basic network.

Figure 3.3 Parts of a Network

In the telephone system, people are both senders and receivers. The telephone set is the encoder/decoder. Telephone lines provide the transmission medium. The information to be transmitted is spoken: encoding enters when your voice is translated to a form sendable over the telephone lines.

In a computer network, computers are both senders and receivers of data. The computer also serves to translate human information into transmittable form.

Collectively, the various networking devices are called either *nodes* or *workstations*. Node is a holdover from mainframe computing. It actually refers to the beginning, intersection, or end of the communications link, not to a specific device. Workstation describes a microcomputer and its attached peripheral(s).

Communications Processing

Communications processing is the collective term for all the activities that help ensure the successful entry, transmission, and delivery of information. Just as data processing involves taking raw data and adding value by changing the inherent information content, communications processing adds value to the raw message by insuring that the message arrives at its destination in a timely manner, in the proper form, at the proper speed, in the proper language, and without errors.

The basic responsibilities of communications processing can be divided into three major areas: editorial, conversion, and arbitration.

Editorial functions include formatting of the message, editing the data, and controlling errors.

Conversion functions include translating transmission speed, and code.

Arbitration functions involve network control and message routing.

Communications processing can be performed in any intelligent device, using the storage and processing capabilities of that device. In the microcomputer based LAN, most communications processing occurs within the microcomputer itself.

Within a network, communications processing is implemented as protocols, the rules that govern the transmission of information.

The following are sample communications processing services:

- Accommodating differing video display characteristics, such as screen size, line length, and paging.

- Translating data into the standard network format and subsequently retranslating the data to meet the requirements of the receiving station.

- Controlling the sequence in which messages are sent.

- Assembling and transmitting messages on the basis of time interval, order received, receipt of particular character, or other characteristic.

- Alerting users to error conditions and possible problems.

Packets

It is neither practical nor advantageous to transmit long messages as a single entity. Therefore, for the purpose of data transmission, and particularly in local area networks, messages are broken down into segments, called *packets*. As shown in Figure 3.4, each packet contains five parts:

- A *start frame*, identifying the beginning of the packet.

- A *header*, containing information for maintaining control of the packet and the network.

- An *information field*, containing a segment of the total text, information, or data to be communicated.

- An *error control field*, permitting the system to verify packet integrity.

- An *end frame*, signifying the end of the packet.

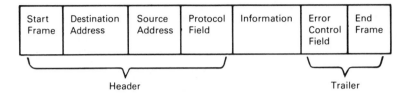

Figure 3.4 Packet

The control information contained in the header includes the *source address,* which identifies where the packet originated; the *destination address,* to which the segment is to be delivered; the packet *sequence number,* which helps insure that the packets can be reassembled in proper order; and a *control block,* which helps prevent duplication, loss, or looping (in which a packet is routed back and forth in an endless circle) of the packet. Additional information to insure proper operation of the network under various overload or impaired operating conditions also may be included. Figure 3.5 further dissects the address fields.

What's in an Address?

Destination Address:

Name—What workstation/resource is being sought?
Address—Where is it?
Route—How to get there.

Source Address:

Name—Who sent the message?
Address—Where is it?
Route—How to send a reply.

Figure 3.5 What's in an Address

Overhead is the additional information that must be transmitted through the network in order to facilitate the proper transmission and delivery of messages. It is created by the system's need to maintain control of all transactions. A percentage of overall network capacity is dedicated to this control information.

Overhead information exists on the network in two basic forms: data appended to each user packet, such as the control and error-checking fields named above. The amount of data appended to a basic message varies from one system to another, and self-contained acknowledgement and control packets, which are transmitted from one device to another. These packets keep the system advised of the status of the components.

Parts of a Microcomputer Network

A microcomputer network consists of the following components:

- *Microcomputer*: Provides the processing power of the network by which messages are created. Microcomputers are a user's main interface to the network, serving as the communicating devices, that is, the devices that actually exchange data with each other.

- *Interface device*: Connects user devices to the network and allows them to interact with other devices. The interface may be a networking card, a modem, or a communications port.

- *Topology*: The physical pattern of interconnection between nodes, a method of creating order out of the potential chaos of randomly attached devices.

- *Communications medium*: Supplies the physical link that carries information from one microcomputer or peripheral to another. The link also is referred to as a *channel*, *path*, *circuit*, or *line*.

• *Protocols*: Formal rules and conventions governing the exchange of information.

For an illustration of a microcomputer network, see Figure 3.6.

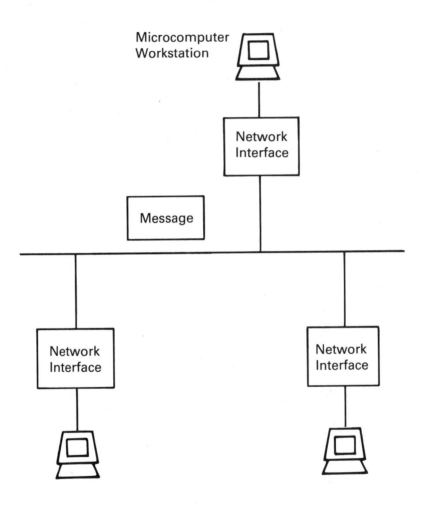

Figure 3.6 Microcomputer Network

The components listed above cover the minimum functional requirements. Missing from our description of a network are all the other devices which assist the transmission process and the software that controls the process. Several different types of software are involved:

- A *network operating system,* to do for the network what the operating systems MS-DOS, CP/M, and UNIX do for your microcomputer.

- *Applications software,* to provide functionality for the user so that work can be done.

- *Network utilities,* to accomplish all the routine procedures like sorting files and troubleshooting that make a system easier to use.

Also omitted from our list are printers; plotters; hard disks; telephones; television and video transmitters and receivers; security alarm systems; environmental monitors such as temperature or humidity sensors; and other peripheral devices that extend the power of the microcomputer.

Part II

4

The Visible Network

To the user, the LAN is composed of the workstation, the shared peripherals, and the network operating system. A *workstation* is an individual, single-user microcomputer with communications capabilities added. The term includes the microcomputer itself as well as all its attached bits and pieces —memory cards, CRT, floppy disk drives, hard disks, and printers. A workstation is distinguished from a personal computer by the network operating system software that controls what the workstations can and cannot do and by a *network interface unit* that supplies the communications capabilities.

Workstations may be divided into two classes: users and servers. User workstations are microcomputers on the network which have a primary responsibility to an individual user. Server workstations perform a service to other workstations on the network.

All workstations on the network communicate and cooperate with one another. The primary difference between server and user workstations is the directly attached resources, and programs which they run.

User workstations normally do not, and cannot, fulfill requests from other workstations. Resources attached to a user workstation, such as floppy disk drives, only can be accessed by the user of that workstation.

In contrast, resources attached to a server are shared by all users of the network. Broadly speaking, any workstation that can supply services to other workstations can perform server functions. More than one server may be attached to a network, with each server providing a different function, or one server fulfilling several roles. See Figure 4.1 for a typical network with servers.

Figure 4.1 Network With Servers

Normally, the server is the most powerful workstation on the network, associated with the disk drive and printer. Some LANs use a small minicomputer or a supermicro with the power of a mini as the server.

Server workstations may be one of two kinds:

- *Dedicated:* The microcomputer is restricted to network functions and often incorporates more powerful capabilities than user workstations do. While a dedicated server is unavailable for running user applications, and hence increases overall system cost, the network can support more features, such as electronic mail service or multiple hard disks, and provides faster system response. Larger networks usually require dedicated servers.

- *Non-dedicated:* The microcomputer can act as an individual workstation even while it controls the network. Network operation usually requires at least 256K of memory. (Many networks require more.) Additional memory is required for all but the simplest tasks. Under light load, performance of a non-dedicated server may be slightly less than that of a workstation; under heavy processing demand, the individual user of the server may find work impossible.

Some network servers are capable of operating in both dedicated and non-dedicated mode, depending on the user's selection.

Network Operating System

The major task of a server is running the network operating system. Network performance is directly dependent on the quality of the network operating system that manages the shared resources of the network. The network operating system is the directly visible aspect of the many layers of internal network software. In broad terms, it is the network's counterpart to MS-DOS or CP/M, the directions that tell how tasks are done on a network. Like a computer operating system, the network operating system works in the background, constantly governing and monitoring network activities.

In most LANs, the network operating system exists in conjunction with the computer's operating system. System requests are processed first by the computer operating system. When a local request is made, that is, one that requires only the immediate resources/capabilities of your workstation, it is fulfilled by the local machine. When a request is made that requires network resources or network activities, it is passed to the network software for processing.

Among other tasks, the network operating system is responsible for controlling access to data, allocating disk space, and controlling sharing of networked printers.

Sharing Data

When the user of a stand-alone microcomputer requests access to a file, a single-user oriented computer operating system reads its internal directory to find where the file is stored and retrieves the file. The table is updated as files are written to disk. By reading the information on unused sectors, the system knows where it can safely write additional data.

In a networking environment, with many users attempting to read the same data and to write to a single shared disk, the network needs some mechanism to synchronize users with each other, to arbitrate between requests, and to govern writing data to the disk, thus allowing several users to access the program's data at the same time.

File and Record Locking

Several alternative techniques exist to handle the difficulties caused by using single-user operating systems and single-user application programs never meant to deal with more than one user at a time. Generally, the techniques may be classified as *file locking/unlocking* and *record locking/unlocking*. Figure 4.2 illustrates file locking.

File locking restricts use of a whole file to one user at a time. When a file is accessed, the program sets a "flag" or marker. Flags consist of bytes of data that are stored along with file names in a table on disk or in memory. Depending on the value of the byte, the file is marked as locked or unlocked. The operating system rejects subsequent requests during the time that the flag indicates that the file is in use. When the original user is finished with the file, the flag is removed or reset.

For file locking to work, the individual applications programs in use must recognize the flags and respond appropriately to them. Effective use of flags is entirely dependent upon the cooperation of all programs involved.

Alternatively, the system may simply post a notice that a particular file is in use. Users are responsible for controlling their own use of a file; no requests are rejected. Other users can still read or write to the file.

Record locking restricts use of a particular record in a file to one user at a time. To lock a record, the network operating system can use a flag to indicate that the record is in use. Just as with file locking, however, the record locking flag must be recognized as a lock.

Some record and file locking functions allow multiple users to simultaneously read the same data, but restrict writing to protect one user from another user's updates.

Locking may be implemented in a network operating system that takes over file management from the microcomputers stand-alone operating system or through applications software specifically designed to run on a network.

Disk Space Allocation

On most LANs, several users share the hard disk. In the simplest network operating systems, the hard disk is divided so that each user "owns" a portion of its storage capacity. Allocation of disk space is fixed. File sizes are limited by the operating system, as are sizes and types of file directories.

Step 1

Step 2

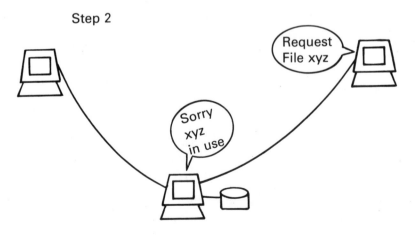

Figure 4.2 File Locking

While such a system permits sharing of storage capacity, the ability to share data is lacking. Only the assigned user can access a particular section. Simultaneous access to a file by two or more users is not possible. However, computers running different operating systems may coexist on the same hard disk.

Many network operating systems possess the ability to view common data and can assign and monitor access privileges. At this level, the server generally supports a single, network-wide operating system and independently operating applications programs. Data transfer between files is limited by ownership privileges and by the type of file. As in single-user systems, data cannot be transferred easily between applications. Changing file size, renaming a file, or other routine operations can upset access by other users.

In many of the newer LANs, hard disks are divided into *volumes*. The portion of total network disk space that is to be devoted to a particular task or set of users is controlled. Volumes may be named or numbered, depending on the operating system.

— A *public volume* contains data that may be read by all network users. It stores basic utilities and shared programs. The files are write protected; they cannot be changed or erased except by the volume's creator. Several network users may access the data simultaneously.

— *Shared volumes* contain files that are available to a defined group of users. Members of the group may both read and write to the volume. To preserve data integrity, when multiple users attempt to change the same record or file simultaneously, some method of data locking is needed.

— *Private volumes* contain personal or confidential data. Access is restricted to the creator ("owner") of the volume, who may read and write data to it.

Each volume usually contains a number of subdirectories. Access privileges to the volume and to individual subdirectories within the volume are defined so that a user can be granted access to precisely the data he needs without access to data he does not have the right to view. Typical user access rights are shown in Figure 4.3.

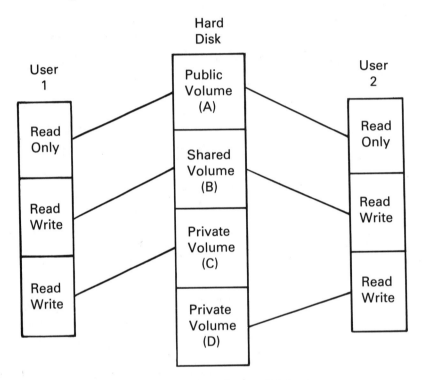

Figure 4.3 User Access Rights

Volume and file sizes are limited by the operating system, the size of the shared disk, and the number of users sharing the disk. The directory structure and size are limited by the specific operating system. For shared volumes, actions by one user can upset others.

Some network operating systems provide for file "caching." Server memory, designated as a "cache block," is reserved for holding current data, much like a mailbox. When a request for information is processed by the file server, the data is read into the available cache block. Subsequent requests to read the data found in a cache block will be retrieved from memory, rather than from the disk. A request to write is first written to the cache block and then completed as a background task to the normal disk or network operating system. Caching improves response time and decreases the number of times the disk is read from and/or written to.

In systems offering file caching, directory caching also may be available. The entire disk directory is stored in memory for immediate access. The location of needed files then can be determined by reading memory, rather than reading the disk. The process is considerably quicker—up to 100 times faster than directly reading the disk—and saves on physical wear.

Network operating system software also may include routines for prioritizing file retrieval requests, for alphabetizing the directory, for password protection, and for error-checking and recovery.

Sharing the Printer

A *print server* is a workstation with an attached printer, a spooler, and software to process and manage printing tasks. *Print spoolers* are designed to help keep the printer from becoming a bottleneck to the entire network.

The simplest spoolers are programs that create a buffer (temporary data storage area) from unused memory. Files to be printed are routed to the buffer and held there until the printer is ready. As writing to memory is considerably faster than most printers, the computer can perform other work while printing tasks occur in the background.

Alternately, the print spooler may write the file to disk. If the printer is busy, the task is entered in the print queue. If the printer is available, or when the task reaches its turn in the queue, the file is read and printed directly from the disk. Figure 4.4 illustrates print queueing.

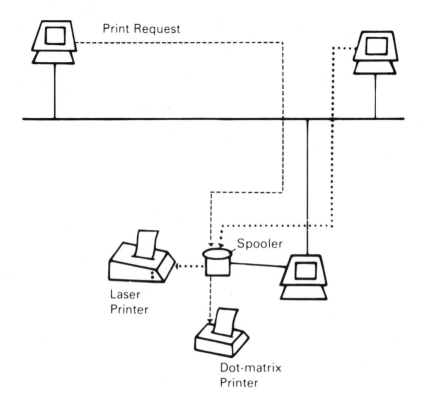

Figure 4.4 Print Server

Newer spoolers are "black boxes" containing additional memory and/or a disk. The device is installed between the computer and the printer. Files to be printed are routed to a print buffer in the spooler. If the printer is in use, the output is automatically queued until the printer is available. As the printer completes one request, the next set of data is sent from the buffer to the printer on a first in, first out basis. The user does not have to wait for printing to be completed, but may proceed to another task.

Sophisticated print servers allow the user to specify the number of copies, the printer to be used, special fonts, and priority. Users may be able to query the state of the print queue, to know when their printing is ready, and to change the order of the queue.

Network Interface Units

The *network interface unit* is a microprocessor based device containing hardware and software which supply the intelligence to control access to and communications across the network and to perform all communications processing. It is the means by which the workstations are connected functionally and physically to the network.

On most microcomputer networks, the network interface is a printed circuit board installed in the microcomputer. Depending on the vendor, it may be called a network card, network adapter, or network interface unit.

On some networks, the network interface may be implemented as a stand-alone box, termed a wiring center, or hub, attached between the main network cable and the workstation. Figure 4.5 shows how the microcomputer is connected to the network through the interface card.

We've made an assumption that networking ability is not already present in the microcomputer, but has to be added. Micros with built-in communications and networking will not need added hardware; the functions of the network interface already will be present in the machine. The crucial factor is not where or how the interface is located, but what functions it serves.

Network interface functions are realized through chips on the interface unit: network bus drivers, communications controller chips, specialized microprocessors, RAM buffers, and ROM code that is executed by the workstation itself. For most LANs, the network interface unit for all user workstations is identical. Server interface units may include additional ROM code to implement additional functions. Physical connection to the network is provided through a standard communications or input/output interface.

Through the network interface, data on the medium is available to all attached workstations and peripherals. System users never need to know what it takes to get from one point to another; they simply indicate the desired destination. The network interface unit provides transmission and

Figure 4.5 Connecting a Workstation to the Network

data control, formats the data into manageable units, translates the data rate and protocols of the attached workstation to that of the network communication medium and vice versa, and supplies address recognition capabilities. Details of network operation are hidden from users of the attached workstations.

Technically, two parts of the network interface can be identified: the *communications interface,* containing network oriented functions, and the *host interface,* containing computer-specific functions. Both parts of the interface are shown in Figure 4.6.

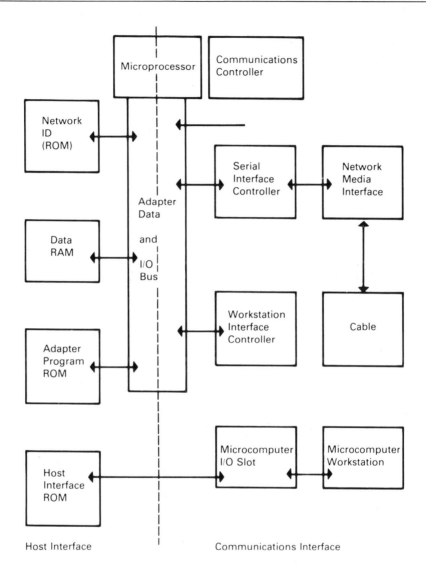

Figure 4.6 Parts of a Network Interface

The communications interface is the unit which logically interfaces to the network. It performs all transmission related functions. It accepts data from the attached workstation, buffers the data until the communication channel is available, and then transmits the data. The communications interface also monitors the channel for messages addressed to its workstation, stores the data, and transfers the data to the device.

The actual physical connection between the workstation and the network is achieved by running a secondary cable between the communications interface and the main network cable. The two cables are joined by a tap.

The host interface supplies the connection between a specific workstation's internal circuitry and the communications interface unit. It fits into the input/output structure of a particular computer, and governs all data exchange between the workstation and the communications-oriented portion of the network interface. Because of the many methods of implementing network and workstation functions, the host interface is workstation and vendor specific.

5

Topology: Arranging the Workstations

Formally, *topology* can be defined as the geometric arrangement of workstations and the links among them. Topologies are designed to create order out of the potential chaos of randomly arranged workstations. The issue is, where do you locate a workstation in relation to the network? At the end of a branch attached to the cable? At a junction point common to two or more cables? At the end of the cable? All of the above?

There are three connection possibilities:

- *Point-to-point* joins two, and only two, adjacent workstations without passing through an intermediary workstation.

- *Multipoint* is a single cable shared by more than two workstations.

- *Logical* implies that workstations are able to communicate, whether or not a direct physical connection actually exists between them.

The workstations in a local area network communicate based on some combination of physical (point-to-point or multipoint) and logical connection.

Given the location of workstations and peripherals, the goal of topology is to find the most economical and efficient way to connect all users to the network resources while providing adequate capacity to handle user demands, maintain system reliability, and keep delay low. The number of parameters and variables that bear on the solution is huge. Rapid change in user demands complicates the problem further.

Control

Control of the network also affects topology. Control and topology are so intertwined that topology often is defined as the means of implementing the control protocol. The two facets of control are *access*—which workstations send messages and when—and *allocation*—how long the workstation has access, and, where broadband media are in use, how much of the channel may be used.

Control may be *centralized*, in which access to the network and allocation of channel is determined by one node. Intelligence also may be concentrated in the central node with the attached workstations primarily terminals. Or it may be *distributed*, in which workstations can access the network channels independently, according to a shared set of protocols. The intelligence of the network is distributed throughout the connected workstations.

Specific protocols and their effects are discussed in Chapter 7.

LAN Topologies

Three topologies are commonly used for microcomputer local area networks:

• *Bus*: illustrated by Figures 5.1 and 5.2

• *Ring*: illustrated by Figures 5.3 and 5.4

• *Star*: illustrated by Figures 5.5, 5.6, and 5.7

Mesh topology, common in long-haul and complex mainframe networks, currently is not used by microcomputer LANs.

Bus networks are multipoint: workstations are connected to the single central communications link by individual secondary lines. Ring and Star networks use a point-to-point topology: each physical segment of cable connects two, and only two, workstations without passing through an intermediate workstation. All three are considered structured topologies.

Combinations of topologies not only are possible, but also they are becoming increasingly popular, particularly star-wired rings. The three basic LAN topologies and the major variations will be discussed below.

Topology Evaluation Factors

Topology is of most interest as it affects LAN use in your installation. To help you select the "best" topology for your situation, a checklist of evaluation factors follows the technical definitions of each topology. Points covered include the following:

- Application: in what size installation is the topology most appropriate?

- Complexity: how technically complex is the topology? This factor affects installation and maintainance of the cabling.

- Performance: how much of a traffic load can the system support?

- System overhead: what is the comparative price in excess capability?

- Vulnerability: how susceptible is the topology to failure? to damage?

- Expandability: when you are ready to extend the LAN, how easily can the topology accommodate additional workstations and cover larger distances?

Importance of the various factors is relative, not absolute, when selecting a specific LAN and is affected most by your requirements.

Bus and Tree

In a bus configuration, all workstations are connected to a single shared communications link through interface units and cable taps, as shown in Figure 5.1. Messages are broadcast along the whole bus. In order to receive a transmission, the workstations must be able to recognize their own address. Devices attached to a bus therefore must possess a high degree of intelligence or have the required intelligence provided by the bus interface unit.

The transmitters and receivers used by the network must tolerate a wide range of signal levels because workstations closest to the sending workstation receive a stronger signal than workstations at the far end of the bus. Signal-strength problems commonly are handled by limiting the length of the cable segments and the number of attached workstations. On some networks, amplifiers or repeaters may be used to maintain strength and clarity of the signal. Bus taps must be designed so as not to greatly reduce the signals reaching the other taps.

Technically, a *tree* (Figure 5.2) is a bus network comprised of a main cable which connects floors in a building (or several buildings), and branches which connect individual workstations in a more limited area. In effect, the network is divided into different segments. This topology is sometimes called a rooted tree and is used to refer to a network employing broadband coaxial cable. An unrooted tree is a baseband network and corresponds to the general definition of bus. Popularly, the terms tree and bus are used interchangeably.

Figure 5.1 Bus

Bus Evaluation Factors

- *Application*: Bus networks are a good choice for small networks and networks with low traffic.

- *Complexity*: Bus networks tend to be relatively uncomplex.

- *Performance*: Excellent under light load, may degrade rapidly as load increases.

- *System overhead*: Comparatively low, particularly because much of the hardware is fully developed and readily available. Some redundancy of communication channel is advisable to reduce the vulnerability to channel outage.

- *Vulnerability*: Failure of one workstation on a bus network does not usually affect the network. Bus networks are vulnerable to failure from damage to the main link and other problems affecting the bus. Problems on the bus are hard to locate. Once located, however, problems are easy to repair.

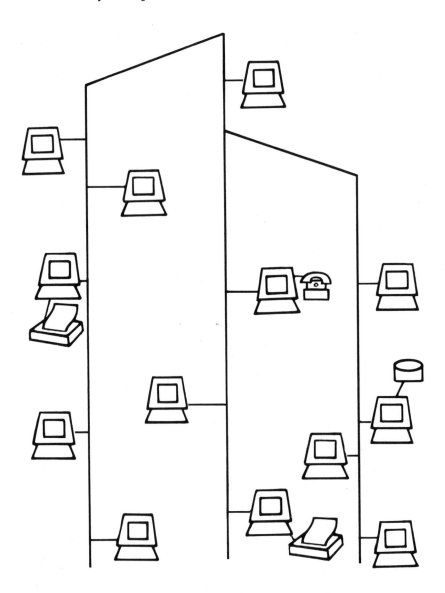

Figure 5.2 Tree

• *Expandability*: Expansion and reconfiguration of a bus network are easy. A new or relocated device may be connected to the nearest convenient network access point with little disruption of the network. Interconnecting microcomputers and equipment from different manufacturers is difficult because all connected devices must be able to accept the same forms of address and data.

Ring

Ring networks (Figure 5.3) consist of an unbroken circle of point-to-point connections of adjacent workstations. Messages travel from workstation to workstation in a round robin fashion. Workstations are connected to the cable through an access unit which is connected to a repeater which, in turn, retransmits messages addressed to other workstations.

In order to receive messages, each workstation must be capable of recognizing its own address. However, no routing capability is required as messages automatically travel to the next workstation on the network. Originally, information flow on the ring was strictly in one direction. Newer, two channel rings transmit information in different directions on each of the two channels.

When a ring topology is used to distribute control in local networks, the protocol used with it must avoid conflicting demands for shared channel.

A *loop* (Figure 5.4) is a ring network using centralized control. One workstation will be designated as server, responsible for access to and control over the channel.

Star-shaped rings, (Figure 5.5), in which the cable between workstations passes through a central wire center, have been gaining favor because of the need to keep the ring operating when a device or the cable fails. Automatic bypass relays which can be used to reconfigure network operations are located at the wire center. If a failure occurs, the "dead" section of the ring may be effectively eliminated. Remaining workstations can keep operating. The star-shaped ring also facilitates maintenance by providing a centralized monitoring and reconfiguration point.

Figure 5.3 Ring

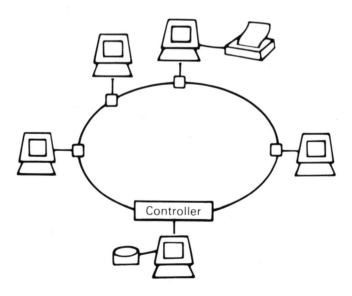

Figure 5.4 Loop

In practice, ring networks have been designed as single loops. Theoretically, a ring network could consist of several interconnected rings and form two or more hierarchical levels.

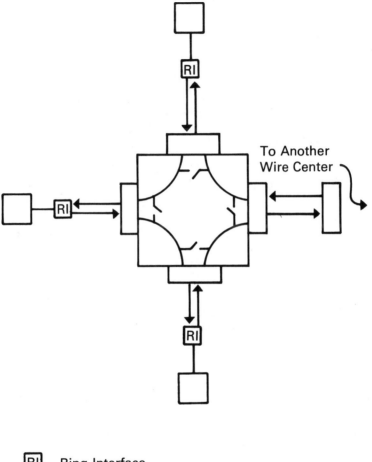

RI   Ring Interface

⟋—   Relay

□   Workstation

Figure 5.5 Star-shaped Ring

Ring Evaluation Factors

- *Application*: A ring is good in situations where capacity must be allocated equally or where a small number of workstations operating at high speeds over short distance are to be connected.

- *Complexity*: A ring requires relatively complex hardware to implement. Message routing, on the other hand, is simple: since only one message path is possible, the sending workstation need only know an address for the destination workstation. Routing information is not necessary.

- *Performance*: Performance under heavy traffic remains stable with less increase in delay and degradation of service than other networks. Average transmission delays are long, however, even under light traffic. Actual performance is dependent on the control protocols implemented.

- *System overhead*: Duplication of resources or a method of bypassing failure points is needed if the ring is to keep functioning when equipment fails.

- *Vulnerability*: Failure in a single workstation or in the channel can cause system failure because of the interdependence of workstations. Locating a failed repeater is particularly difficult; in a system with wide geographical distribution it may not be possible to immediately repair or circumvent the problem.

- *Expandability*: It is moderately easy to add or delete workstations on a ring network without making numerous connections for each change. Therefore, system modification costs are relatively low. Expansion does disrupt the whole system, although it may be only briefly.

Star

In a star configuration (see Figure 5.6), each workstation is connected to a central server through a dedicated point-to-point channel. Messages are passed from a workstation to the server.

Control of the network may be allocated in one of three ways:

1. Control resides in the central server which performs all routing of messages. Data received by the central workstation may either be processed internally or forwarded for processing. In this case, the server normally provides the main computing power.

2. Control may be exercised by an outlying workstation rather than the central device. The server operates as a switch, establishing connections between workstations.

3. Control may be distributed equally to all workstations. The server is used to route messages to their destinations and to resolve conflicting requests for connections between workstations.

In all three cases the central server is the critical node: if it fails, the whole network stops.

The server provides a logical location for directly attaching the major shared resources. Generally, individual workstations do not have to make routing decisions, as all communications must pass through the central workstation before going to their destinations. *Compound star networks* (Figure 5.7) are those in which a workstation on one network may act as server and/or controller for a secondary network. The term *snowflake* is used sometimes to refer to a compound star.

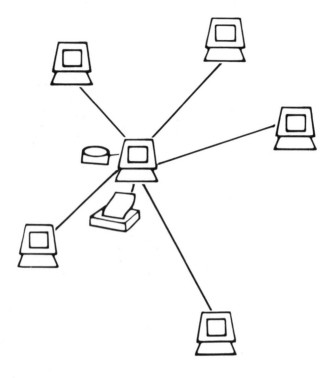

Figure 5.6 Star

The size and capacity of the network is a direct function of the power of the central workstation, with the burden of compatibility placed on the central server. Workstations do not compete for local capacity: heavy demand by one workstation does not necessarily cause a delay in network response time.

The star topology eliminates the need for each workstation on the network to make routing decisions. All message routing is localized in the central server.

Conceptually, a star is compatible with basic telephone services and is often implemented on the same lines through use of a data PBX.

Star Evaluation Factors

- *Application*: Presently, a star network is the best way to integrate voice and data services. A star-based data network using the newer digital PBXs often can be justified by the savings and features for voice-based telephone services alone.

- *Complexity*: The star can be quite complex: workstations attached to the central workstation may in turn act as the central server for other workstations or may be connected to remote communications links.

- *Performance*: Good for moderate load. However, the size and capacity of the network, and hence the performance, is a direct function of the power of the central node.

- *System overhead*: Network overhead is high: the server usually cannot be used for any other purpose while acting as network server. The number of separate lines is also high.

- *Vulnerability*: System reliability is dependent on central server. If the server fails, all activity on the network ceases. Failure of an individual workstation does not affect system. In either case, identification and repair of problems is simplified by centralized control.

- *Expandability*: Expandability may be severely restricted; most servers can support a limited number of network interfaces. Bandwidth and data rate limitations are often imposed on each user. The limits are necessary to protect the central processing functions from overload due to the aggregate rate of all the service ports and to keep the cost of each port on the central server low.

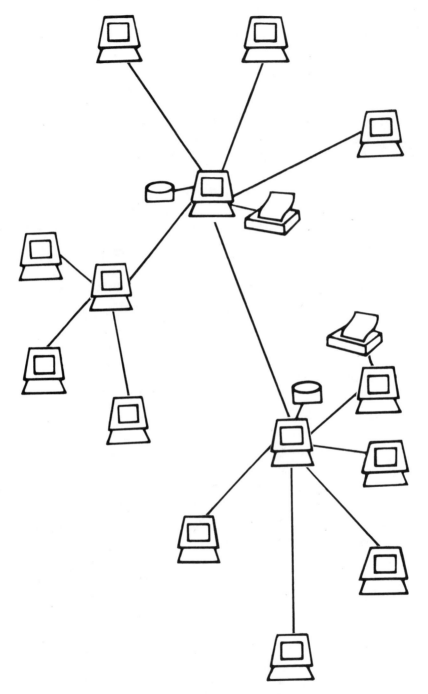

Figure 5.7 Compound Star or Snowflake

6

Communications Links

Transmission lines, the backbone of the network, come in two basic varieties: baseband and broadband.

Baseband communications links are *twisted pair wire* (see Figures 6.1 and 6.2) and *baseband coaxial cable* (see Figures 6.3 and 6.4). Broadband media are *broadband coaxial* (see Figures 6.5 and 6.6) and *fiber optic cable* (see Figures 6.7 and 6.8).

Descriptions of the cables, along with the additional devices required to turn a piece of cable into a network, will occupy the rest of this chapter.

Media Evaluation Factors

Each media is better suited to certain types of installation than to others. Factors influencing media choice follow the descriptions of the media and network components. Topics covered include the following:

- *Application*: In what size installation is the media most appropriate? How great a distance can it cover easily?

- *Application restrictions*: Under what conditions should the media be avoided?

- *Topology*: Which topologies use the cable?

- *Attraction*: In what situation is the cable to be preferred?

- *Network Reliability*: How dependable is the necessary equipment (other than the microcomputer workstations and the network interface cards)?

- *Vulnerability*: What are the major causes of equipment failure?

- *Susceptibility to noise*: How prone to interference is the network?

- *Implementation costs*: Installation of cabling and associated equipment is the great hidden cost of networking. For all media, the cost of installation easily exceeds that of the cost of the wire itself.

- *Security*: How open to tapping is the media?

See Chart 6.1 for media comparison.

	Twisted Pair Wire	Baseband Coaxial Cable	Broadband Coaxial Cable	Fiber Optic Cable
Bandwidth (partial)	Low	Moderate	High	Very High
Data Transfer Reliability	Low	High	High	Very High
Noise Susceptibility	High	Moderate	Low	None
Transmission Security	Low	Low	Low	High
Length	Low	Moderate	High	Very High
Installation	Easiest	Hard	Hardest	Moderate

Chart 6.1 Media Comparison Chart

Twisted Pair Wire

Twisted pair wire (Figure 6.1) is familiar as the cable used for telephone systems. Since the start of the computer age, it has been used to connect terminals and other low-speed data equipment to the mainframe. Use of twisted pair wire is so widespread that it is frequently pre-installed in buildings.

Figure 6.1 Twisted Pair Wire

As the name implies, pairs of wires are spiraled about each other. Gauge (size) of the base wire varies, as does the number of twists per foot. The twisting standardizes the electrical properties throughout the length of the cable and minimizes the interference created by adjacent wires in multipair cable. Normally, copper is used for the wire. Twisted pair tends to be unshielded or only minimally shielded. As a result, the cable is light and relatively easy to install.

Components of a Twisted Pair Network

A twisted pair wire network (Figure 6.2) consists of the main cable, plus the following:

- *Transceivers*: Network interface units which provide the intelligence for reading message addresses and for other network-oriented communication functions.

- *Cable taps*: Connect the transceiver to the main cable.

- *Repeaters*: Boost the strength of the signal as the messages pass from one cable section to another. The distance unamplified digital signals can travel on twisted pair is limited—approximately 8,000 feet under favorable conditions, without a repeater. The higher the speed of the signal, the shorter the distance it can travel.

Twisted Pair Evaluation Factors

- *Application*: Twisted pair cable is most suitable for point-to-point applications where low speed, low demand devices are interconnected. Average data rates are severely restricted, dropping rapidly as the distance between devices increases.

- *Application restrictions*: Most implementations restrict the number of workstations on the lines and limit distances to the area within a single building.

- *Topology*: Twisted pair is used in star, bus, and ring topologies.

- *Attraction*: One major attraction of twisted pair is its wide use for other communication purposes, particularly telephone networks. A second attraction is cost: wiring and installation are relatively inexpensive. To date, it has been the main transmission media for local networks.

- *Network Reliability*: Reliability is excellent. How often does your in-house telephone system fail because of cabling problems?

- *Vulnerability*: Although the medium is extremely flexible, physical ruggedness is low. Twisted pair is susceptible to damage from improper installation, sharp bends, and contact with rough surfaces.

- *Susceptibility to noise*: Lack of shielding leaves the medium vulnerable to interference from electrical noise, resulting in high error rates. Twisted pair wire should not be routed near any device that has a strong

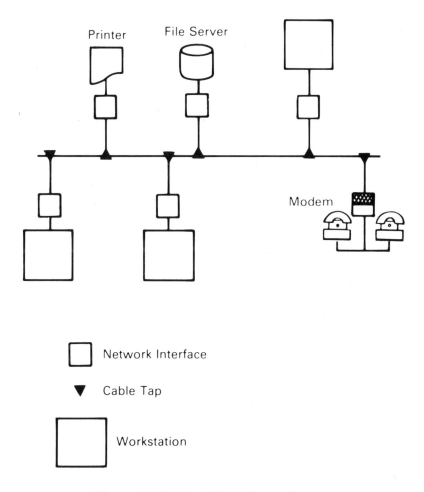

Figure 6.2 Twisted Pair Network

electromagnetic field, such as a radio transmitter or power transformer. Electric motors, gasoline engines, industrial machinery also must be avoided.

• *Implementation costs*: Cable cost depends on the number of twists per foot; the type of insulation and shielding; and the gauge of the wire. Based on cable costs alone, twisted pair is the least expensive medium. Additionally, it already is installed in many buildings. If not, or in cases where existing wiring cannot be used, installation costs are moderate, slightly less than that of coaxial cable.

- *Security*: Twisted pair networks are severely deficient in security due to lack of shielding. Electrical signals on the network are broadcast and may be intercepted by stations not actually connected to the network.

Baseband Coaxial Cable

Coaxial cable has been used for many years in the telephone network in applications with requirements similar to those of a LAN. It also is used for CATV (Community Antenna Television) systems. Both baseband and broadband coaxial cable are available. Although they are similar in construction, their installation and applications differ. Therefore, they will be discussed in separate sections.

In baseband coaxial cable (Figure 6.3), a central carrier wire is surrounded by a fine woven mesh of copper which forms an outer shell. The space between the wire and the outer shell is insulated to separate the two conductors and to maintain the electrical properties. The entire cable is covered by protective insulation to minimize electrical emissions. The cable is usually approximately 3/8 inch diameter.

The cable carries a single digital signal at a very high data rate—up to 10 to 12 megabits per second. Transmission frequency is relatively low. Bits are put directly on the cable without modulation.

Components of a Baseband Coaxial Network

In most respects, baseband coaxial is similar to twisted wire pairs. To transform a simple cable into a network (Figure 6.4), the following parts are needed:

- *Transceivers*: Network interface units, which provide the intelligence for reading message addresses and for other network-oriented communication functions.

- *Cable taps*: Connect the transceiver cable to the main cable.

- *Repeaters*: Amplify the signal as the messages pass from one cable section to another.

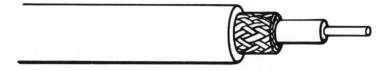

Figure 6.3 Baseband Coaxial Cable

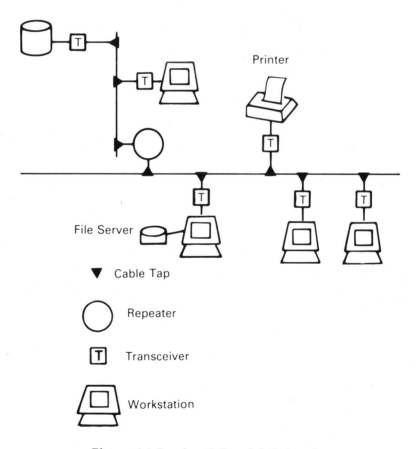

Figure 6.4 Baseband Coaxial Network

The main network cable is installed in a wire trough, which may be located beneath a raised floor, inside walls, or above a dropped ceiling. Local outlets may be provided in each office to facilitate connecting an individual workstation to the network.

Baseband Coaxial
Evaluation Factors

- *Application*: Baseband coaxial cable may be interchanged with twisted pair for many, but not all, purposes.

- *Application restrictions*: Most baseband coaxial networks limit the distance covered and the number of workstations.

- *Topology*: Baseband coaxial cable is frequently used for bus networks.

- *Attraction*: Baseband coaxial offers greater resistance to noise and better performance than twisted pair for an only slightly higher cable cost.

- *Network Reliability*: Reliability is good to excellent.

- *Vulnerability*: The cable itself is physically rugged.

- *Susceptibility to noise*: Although less susceptible to electrical noise than twisted pair, it is still noise sensitive. Baseband coaxial cable is not recommended for installation in sites with high levels of electrical noise.

- *Installation costs*: Installation costs are comparable to twisted pair.

- *Security*: Security of baseband coaxial is a problem: the cable may act as an antenna, broadcasting the signal, inadvertently permitting unauthorized taping. The broadcast signal may interfere with radio, television, and other broadcast systems located nearby.

Broadband Coaxial Cable

Broadband coaxial cable (Figure 6.5) comes in several different diameters with varying amounts of insulation. The cable may have the same construction as baseband coaxial, or the central carrier may be surrounded by an aluminum sleeve. The space between the core and the shell is filled with insulation, and the whole is enclosed in a protective coat of insulation.

Broadband coaxial cable can carry 50 to 100 television channels or thousands of voice and low speed data channels at rates of 9.2 to 50 kilobits per second.

Figure 6.5 Broadband Coaxial Cable

Components of a Broadband Coaxial Network

Broadband coaxial networks (Figure 6.6) usually are implemented with off-the-shelf CATV hardware. The radio frequency signal carrier propagates in one direction only.

If the system uses a single cable, the signal is divided into inbound (transmit) and outbound (receive) frequency ranges. Workstations receive messages within the outbound frequency range and transmit within the inbound frequency range. A translator at the head end converts inbound frequencies to outbound frequencies. On a 300 MHz or 400 MHz line, 40 to 50 channels of 6 MHz can be provided.

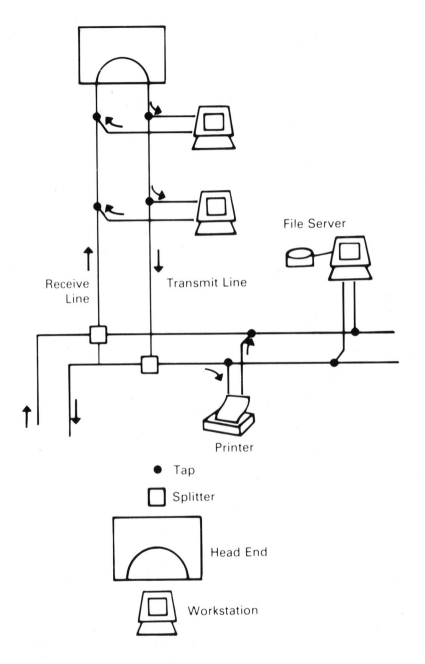

Receive
Line

Transmit Line

File Server

Printer

● Tap

☐ Splitter

Head End

Workstation

Figure 6.6 Broadband Coaxial Network

For local area networks, approximately one-half of the available channels are used for each direction, a scheme called *Mid-split*. The "split" in the name refers to the placement of unassigned frequencies, required as guardband to minimize interference.

The head end, located at the midpoint of the single cable, serves as the point of origin of all radio frequency signals and the collection point for all signals being generated on the network. It acts as the inbound-outbound crossover point which divides the network into a transmit half and a receive half. Shared devices frequently are located at the cable head end. As noise also returns to the head end, the return signals may be subject to noise degradation.

In a dual cable system, one cable carries inbound transmissions, the other outbound transmissions. The head end passes signals from the inbound line to the outbound line across all frequencies. Workstations send and receive on the same frequency, but on different cables.

In both systems, when the network cable is installed, the two halves are positioned parallel and physically adjacent to each other. Operational differences between LANs using mid-split single cable and dual cable systems are minor.

The coaxial network contains three levels of line:

- *Trunk*: The main network cable, which transports radio-frequency signals between amplifiers. Each floor in a multi-floor installation will have a trunk cable. It also is used for long runs between buildings. Trunk cable is normally thicker and more rigid than other cables in the network.

- *Branch*: Carries the network to the general area of the user. Branch distribution cables may extend from other branches, subject only to signal quality considerations.

- *Drop*: Connects the user outlet to the branch. The cable used is thin and more flexible than other broadband coaxial cables. Several drop cables may be attached to each connector.

The cable is installed above a dropped ceiling or below a false floor where it can be "pulled" into position. Risers bring the main cable from one floor to another. Usually a building will have only two riser cables. Each floor will have a pair of trunk cables split at various points into branches. The cable may be buried for runs between buildings or hung on poles (as is done for CATV).

To the lines are connected:

- *Radio-Frequency Modems*: Used as network interface. Broadband systems require modems to translate the data onto and off of the carrier signal. The modem must be able to transmit and/or receive on a variety of frequencies and is therefore sometimes called frequency-agile.

- *Amplifiers*: Used to "boost" the signal. Amplifiers (also called Repeaters) are necessary over long distances, such as an installation encompassing multiple floors of a building or multiple buildings.

- *Power supply*: The system as a whole runs on electrical power. Distributing power over the coaxial cable eliminates the need for a separate power supply at each amplifier location, resulting in greater flexibility in the placement of amplifiers. For reliability, electrical grounding is necessary.

- *Directional couplers*: Insure that signals transmitted by any network device will be transmitted only toward the head end.

- *Splitters and combiners*: Permit branching of cable.

- *Taps*: Pre-installed, stand-alone outlets with two sockets, one for transmitting and one for receiving. Workstations can be plugged into the network or unplugged from it without affecting service to other users.

- *Terminators*: End a line. Terminators limit noise reflection in the system and minimize undesirable signals.

To run the system, a power supply is necessary. Power may be provided at the head end or with a power outlet at each amplifier.

In installations where user outlets have been liberally supplied, adding workstations or moving existing workstations from one location to any other location served by the network is achieved easily. In many cases, connection and/or disconnection of a workstation will not affect the operation of the network as a whole. Reconfiguration of the network into a hierarchy with subnetworks is possible.

Broadband Coaxial Evaluation Factors

- *Application*: Coaxial cable is preferred for high-frequency, wide bandwidth, high-speed applications. It is currently the most practical choice for networks covering moderate distances; requiring digital, voice, and video transmission; and/or having a large number of workstations.

- *Application restrictions*: The cost of the system makes broadband coaxial impractical for small networks.

- *Topology*: Basic broadband coaxial topology is extremely flexible. Star or tree are suggested by the transmission technology.

- *Attraction*: All transmission devices are readily available CATV components with proven high reliability.

- *Network Reliability*: The basic technology is highly dependable. Network reliability depends on the reliability of individual parts. Cable amplifiers tend to be the major point of failure, particularly when new. If amplifiers survive the first several months, they usually do not fail until near end of guaranteed life.

- *Vulnerability*: The cable is susceptible to damage from careless installation, improperly installed devices, and failure in cable components. It cannot make sharp bends around corners. In addition, the cable is sensitive to temperature changes.

- *Susceptibility to noise*: Transmission is susceptible to interference from low-frequency electromagnetic noise. The actual noise immunity is dependent on the physical location and method of implementation. Coaxial cable can be used in many environments where twisted pair wire or other unshielded cable could not be used.

- *Implementation costs*: While the cable itself is not expensive, system costs are high because of initial equipment and upkeep costs. Installation and maintenance of CATV equipment is routine.

- *Security*: Unlike baseband coaxial, broadband coaxial cable does not broadcast the electrical signals that it carries. Security, however, still may be a problem: coaxial cable can be easily tapped by anyone who can gain physical access to the cable.

Fiber Optic Cable

Fiber optic cable (Figure 6.7) is a relatively new media for local area networks. Light signals are transmitted through a cable/waveguide composed of a bundle glass or plastic fibers. Each individual strand has a center core of plastic or glass with a high refraction index, surrounded by a cladding layer (overcoat) with a slightly lower index. The cladding layer isolates the fibers and prevents interference between adjacent strands, as well as providing some physical protection for the core. The whole usually is enclosed by additional protective outer layers which play no role in the actual transmission.

Figure 6.7 Fiber Optic Cable

Three basic types of cable are available:

- *Single mode fibers* have an extremely thin core diameter. While the thinness provides high performance, it makes connection to light transmitters and other cable segments extremely difficult. Single mode fibers are not commercially available in any quantity at this time.

- *Stepped index fibers* contain a core of high resolution within a shell of lower resolution. The boundary between core and cladding is abrupt. Connections are easier than with other types of fiber.

- *Graded index fibers* vary in density from the core outward. The gradation moderates the dispersion of signals. Graded index fiber is currently the most commonly available, because it is preferred for telecommunications. It has the highest transmission rate of the three types of cable.

Cable segments must be aligned precisely for the signal to continue from one segment to the next, because light tends to travel in a wave-like motion rather than a straight line. The greater the fluctuations in the light wave, the more rapidly the performance degrades and the greater the dispersion of the signal. The thinner the optic fiber and the narrower the light source, the straighter the wave is forced to travel and, therefore, the more efficient the network as a whole.

Components of a Fiber
Optic Network

In addition to the cable, the fiber optic network (Figure 6.8) requires the following:

- A *Transmitter*: Consisting of a light source and a power supply. Light is supplied by either a LED (Light Emitting Diode) or a laser diode.

- *Receivers*: Also called detectors, which sense the light signals and convert them back to electrical signals.

- *Repeaters*: Necessary for very long networks. Fiber optic systems use far fewer repeaters than any other media.

- *Couplers and connectors*: Used to join two lengths of cable. Any mating of fiber optic cable requires a great deal of care, because minor mismatches can cause a large loss of efficiency.

In operation, a workstation sends data in standard electrical form to a transmitter, where it is converted into light pulses. The light signals are collected by the waveguide and carried to a receiver. At the receiver, the light pulses are retranslated to electrical pulses and delivered to the destination workstation.

Unlike coaxial cable, fiber optic systems generally do not require repeaters over the distances typically found in LANs. Repeaterless runs of up to 4 kilometers or more can be accommodated, as compared to only 1 1/2 kilometers for coaxial cable.

The light signals may be digital or analog. Digital light signals are created by on/off pulses; analog signals use varying light intensity. Each cable can transmit in one direction only. Two-way communications require two optic cables.

Performance of the system is a function of transmission speed, bandwidth, and the amount of signal dispersion, or degradation, over the length of the cable. The wider the range of light wavelengths at the source, the sooner the signal disperses.

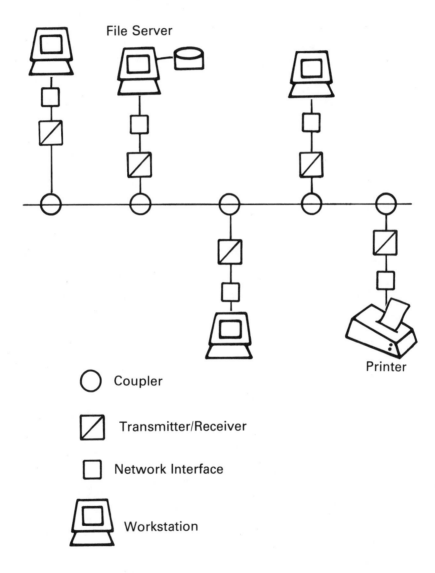

Figure 6.8 Fiber Optic Network

Fiber Optic Evaluation Factors

- *Application*: Fiber optic is particularly suited to systems with very-high speed data and video transmission requirements; to transmission over distances greater than other media can support; for installations which anticipate rapidly increasing demand for communication capabilities; and where space and signal interference cause problems.

- *Application restrictions*: Fiber optic is not suitable for small installations or where cost is a major factor.

- *Topology*: Currently, fiber optic systems are most suitable for point-to-point transmission, suggesting star or ring topologies. Bus topology is possible, but currently is infrequently implemented.

- *Attraction*: Fiber optic networks support an extremely high data rate—over 1 gigabit per second (10 to the 9th power bits per second)—on a potentially unlimited bandwidth, with extremely high reliability and high quality output. Fiber optic cable is thin, light weight, very flexible, and extremely resistant to ordinary transmission hazards.

- *Network Reliability*: Fiber optic cable is rugged, has a long life, and has displayed high reliability under adverse physical conditions.

- *Vulnerability*: Fiber optic networks are susceptible to signal loss from improper splicing or interfacing, bending, and pressure. The light source may be heat sensitive.

- *Susceptibility to noise*: Due to its resistance to electrical, electromagnetic, and radio frequency noise, fiber optic may be the only functional choice for a heavily industrial installation. The fiber optic cable is electrically isolated and therefore cannot broadcast its signal outside the network. It has the added advantage of not emitting sparks and thus does not present a potential fire hazard.

- *Implementation costs*: Currently fiber optic networks are very expensive. Installation and equipment, particularly coupling and interfacing devices, are high. The installation is complex, especially as connections must be precise. However, costs of all parts of the network are dropping rapidly and will continue to do so.

- *Security*: Fiber optic is the best choice where tight security is mandatory. It is virtually invulnerable to tapping.

7

Controlling Communication on the Network

Protocols are the formal rules and conventions governing the exchange of information between computers, defined to provide reliable and efficient transfer of information. Without protocols to guide the orderly exchange of data between points in a network, there would be chaos, not communication.

Detailed protocols are required to precisely define the format in which data and system messages are to be sent; describe how a message is addressed; and govern network traffic flow by controlling priority, routing, and sequencing of messages. Only when two devices agree on the specific conventions to be used can conversation take place.

Qualitatively, protocols may be said to insure that the system is capable of "useful" work. As part of the task, the protocols must be implemented uniformly throughout the network. For computer-to-computer communications, the protocols are, of necessity, complex.

No protocol works in isolation. Rather, it functions as part of the total set of instructions which determine the operations of a device or network. Each set of protocols is designed to work under different conditions and to satisfy different requirements.

The range of possible methods for passing messages between computers is enormous. The following are specific communication protocols of interest for local area networking:

- Contention:

    — Simple contention: Figure 7.1

    — Carrier Sense Multiple Access (CSMA): Figure 7.2

    — Carrier Sense Multiple Access with Collision Detection (CSMA/CD)

    — Carrier Sense Multiple Access with Collision Avoidance (CSMA/CA)

- Polling: Figure 7.3

- Token passing: Figures 7.4, 7.5

Protocol Evaluation Factors

Precise protocol specification could fill several books with complex mathematical formulas; we will avoid mathematics in favor of general functional descriptions. When selecting a protocol, the following factors may influence your choice:

- *Message length*: How long a message may be passed between workstations at any one time?

- *Traffic volume*: How many messages can be passed?

- *Network size constraints*: How large can a network using the protocol be?

- *Performance*: Under what conditions does the protocol perform well? Poorly?

- *Overhead*: How much traffic capacity is required to pass control messages?

- *Access Delay*: Does the protocol have built-in delays before a workstation can access the network?

- *Station Failures*: What happens to the network if a workstation fails?

- *Expansion*: How easily can the protocol accommodate additional workstations?

Contention

Contention is what happens at a staff meeting when several people start to talk at the same time. In contention protocols, no "policeman" controls usage of the communications channels.

All workstations on a contention network share a common transmission channel. Messages are broadcast on that channel and may be overheard by all attached workstations. (See Figure 7.1.) A workstation responds only to messages with its address: messages intended for different destinations are ignored. When not responding to a specific message, workstations are passive, simply listening in on the channel rather than being actively involved in transmitting messages.

Messages to be transmitted are converted to *packets* (Figure 3.4) and are sent when ready, without verifying the availability of the channel. When transmission of a packet from one workstation overlaps that of another, collision occurs. Colliding packets, with their embedded message, are destroyed.

While the basic contention protocol makes no provision for knowing if another message is already underway, it does provide for acknowledging the successful receipt of a packet. If the originating workstation does not receive an acknowledgement, it assumes that transmission was garbled or destroyed. The sending workstation waits a random amount of time and then retransmits the packet. The waiting time must be random or the same messages will collide repeatedly.

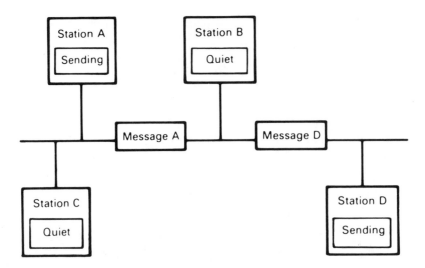

Figure 7.1 Contention

In some cases, the receiving workstation receives only part of a packet. The receiver may then return a negative acknowledgement to the originator, requesting retransmission.

More than any other network, the contention network is characterized by *bursty traffic*: the time interval needed for each transmission is short in relation to the interval between transmission.

Contention Evaluation Factors

Smooth functioning of a contention-based network is dependent upon high availability of the transmission media and a low collision rate. The network is characterized by the following:

- *Message length*: Messages are divided into short packets in order to reduce the amount of data that must be rebroadcast after collisions. Normally, the original message is also fairly short.

- *Traffic volume*: Contention protocols are designed for networks with low traffic volume, that is, one with few workstations attempting to use the network at the same time. Low traffic volume implies a limited number of attached workstations.

- *Network length constraints*: The longer the network, the greater the chance of collision. Contention networks are limited by the time needed for a signal to travel the length of the transmission media and have an acknowledgement returned (that is, propagation delay).

- *Performance*: Contention networks are most effective under light to medium load. Performance under those conditions is excellent. Under heavy load, a contention network tends to be unstable, with service rapidly degrading.

- *Overhead*: Contention networks have high overhead because of collisions and the need to acknowledge the successful receipt of messages.

- *Access Delay*: Delay on the network is generally moderate to long, depending on traffic. Delay under heavy load can be significantly higher than load alone would seem to dictate.

- *Station Failures*: Because operation of the network is not dependent on the presence or absence of any one workstation, failure of a workstation inconveniences only its users. Rarely does failure of a single station disrupt service on the whole network.

- *Expansion*: Addition of new workstations is relatively easy, because to be included in the network, the workstation simply must recognize its own unique address. Expansion may be achieved with minimal disruption of the network.

Refinements on contention procedures are used by many of the current microcomputer local networks. These refinements are: Carrier Sense Multiple Access (CSMA) in

Figure 7.2; Carrier Sense Multiple Access with Collision Detection (CSMA/CD); and Carrier Sense Multiple Access with Collision Avoidance (CSMA/CA).

Each will be discussed in a separate section below. For all practical purposes, characteristics of these refinements are identical to the characteristics of simple contention.

Carrier Sense Multiple Access

Carrier Sense Multiple Access (CSMA) is a polite staff meeting, with colleagues beginning to talk only when no one else is talking. As in simple contention, members of the network share a single communications channel. (See Figure 7.2.)

Before information is sent, the workstation "listens"—usually on a secondary frequency—to sense whether any other workstation is using the primary transmission channel (the "carrier"). Only when the line is clear will the workstation transmit.

If a workstation becomes ready to transmit while another workstation is active, it detects the signal passing on the cable and does not send its message until the current transmission is complete. For microcomputer networks the waiting station has two options, depending on system design:

1. It can continually sense the channel while waiting for the busy signal to cease and then transmit immediately. This is called *persistent carrier sense*, as the terminal actively waits to seize the channel as soon as it becomes free. If other workstations are equally persistent, a collision may occur immediately after the busy signal ceases.

2. Alternatively, if the channel is sensed busy, the terminal reschedules its transmission for a later time, using a random delay, and tries again—*nonpersistent carrier sense*. Fewer collisions occur, resulting in

higher throughput. However, delays may be slightly longer, at least in networks with low channel utilization.

In addition to transmitting its message on the main channel, the active workstation broadcasts a carrier-sense signal on the secondary channel to inform other workstations that the line is busy.

After transmitting, the workstation waits for an acknowledgement, indicating that transmission was successful. If no acknowledgement is received, or if a negative acknowledgement (indicating unsuccessful transmission) is received, the workstation assumes a collision has occurred. The workstation then waits a random amount of time before starting the process again.

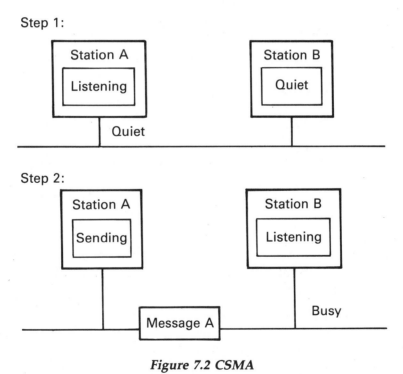

Figure 7.2 CSMA

In. a CSMA network, collision between transmitting workstations is still inevitable. A "ready" signal on the secondary channel does not necessarily mean that the network is free of other traffic. Because of the length of time required for a signal to travel the channel (propagation delay), two or more workstations may sense an idle line simultaneously, and thus both attempt to transmit at the same time. If the propagation delay is short, the information the workstation hears by monitoring the channel is sufficiently current to permit a useful decision. The probability of success will be significantly higher than in simple contention. If, however, the information is old, that is, the propagation delay is long, CSMA offers only slight improvement over plain contention.

The secondary channel which carries the busy tone does require some bandwidth. This bandwidth is generally minimal. There is a brief delay involved in sensing the busy signal.

Carrier Sense Multiple Access with Collision Detection

Carrier Sense Multiple Access with Collision Detection (CSMA/CD) provides the proper etiquette for the times when polite colleagues inadvertently start talking at the same instant. At our theoretical staff meeting, both speakers would stop, and wait for the other to continue. The one who resumes first would have the floor.

In CSMA/CD, in addition to sensing whether the transmission channel is in use before beginning to transmit, workstations monitor the link during transmission. When a collision is detected, transmission is halted.

As in the other contention-based protocols, the message is retransmitted after a brief interval. For CSMA/CD, the interval may be either random or pre-defined as a unique period for each workstation. Because of the ability to listen before and during transmission, the number of collisions is relatively low. Successive collisions between the same workstations is rare. Additionally, since transmission ceases as soon as a collision is detected, less delay occurs.

Carrier Sense Multiple Access with Collision Avoidance

Carrier Sense Multiple Access with Collision Avoidance (CSMA/CA) is analogous to several people wishing to contribute information at a meeting, and therefore all raising their hands at the same time. At the meeting, the moderator selects the next speaker. In CSMA/CA, the protocol determines who speaks next.

A station with a message to transmit monitors the medium and waits for the line to be available. When the channel is clear, the workstation signals its intention to broadcast. If multiple workstations are waiting, the order of precedence is determined by a pre-established table.

Just as human meetings tend to be biased in favor of allowing the main speaker or resident expert the greatest opportunity to talk, most CSMA/CA schemes are biased in favor of the lower-numbered workstations. That is, after any transmission, the workstation designated as first by the table has the right to transmit. If it has no message to send, or if it fails to transmit within a pre-defined time for any reason, the next workstation has the chance, and so on.

Once any workstation transmits, the network begins again at the top of the list of precedence. Refinements are possible. Some implementations are designed to avoid having the network dominated by any one workstation: a station which has just transmitted may not be allowed to transmit again until all other stations have had an opportunity.

To accommodate multimessage dialog, the workstation receiving a message may have the first right to transmit. If it does reply, the original sender would again have a chance. Unfortunately, two workstations may seize the medium, with one station sending messages and the other replying.

In the case when no workstation has a message to transmit, the network may reinitialize, starting again with the first workstation. In other cases, the network may enter a free-for-all period, in which the first workstation to transmit gains the channel. During the contention period, collisions are allowed.

Polling

Polling (Figure 7.3) involves the central control of all workstations in a network. The central, or primary, workstation acts like a teacher going down the rows of the classroom asking each student for homework. When one student has answered, the next is given a chance to respond.

A polling network contains two classes of workstations: the primary workstation (also termed the central controller or server), and the multiple secondary workstations connected to it. A buffer that can temporarily store messages is associated with each secondary workstation. When a workstation has information to transmit, the data is passed to the buffer. The message is held until the workstation is polled by the central controller.

The primary workstation queries each secondary in turn to determine if it has a message to transmit. If the answer is affirmative, the workstation is either given permission to transmit immediately or assigned a transmission time. The amount of time a workstation may have in which to transmit once channel access is gained is determined by system parameters.

If a workstation does not have data to transmit, it still must respond with a short control message. Rather than returning a message to the primary, some networks allow a polled workstation with no data to send to pass the polling signal to the next secondary station.

Each time a workstation is polled, the primary workstation must wait for a response to be returned. After a workstation responds, the next station is polled. The primary workstation determines which workstation has access to the network at any one time.

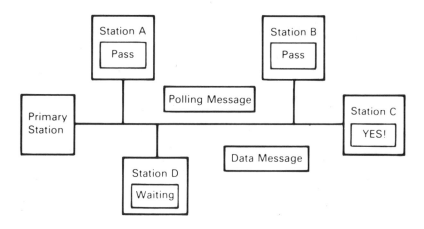

Figure 7.3 Polling

There are two possibilities for the path of a message from source to destination workstation:

1. All messages may be required to pass to the central workstation, which routes them to their destinations.

2. Messages may be sent directly from the originator to their destinations.

In either case, communication between workstations is possible only under the direction of the polling computer.

Variations on polling tend to be concerned with how often workstations are queried. The basic protocol calls for all stations to have equal opportunity to broadcast. This is not always so. In some networks, workstations considered to be very active or to have priority may be polled several times within a single cycle. In other cases, an inactive device may not be polled every cycle. A third alternative is that the frequency with which individual workstations are polled may be varied to reflect their current activity level.

Polling techniques can be said to maintain a tighter control over the network than do contention-based protocols.

Polling Evaluation Factors

The polling network is characterized by the following:

- *Message length*: Allowable message length tends to be longer than in contention networks, as no workstation can pre-empt the network through frequent, lengthy messages. However, if all workstations have long messages, the transmission delay is high.

- *Traffic volume*: Polling networks support moderate to high traffic volume, limited primarily by the need to wait for permission to transmit. Direct conflict for time to transmit, as in contention techniques, is avoided. Therefore, a large number of workstations can share the common channel.

- *Network length constraints*: The distance between workstations and the overall length of the network is limited by the transmission medium, rather than by the polling protocol. As in any network, the greater the length, the longer the time required for messages to travel between sending and receiving stations.

- *Performance*: Polling networks perform best under moderate load. Under heavy load, transmission delays may become unacceptably long. Polling is inefficient for networks with light loads. In the extreme case, most network traffic may be comprised of polling signals and negative acknowledgements, rather than actual messages.

- *Overhead*: Administrative overhead on a polling network is high. The query and response use a measurable part of the total network capacity. Furthermore, in many polling networks, the server unit cannot be used as a workstation.

- *Access delay*: Delays in most polling networks are relatively long. In most implementations, a workstation is polled only once each cycle. If the network is very large, delay may be unacceptably long.

- *Station Failures*: Little or no disruption of the network is caused by a failed secondary workstation. The inactive workstation is "invisible" to the network; that is, it simply fails to respond when polled. However, if the central workstation fails, all communication on the network ceases.

- *Expansion*: In order for the network to be expanded, the primary workstation must be informed and the order of polling revised to reflect the addition. Therefore, expansion is more complex than expansion of a contention network.

Token Passing

Token passing can be seen as the children's game of hot potato in reverse. Like the players, the network continuously circulates a special bit pattern known as a token. Rather than being out if you are holding the object being passed, holding the token confers the right to communicate. Only the workstation holding the token can put a message onto the network. Control of the network is decentralized.

Each token contains network information, comprised of a header, a data field, and a trailer. (See Figure 7.4.)

When a workstation that wants to transmit receives an empty token, it inserts routing information, inserts the data, and sends the token on a complete circuit of the network.

The workstation holding the token may transmit messages up to a specified maximum length. If it does not have anything to communicate, it passes the token to the next station in the network. Figure 7.5 illustrates token passing.

In most token passing networks, the token passes from one workstation to the one immediately adjacent. However, the token may pass from workstation to workstation in a sequence established at network implementation time, without requiring nodes to be physically adjacent. In such implementations the workstation knows the address of the next workstation to receive the token, as well as its own address.

Empty Token:

In Use:

Figure 7.4 Token

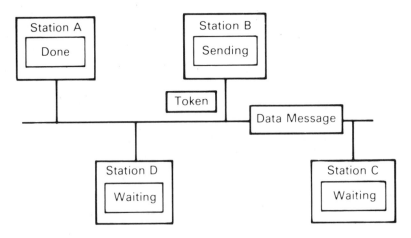

Figure 7.5 Token Passing

All the workstations on the network read the address in an occupied token; if it is for a different workstation, it is passed on unchanged and unread. At the destination, the receiving workstation reads the message, marks the token as copied or rejected, and continues passing it. Only the workstation which has placed a particular message onto the network may remove that message. If a workstation is disassociated from the network, it simply does not read its message.

When the token returns to its original sender, the message is removed. The token is marked as empty and forwarded to the next workstation. The sender can either save the message, in order to compare it with the original data as part of a network reliability monitoring scheme, or discard it. Acknowledgement or lack thereof notifies the sender of the status of the message. If the receiving workstation is absent from the network, no acknowledgement will be received. If the message has been rejected because it is garbled, the sending workstation can retransmit it.

Complex error-recovery protocols are required to recognize and recover from events such as lost or garbled tokens, the failure of a workstation to forward the token, or any time that no token exists, such as at network start-up. In such cases, a method of generating a token and beginning to circulate it must be specified. Controlled contention or a priority access scheme based on workstation address may be used to re-establish token ownership.

Token passing ensures relatively tight control over the network. The elimination of inefficiencies caused by collisions between contending units is a major advantage for users.

Token Passing
Evaluation Factors

- *Message length*: Token passing can accommodate moderate to long messages. Since messages are embedded within the token, multiple types of data may be handled.

- *Traffic volume*: Traffic on a token passing network can be quite high. Because each workstation may broadcast a single message on each turn, availability of the network is equitable. There is little possibility that any one workstation will claim more than its fair share of network capacity.

- *Network length constraints*: Token passing networks are limited primarily by the transmission medium, not by the protocol.

- *Performance*: Token passing networks perform well under most conditions. Given a moderate to high traffic load when the network is in almost constant use, performance is excellent.

- *Overhead*: Administrative overhead on token networks is comparatively high.

- *Access Delay*: Under any given volume of traffic, line delays on the token network tend to be constant and predictable. Heavy traffic creates a moderate delay. Under moderate traffic conditions, delay is short.

- *Station Failure*: In older token rings, failure of any one workstation blocked all transmission. Recently developed token rings have eliminated this problem.

- *Expansion*: Expanding a token passing network is a complex process which may involve re-wiring the network to include the new workstations and identifying a new token circulation pattern. During expansion, service on the network may be disrupted for extended periods.

8

Standards: Bringing Order to LAN Design

To form a viable network, all the diverse elements—equipment, topology, communications links, protocols—must be assembled into a unified system. While the actual design of each component of the communications system can and does vary depending on the specific system involved, no single component can be selected or designed in isolation. Parts of the system must be balanced for effective communication to occur. If any one component does not interact successfully with the others or is absent, communication cannot occur.

Thousands of possible viable LAN combinations exist. Given that creative engineers love to experiment (inherent in all new technologies is an almost overwhelming desire to play, to see how many different things can be done), how do you coordinate all the pieces?

More importantly, how do you insure that a local area network is able to interconnect diverse types of equipment from multiple sources when there is no common language that computers can use to communicate with each other?

Standards that bring order to the design process are required. Currently, the work of two organizations is relevant to local area networks. They are the International Standards Organization (ISO) and the Institute of Electrical and Electronic Engineers' (IEEE) Project 802 committee.

The Open Systems Interconnection Model

In 1978 the International Standards Organization (ISO) proposed a broad model for mainframe wide area network communications, which they titled "The Reference Model of Open Systems Interconnection."

Open Systems Interconnection refers to the exchange of information among terminal devices, computers, people, networks, and processes. The systems are open to one another by virtue of their mutual use of the standards developed from the original reference model. Openness does not imply any particular implementation, technology, or interconnection means.

The Open System Interconnection Reference Model is not, by itself, a standard, nor is it a literal description of computer communications. While it defines *where* to perform tasks, it does not detail *how* to perform them. Individual services and protocols are not specified. Within the model, communication functions are addressed from the perspective of computer-to-communications network interconnection.

The Reference Model is intended to provide a common basis for coordinating the development of standards aimed at systems interconnection, while allowing existing standards to be placed in perspective within a common framework.

OSI Layers

As shown in the chart in Figure 8.1, each system is viewed as being composed of an ordered set of subsystems, or layers. The layers of the Reference Model are separated by interfaces. Adjacent layers communicate through their common interface.

Layer 1   Physical Link.
Defines the electrical and mechanical
characteristics of network interfaces, as well as
their functions.

Layer 2   Data Link.
Establishes, maintains, and terminates
communications between users.
Responsible for maintaining an error-free
channel.

Layer 3   Network.
Establishes, maintains, and terminates
communications between systems.
Controls transmission of data through the
network.

Layer 4   Transport.
Provides trnsparent transfer of data between
source and destination. Manages the end-to-
end data flow.
System independent.

Layer 5   Session.
Organizes, synchronizes, and manages the
dialogue between users.
System dependent.

Layer 6   Presentation.
Translates information from machine format
into that understandable by user.
Provides frequently requested services for the
network.

Layer 7   Application/User.
Manages the exchange of information between
the user and the system.

Figure 8.1 The ISO Reference Model of Open System
Interconnection

Each layer in the structure provides a defined set of services for the layer above and requests specific services from the layer below. Layers are defined by function: protocols are defined to control the processes managed by each layer. Relationships between layers, and the information that must be passed between layers are identified.

Interfaces are located where one layer interacts with another and serve to isolate one layer from the next. Because the mechanisms and functions of the layers can be expected to change as technology develops, the functions of the interfaces are precisely defined, but the format of the data interchanges between layers is not. This permits the characteristics of a layer to change without affecting the rest of the model.

The arrangement of the layers begins with the most concrete—the physical layer, which defines cables—to the abstract—the application layer which defines user interfaces.

Layers one through four are considered system independent. Protocols associated with these layers are relevant to all systems. Layers five, six, and seven are considered system dependent. Protocols must be defined individually for each different device. Some experts consider the first four layers to specify the communications functions: the remaining, higher, layers specify data processing functions.

Briefly, the functions of the layers are defined below.

Layer 1: Physical

The *physical layer* is concerned with transmitting raw data over a channel. It defines the mechanical, electrical, functional, and procedural characteristics necessary to establish, maintain, and disconnect the physical connection. The layer is designed to accommodate a variety of physical media and differing control procedures.

Aspects of the network affected by physical layer protocols include cables and connectors; electrical signaling methods; and computer and data communications equipment interfaces. Design problems focus on making sure that when one device sends a one, it is received at the destination as a one, not a zero. Typical issues are how many microseconds a bit occupies; how many volts are used to represent a one and how many for a zero; how many pins the network connector has and what each pin is used for; and whether or not transmission may proceed simultaneously in both directions.

Layer 2: Data Link

The *data link* layer aims at taking a raw transmission facility and transforming it into a line that appears free of transmission errors to the network layer. The layer acts to maintain an error-free channel by detecting and possibly correcting errors on the transmission medium.

The data link layer is responsible for providing the functional and procedural means used by higher layers to establish, maintain, and terminate communications between users. Protocols associated with the data link layer affect the format of data blocks; address code; detection and recovery from errors; and sequence of transmitted data.

Layer 3: Network

The *network layer* is concerned with the transmission of data through the network. Within the network layer, data from the transport layer is accepted, converted to packets, and routed toward the destination. In some sources, this is called the communications subnet layer because it is a subsystem/segment of the network as a whole.

The network layer provides the means to establish, maintain, and terminate network connections between systems, and it controls routing of packets. Associated protocols cover administration and management of data; delivery of status messages; regulation of traffic flow; and the division of labor between the Network Interface Units and the host, in particular who should ensure that all packets are correctly received at their destinations.

Layer 4: Transport

The *transport layer* provides for the transparent transfer of data between users from source system to destination system; that is, it manages the end-to-end data flow. Its basic function is to accept data from the session layer, split it up into messages if necessary, and pass these to the network layer. It must ensure that the pieces all arrive correctly at the other end.

Layer 4 represents the vaguely defined boundary between data communications and data processing. Transport layer protocols control distribution of messages, data integrity, loss or duplicate message prevention, and proper addressing of user equipment.

Layer 5: Session

The *session layer* establishes a connection between users: in effect, it provides the user's interface into the network. The user must negotiate with this layer to establish a connection with a process on another machine. Once that connection has been made, the session layer synchronizes the dialog and manages the data exchange; that is, it manages the session, as the dialog between users generally is called. (Technically, a session is a dialog between two presentation layer processes.)

The session layer takes the communication service of the transport layer and adds application-oriented functions. Layer 5 protocols include rules for establishing and ending connections; verifying that proper communications is occurring; and interfacing the network to the operating system.

Layer 6: Presentation

The *presentation layer* transforms information from machine format into that understandable by user. It performs functions that are requested sufficiently often to warrant finding a general solution for them, rather than letting each user solve the problem.

One major function is translation—between differing file formats, between different terminal formats, between different codes (ASCII to EBCDIC, for instance). The presentation layer is designed to represent information to communicating application-processes in a way that preserves meaning while resolving syntax differences. Typical presentation layer services include data translation, conversion of file formats, and encryption.

Layer 7: Application

The *application layer* provides the user with a window into the system. All exchange of information between the user and the network occurs through this layer. Application services are the only Reference Model services directly comprehensible to users.

Layer 7 protocols are responsible for user and application program support such as passwords, resource sharing, file transfer, and network management.

Operation of the OSI Model in a Network

To a user, communication appears to be taking place directly between systems, with messages going directly to the destination. Communication is perceived as peer-to-peer, that is, as between corresponding layers in a connected system, as diagrammed in Figure 8.2.

In actuality, the process is quite complex, as shown in Figure 8.3. When a user sends a message, the original message is embedded in a protocol and passed downward through the interface to the next lower layer. This layer in turn envelopes the expanded message within its protocol before forwarding the message. As the message passes downward, each layer adds its protocol, and performs its translation/transformation on the message received. A message must pass through all layers between its origination point and the data channel.

Once on the data channel, the message is passed upward through the layers until the requisite layer is reached. As the message moves upward, the surrounding protocols are stripped away and transformations are reversed, layer by layer, until the embedded, original message is revealed.

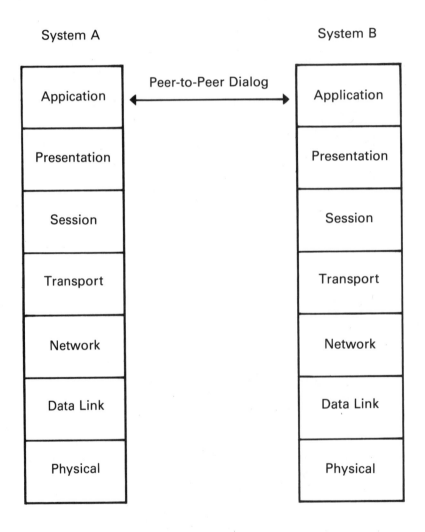

Figure 8.2 The User's View of Communications Through the ISO Layers

Each layer manipulates or changes the message in some way:
In System A, information is added. In System B, the added information is stripped away until the original message is revealed.

H   Message header, added by a layer for its counterpart
Data Unit   Original message, plus headers
F   Flag
A   Address
C   Control
FSC   Error Checking

Figure 8.3 The System's View of Communications Through the ISO Layers

IEEE 802 Project

A local area network, as defined by the Institute of Electrical and Electronic Engineers' (IEEE) Project 802, is a data communications system allowing a number of independent devices to communicate directly with each other, within a moderately sized geographic area, over a physical communications channel of moderate data rates.

The number and kinds of devices a data local area network should connect, the types of services supported, reliability, and so forth, have been precisely defined in the various 802 committees. Two levels of requirements exist: requirements applicable to networks in general and requirements for specific types of networks. A few of the more

general (and hence more relevant for our purposes) requirements have been summarized below. This list is not of all the
general requirements, however, nor even of all the relevant
requirements.

- Size: One LAN should support at least 200 devices and
  should be able to span at least 2 kilometers. LANs must
  be capable of being linked to provide service over a
  greater area.

- Transmission rate: Data shall be transmitted through
  the network at a rate between 1 Megabit per second and
  20 Megabits per second.

- Data communications functions: The data communications supported should include, but are not restricted
  to, file transfer; transaction processing; file and database access; terminal support ("dumb" terminals,
  "smart" terminals, high-speed graphics terminals, etc.);
  electronic mail; voicegrams.

- Attached devices: Devices interconnected by the LAN
  should include computers and terminals; mass storage
  devices; printers, plotters, network and site monitoring
  and control equipment; bridges and gateways to other
  networks; telephones; video cameras and monitors;
  photocopiers; facsimile transceivers.

- Services: The LAN should allow a variety of network
  processes to coexist.

- Expandability: Adding or removing devices must be
  easy. Changes should cause minimal disruption,
  defined as a transient fault lasting no more than one
  second.

- Resource sharing: When devices need to share LAN
  facilities, especially the bandwidth of the bus, this sharing must be fair to all devices, even in overload
  conditions.

• Reliability: The LAN should be highly reliable. No more than one packet per year may contain an undetected error.

Very early in the process of defining a LAN and developing standards, the members of the 802 project recognized that no single technology would satisfy all requirements. Specific applications, with their differing priorities, demand different technologies. Therefore, the 802 project divided into several different committees, listed in Figure 8.4, each focused on creating separate standards.

Figure 8.4 IEEE 802 Committees

802.1—Higher Layer Interface Standard

The 802.1 committee is not developing standards, but has focused on issues relevant to all other committees such as addressing of messages, internetworking, network management, and higher layer interfaces.

802.2—Logical Link Control Standard

The 802.2 committee has concentrated on functions necessary to provide a reliable communications path between two devices. Levels of service and standard frame format have been defined and accepted by the IEEE as a standard. Currently, the committee is working on network management.

802.3—CSMA/CD Bus

The 802.3 is aimed at developing a contention bus network. The standards proposed by the committee were virtually identical to Ethernet specifications published by the DEC-Intel-Xerox collaboration: a 10 megabit per second network, which would allow up to 1000 devices to share a baseband coaxial cable. Although the initial proposal was accepted by the IEEE and the ISO as a standard, the committee has been considering changing the type of cable specified to permit use of a thinner wire.

Currently, two other efforts are underway by 802.3. Part of the committee is studying low cost CSMA/CD broadband using a star topology and is in the process of defining how it would work. A second subcommittee has defined a broadband modem which will allow Ethernet to plug into a broadband cable.

802.4—Token Passing Bus

The 802.4 committee has focused on defining a logical ring on a physical bus so that token passing protocol can be used. Broadband operation with a variety of data rates has been defined.

The specifications have been accepted and are being published as standards. One major problem affecting the usability of a token bus is that the committee is standardizing protocols for a complex network that has not been widely implemented yet.

802.5—Token Passing Ring

The 802.5 has defined a token ring using the star topology to access workstations sequentially. Baseband and broadband versions have been developed. IBM has contributed extensively to this subcommittee. The proposal of the token ring committee was accepted in fall, 1984.

New Committees

Three new 802 committees were formed during 1984:

- 802.6—Metropolitan Area Network: 802.6 is exploring the use of a variety of techniques to send data in a city-wide area. Both CATV and cellular radio are being considered.

- 802.7—Broadband Technical Assistance: 802.7 was formed to define broadband LAN standards.

- 802.8—Fiber Optic: The 802.8 committee is the most recently formed group. Members have begun exploring the use of fiber optics for a very high speed local area network.

802 Reference Model

Although the 802 Project committee's overall approach is based upon the structure of the International Standards Organization (ISO) Reference Model of Open System Interconnection, it does differ from the layers defined by the ISO.

Moreover, 802 is focused on the lowest ISO layers only, sharing the media. No higher layer protocols are under 802 study.

The 802 Reference Model has three layers, as shown in Figure 8.5:

- Physical: concerned with the nature of the transmission medium and the details of device attachment and electrical signaling.

- Medium Access Control: focused on methods of sharing a single transmission medium. Typical issues center on controlling access to the medium, capacity sharing algorithms, station addressing.

- Logical Link Control: concerned with providing a reliable communications path between two devices. The relevant protocols cover the flow of frames between stations; establishing, maintaining, and terminating communications between devices; error control.

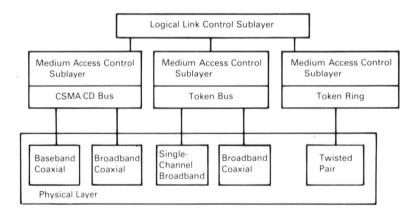

Figure 8.5 IEEE 802 Layers

Figure 8.6 contrasts the 802 layers to the ISO layers. Basically, the 802 Physical Layer is designed to correspond to the ISO Physical Layer. However, rather than being a single layer as in the ISO model, the 802 Physical Layer is itself divided into three parts:

- The physical signalling sublayer.

- Access-unit interface.

- The physical medium attachment.

This division is intended to permit the most complex part of the layer, the physical signalling sublayer, to be physically combined with the station logic in the network controller.

Jointly, the 802 Medium Access Control Layer and the Logical Link Control Layer correspond to the ISO Data Link Layer. Again, the division has been made to allow combining with other network functions.

Figure 8.6 IEEE 802 Layers Compared to ISO Layers

9
Network Architecture

The term most frequently used for the overall design of a network is *architecture*. The goal of architecture is to achieve a high level of performance at a minimal cost. Although local area networks cannot be classified solely by architecture, the specific combination of elements determine the characteristics of a particular LAN.

Specific protocols tend to be associated with specific topologies to the point that topology is often considered the means of implementing the communications protocol. The control strategy used by a network determines the number and type of connected workstations, the nature of interactions between workstations, and the particular transmission link used.

No one architecture is innately superior to another: too many variables affect each individual situation. The most that can be said is that given a specific set of circumstances, one network design seems to accommodate more of the user's requirements than another. Ultimately, the architecture of a network is determined by the location of the workstations to be connected, the demands of the information being transmitted, the available resources, and the nature of the organization creating the network.

Ethernet

One of the best known and more successful local area networks is Ethernet (Figure 9.1), developed at Xerox's Palo Alto Research Laboratories. The original Ethernet was designed to link a set of single-user minicomputers that were scattered throughout the research center. Xerox's immediate goals were to enable the exchange of programs and data and to provide access to various specialized peripherals.

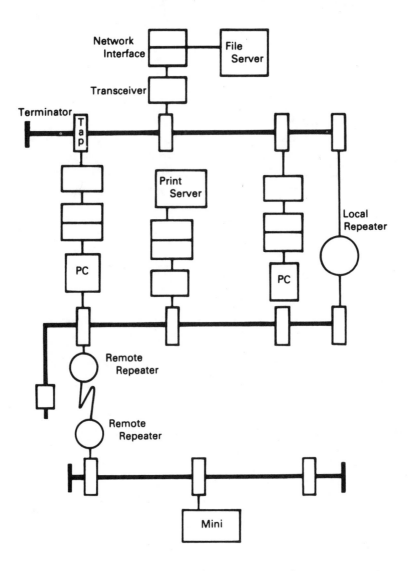

Figure 9.1 Ethernet Network

Ethernet workstations are connected by a single, multidrop, baseband coaxial cable bus using CSMA/CD. As in all contention schemes, the shared channel is a passive broadcast medium with no central control. Access to the channel by stations wishing to transmit is coordinated by the stations themselves.

Workstations are attached to the main bus through a network interface module. The interface buffers and formats messages and subsequently broadcasts the data onto the cable in bursts. The data is in a fixed-length packet containing address information in the header. Current packet size has been defined as 256 bytes, although the technical specification allows packets ranging from 72 bytes to 1526 bytes.

Each station contains address recognition mechanisms, used to identify and accept packets. Every Ethernet workstation, no matter what network it is on, has a unique 48-bit address that is assigned to it and to no other workstation. Hence, when a workstation is moved from one network to another, there is no chance of conflict.

This assigning of unique identities has the advantage of flexibility: networks within a company can be physically reconfigured with minimal operating system reconfiguration.

Data on the network moves at a speed of 10 Megabytes per second, over a maximum distance of 2.5 kilometers. No more than 100 workstations can be connected in a 500 meter segment.

Ethernet's strength is that it provides efficient, high-speed resource sharing services within a limited geographic area, at a relatively low cost.

Interest in Ethernet, and in local area networks in general, was focused by the 1980 announcement from Digital, Intel, and Xerox of a joint project to develop specifications for a local communications network. The project's aim was compatibility, providing sufficient information for various manufacturers such that their widely differing machines could communicate with one another. In effect, the group was establishing a *de facto* standard.

The attempt was largely successful. The IEEE 802.3 contention bus specification is similar to Ethernet in most details. The two designs are not identical, but are extremely close.

Spurred by these factors, quite a number of vendors have announced hardware and software intended to connect microcomputers into an Ethernet compatible network. At the moment, in fact, the majority of microcomputer LANs use a variation on Ethernet.

- "Ethernet on a chip," that is, an implementation of Ethernet protocols on a single silicon chip, is available from Intel and other chip vendors.

- A fiber optic implementation of Ethernet.

- "Cheapernet," a low cost implementation of Ethernet, is close to being accepted as an IEEE 802.3 standard.

ARCNET

ARCNET began as a minicomputer distributed processing system offered by Datapoint. It was the first minicomputer local area network to gain a substantial user base. Since 1982, ARCNET has offered interfaces to several microcomputers.

ARC stands for Attached Resource Processor. Interface units, called a *resource interface module*, or RIM, are microprocessor based. The RIMs monitor and control the operation of the network, particularly data transmission, buffer management, error detection, system reconfiguration, and related tasks, leaving the attached computers free for user applications.

As Figure 9.2 shows, the RIM consists of four components:

- A controller, consisting of the RIM chip, node ID switch, address and data path information, and RAM buffer.

- A clock which provides synchronization and timing for the network.

- A link interface which connects the controller to the communications media via a serial data link and provides the transmitter and receiver capabilities.

- A processor interface which provides the address decoders, bus drivers, buffer access, and other functions required to interface the controller to the system bus of the host processor.

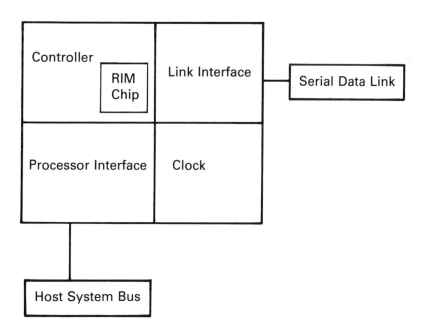

Figure 9.2 RIM

Each workstation is connected by baseband coaxial cable to a RIM which is, in turn, connected to a port on a "hub." The hubs serve as amplifiers and connectors for the RIMs within the network. While any one hub can contain a maximum of 16 RIMs, two or more hubs can be joined for larger systems. Although physically the ARCNET resembles a compound star, logically it works as a token passing ring. (See Figure 9.3.)

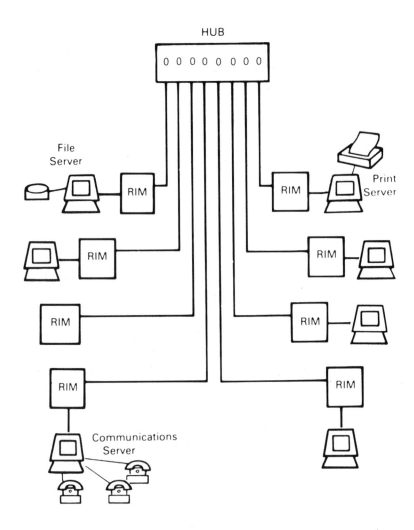

Figure 9.3 ARCNET Network

To send a message, the workstation writes the message into a RIM buffer and issues a transmit command. The RIM sets a status flag when the token is received and the message is sent. To receive a message, the workstation assigns a RIM buffer to the RIM receiver. Acknowledgement is provided of successful or unsuccessful message receipt.

Control tokens are dispersed among the workstations of the network. All nodes share responsibility for the detection and re-creation of lost tokens, and for recreation of tokens after system reconfiguration. The user is unaware of, and has no control over, details of the token passing.

Each RIM has two addresses. The first is a fixed unique identifier. The second address is a relative one and identifies where on the ring the unit logically falls. When a new RIM becomes active, it sends a reconfiguration burst which terminates all activity on the network. The RIM that had control of the line releases it; no other RIM claims control. When the RIMs see an idle line, they know the system is being reconfigured. After a quiet period, all workstations reset their id and begin looking for network activity.

Communications services are restricted to a transfer between a file server and an attached computer. Actual computing is performed separately from where the data are stored, permitting more data to be stored in one location and freeing the computers to process a greater amount of data.

ARCNET imposes few restrictions on the transmission medium. Basically, the receiver at any station must be able to hear the transmitter at any other station. Any two stations must be connected by a single path. Data is transmitted on the network at 2.5 megabits per second. At that rate, the maximum propagation delay between any two stations must be 31 microseconds or less.

Datapoint has made the technical details of its protocol and communications available to the public domain as a way of encouraging other vendors to develop ARC compatible systems. Because only a few relatively inexpensive components are necessary to implement ARC, the appeal is growing.

IBM PC Network

In the fall of 1984, IBM announced a single-wire broadband coaxial CSMA/CD network designed to link IBM PCs. The system is based on an existing network (LocalNet) developed by Sytek, Inc. Although targeted at IBM's three microcomputers—the PC, XT, and AT—the network can support other microcomputers that supply a strictly IBM-compatible internal operating system and that are physically bus-compatible with the IBM PC.

The network, shown in Figure 9.4, has two major components:

- A network translator unit, containing a radio frequency modem and one eight-way cable splitter. The translator is the network's head end.

- PC Network Adapter, to be installed in each PC. The adapter card contains most of the network intelligence; it provides encoding and decoding services for the signals and control.

To the basic components must be added the microcomputers (you supply), and broadband coaxial cable, which IBM has thoughtfully made available in the form of cable kits containing all relevant hardware plus pre-cut cable. Short (1 foot), medium (400 foot maximum), and long (800 foot maximum) distance kits with splitters are available.

The minimal network supports up to eight PCs, each of which may be up to 200 feet from the translator's 8-way splitter. Expander kits, containing additional cable taps, are available for users who want to connect more than nine PCs. The expanded network will interconnect up to 72 micros, at a maximum distance of 2000 feet.

The IBM PC Network is, at the moment, one of the few which provides some level of network security. Although logon passwords are not required, files may be protected by a password.

The real lack is the continuing shortage of network software. Despite being based on an existing network, the network operating system is quite limited. Disk caching and print spooling are possible, system management is not.

Figure 9.4 IBM's PC Network

Network utilities such as electronic mail are missing. Applications software is virtually nonexistent.

IBM Token Ring

In October 1985, IBM announced its long expected token ring network. The token ring, Figure 9.5, is intended as a general purpose local network, aimed at customers who require high-speed communications between intelligent workstations. The initial release supported only microcomputers and gateways to host systems.

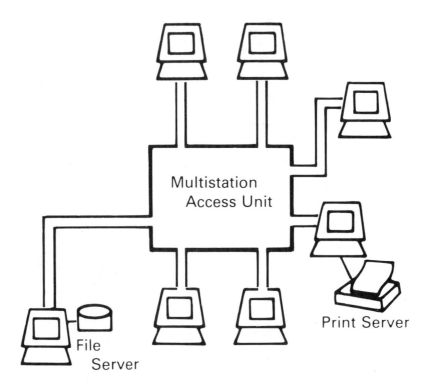

Figure 9.5 IBM Token Ring Network

Conforming to the IEEE 802.5 standard, the token ring is a 4M bit per second star-wired baseband ring using a token passing protocol. It can support up to 72 microcomputers using twisted pair wiring, or up to 260 micros using shielded data-grade (coaxial) cable. Distance between networked devices is limited to 100 meters on twisted pair, 300 meters on data-grade cable.

Hardware components include the following:

- Network PC Adapter card, which must be installed in each microcomputer connected to the network.

- Network Multistation Access Unit, an eight port wire concentrator which serves as the center of the star ring.

Required software components includes the most recent version of DOS, the IBM PC operating system. The token ring supports IBM's NetBIOS (Network Basic Input/Output System). Programs written for the IBM PC Network will run on the token ring.

Other available software includes the following:

- IBM token ring Network/IBM PC Network interconnect program, which enables the two IBM networks to be coupled. The interconnect program runs on a micro dedicated as a gateway.

- Asynchronous Communications Server Program, which provides a gateway between the token ring, the PC Network, and ASCII applications. The program supports two simultaneous dial up lines per server.

- Advanced Program-to-Program Communications for the Personal Computer, providing a Logical Unit 6.2 Systems Network Architecture (SNA) applications program interface. This interface eventually will enable PCs to communicate as peers with larger IBM systems, a task they cannot perform now.

- Series 1/PC Connect Program, to be available in mid-1986.

- IBM PC Network SNA 3270 Emulation Program, which has been tested on the token ring, also will be available in 1986.

Part III

10

Considering the User

Users measure the value of a system by the time and effort required to learn to work with it effectively. For the average, non-technical user, learning to use a microcomputer is like embarking on Alice's journey down the rabbit hole: a mad adventure in an unknown land, where people seem to be talking in English, but the words don't quite make sense. The machines demand endless changes in normal routine. Operating systems are impossible to understand. Software is difficult to use, inefficient, and full of errors. Despite the marvelous promise of technology, the benefits somehow don't seem worth the hassles.

Any new system must:

Solve the problem that it is addressing without creating new ones.

Speak the user's language.

Help do the job more efficiently and productively than it is being done now.

Figure 10.1 New System Requirements

The key to acceptance is knowledge. Familiarity with the network and the microcomputers on it plays a large part in efficient, productive system usage. Realistically, you must assume that even experienced computer users will need some re-education to carry them from what they know to what you need them to know before they use the network. The amount of training required to bring users up to speed on the network depends on three major factors:

- the user's previous experience with microcomputers and/or networks

- the type of network operating system (menu-driven or command oriented)

- the complexity of the application program

For the majority of users, the training sessions will be the first time that they have a chance to learn what the network can do and how to do it. Most users will not need nor want to know the technical details of local area networking; rather, they need the practical, task-oriented information which will allow them to perform their job. Training sessions must present how to work the system in a logical and understandable manner. Stick to essentials: users need a solid foundation on which to begin learning, not endless details that never reach the main point.

Figure four days of hands-on instruction for minimal microcomputer familiarity. Add two to four days for each new application program. Add an additional half to one full day for basic network commands. Short (one or two hour) sessions to reinforce learning should be scheduled once every week for the first month, then once a month as necessary.

Documentation

Documentation plays a major role in providing a truly functional system: the better the documentation, the easier the system will be to install and maintain, and the quicker users will learn to take advantage of the network. Documentation requirements vary with who will use the information and the purpose for which it is employed.

Network documentation is a complete description of the network—workstations, peripherals, routing of cables, and so forth. It is required during configuration and whenever changes are made. Administrator documentation contains all information needed to maintain a functioning network. It includes, but is not restricted to, operators' guides for all equipment; error messages and codes for network, nodes, and major applications; and problem determination guides. User documentation includes information on how to use the workstation, how to use the network, and how to use major applications. For the majority of users, facts are important only in relation to tasks, transactions, and procedures. The actual mechanics of a system are less crucial than ease of discovering what to do next.

No installation is successful until the users are up and running. No matter how good the hardware, no matter how sophisticated the software, the system is a failure if people cannot easily learn to use it. If the existing documentation is confusing, you may need to write your own user manuals.

Good network documentation facilitates learning. The documentation should contain tutorials and practical exercises for novice, non-technical users. Step-by-step instruction on all facets of the workstation and the network are mandatory for all but the most experienced users. Brief descriptions of what each command does and when to use it also should be provided. Detailed information on specialized functions and a reference manual which explains technical complexities (including obscure points) must be provided for the network administrator.

Technical terms should be kept to a minimum in sections aimed at the average user. Terms that are used should be carefully defined. If the concept is too complicated to explain in a few understandable sentences, it should be broken into coherent segments. Illustrations should be plentiful.

In addition, information in the manual must be readily findable through the table of contents and index. Instructions for logging on and off the network and major network commands should be summarized on a reference card.

Ergonomics

Ergonomics means fitting the tool to the hand that uses it and to the task for which it is employed. Understanding how people regard the tasks they do and the tools they use can help make sure you get the most from the LAN. Recent studies demonstrate that productivity increases in an ergonomically sound environment.

In Europe, ergonomic standards have been adopted and must be implemented at all sites where video displays, workstations, and computers are used. Many of the suggestions make excellent sense is any office. While the aim of the European regulations is to increase the typist's comfort and reduce fatigue, not to increase typing performance, common sense suggests that an uncomfortable worker is less efficient than one who is comfortable.

Although ergonomic considerations cost money in the short run, they will lead to greater productivity in the long run. The following excerpt from that list focuses on some of the measures which are comparatively easy to implement.

Workstations

- *Keyboard*: The workstation keyboard is the primary channel of communication between user and LAN resources. Even small differences in design can make a great difference in the ease of using the keyboard. For best results, the keyboard and display should be separate. Stops on the underside of the keyboard will help keep it from sliding around on the desktop. Users should be able to adjust the angle of the keyboard; a 12 degree slant seems to improve typing productivity. The keyboard and cover should have a matte finish to prevent glare and be of a neutral color, neither too bright nor too dark. Light keytops with dark legends are preferred.

• *Key layout*: Although key arrangement is debated hotly, the important factor seems to be consistency so that all workstations use the same key arrangement. People type best (fastest and with the fewest mistakes) on whatever key layout that they are used to and improve with practice. Typing efficiency drops when users change from one keyboard layout to another. Users who routinely work on two or more different keyboards rarely adapt to any: they type more slowly and make many errors because keys are never where expected.

• *Display screen*: The display should be mounted to tilt and swivel. Adjust the display so that the center of the screen is about 20 degrees below eye level and between 14 to 20 inches away. The screen should be anti-glare, have green or amber characters on a dark background, and have adjustable contrast and focus. Screen brightness should be set at three to four times as bright as the room, but not so bright that there is an after-image when the user looks away from the screen. Image quality must be high, with no flicker.

Environment

• *Lighting*: Many offices are too bright for video display work. A light level of 30 to 50 foot-candles is recommended. Reduce overly bright lighting by removing overhead fluorescent bulbs. Provide small, adjustable lights such as an architect's drafting lamp with adjustable arm, by workstations to illuminate papers, etc. Lights should be neither directly above or directly behind the user. Fluorescent lights should have diffusers which direct the light downward.

• *Glare*: Glare from windows and overhead lights must be controlled. Avoid placing workstations near sunny windows, or use shades and/or horizontal blinds to reduce glare.

- *Seating*: Chairs should fit the users, not designer specifications. Orthopedic swivel desk chairs should be provided. Seats should be adjustable for height so that the user is able to keep his or her feet on the floor. Backrest angle and height should be adjustable to provide lumbar support. The chair's design should minimize pressure on the upper legs and behind the knees. A five-legged, untippable star-shaped base with casters is suggested.

- *Desks and tables*: Work surfaces should be tailored for the task. Desks supporting workstations need to be lower than normal desk height and provide an adjustable shelf for the keyboard.

- *Noise*: An office filled with computer noise is a nonproductive workplace. Supply acoustic enclosures for printers or isolate the printers in a secluded area. Enclose or isolate other noise-generating peripherals. In open plan offices, use sound-absorbing dividers rather than panels with a hard surface.

- *Air*: The temperature should be reasonable, with air conditioning and heating systems. Humidity and air quality should be controlled. Air should circulate at least four to five times an hour. Stale air should not recirculate; dust, office contaminants like copier fluid or ink solvents, and tobacco smoke buildup must be avoided. This measure is good for equipment as well as for users.

Work

- *Breaks*: Encourage regular rest breaks. Recommendations range from hourly five minute breaks, to fifteen minutes away from the screen every two hours, to alternating between video display and non-video display jobs. A twice daily stretch period in addition to other breaks is a must.

- *Pregnancy*: Pregnant women should be able to transfer to non-video display jobs, with no loss of pay or seniority.

- *Work content*: To maintain worker motivation, jobs should provide challenge and variety.

11

Configuring and Managing the Network

Coordinating a local area network is a large job, demanding a large variety of skills. Where prior MIS or DP structure does not exist (and possibly even in organizations with well-developed mainframe MIS departments), installation of a microcomputer LAN calls for the creation of a new position, that of network coordinator.

The goal of the network coordinator is to maximize services while minimizing costs. To do so will take time, equipment, money, and lots of attention to details. Shortchanging any part of the effort will cripple the network. For example, when designing the network, particular attention must be paid to type and location of wiring. Just having diagrams isn't enough: every cable should carry an identifying label. Wiring troughs, if used, must have room to trace existing cable and to pull new cables. Adequate provision must be made for future network growth.

Once the LAN is installed, the coordinator must deal with every aspect of daily network operation, from starting up the network in the morning to shutting it down at night, and all that happens in between: interconnecting equipment; providing services; assigning user access rights; setting up menus with network software or batch files; making provisions for data security, back-up, and recovery. To be effective, the coordinator must be aware of how the network is being used within the organization, and stay current with new developments in network and microcomputer technology.

The responsibilities of the LAN coordinator can be broken down into seven areas:

- *Respond* to users' needs.

- *Design* the network installation, including wiring, workstation location, user access rights, user interfaces, and security.

- *Configure* the network at startup and whenever changes are made.

- *Maintain* and *monitor* the network on a day-to-day basis or oversee maintenance provided by a technician.

- *Diagnose* problems and initiate repair.

- *Evaluate* network performance.

- *Plan* for change and expansion, both immediate and future.

A local area network does not exist for its own sake; it was developed as a tool to help people get work done. *People* are the crucial part of the system, not machines. The coordinator is going to need to be as aware of the users as he or she is of the technical issues. Using the network, tinkering with the bits and pieces isn't sufficient. As much as she knows the technical side of the LAN, the coordinator must know the people who use it.

Configuring the Network

Before a network can be brought into operation, network hardware must be installed and system configuration must take place. For most microcomputer networks, the following steps are included:

- Installing network cabling.

- Installing network interfaces for all workstations.

- Installing additional memory cards in some or all of the microcomputers.

- Installing hard disk, printer(s), and/or other peripherals.

- Connecting all equipment to the network.

- Formatting disks and copying the LAN software.

- Identifying all installed equipment for the network operating system.

On the simplest level, configuring the network software parallels applications program configuration. You will need to format blank disks, copy the microcomputer operating system onto the disk, and copy the network software to working disks.

The crucial step is identifying each node for the network. In a few systems, the program is smart enough to read information directly from the interface card, making configuration relatively simple. Typically, the following information is requested for each workstation: (See Figure 11.1 for a sample configuration chart.)

- *Workstation ID*: a unique name for each workstation on the network. If you are lucky, the ID will be in English, and perhaps user-selectable. Some systems use the serial number from the Network Interface Unit or a hexadecimal identifier.

- *Attached Devices*: a list of devices, such as printer or hard disk, which are connected to the workstation and can be shared by other users.

- *User Name:* the name of the person using the workstation. This name identifies the user to other people on the network and may be used by the security system.

- *Usable Devices*: a list of devices attached to other work-stations which can be used from this workstation.

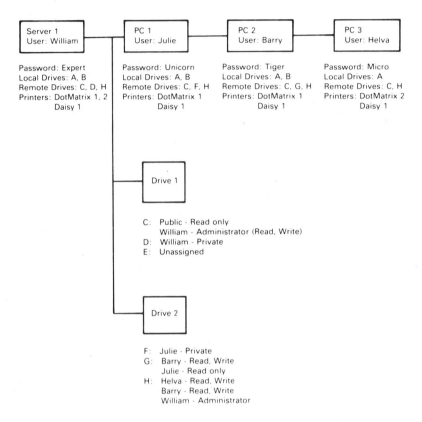

Figure 11.1 Network Configuration

On some networks, the server workstation(s) and user workstations run the same program. On others, the different classes of workstation use different software. Many systems require a special configuration program which is run from each workstation. In other systems, all configuration can be accomplished from a network server. The whole configuration process may have to be repeated every time a physical change (that is, when workstations are added or removed) is made to the network.

The final step is initialization, the process of turning on the network, as a whole and as individual workstations. Some systems are turned off at night and re-initialized each morning. If you have more than six or eight workstations on the network, daily shutdown should be avoided. However, do have all users sign off.

Most systems allow initialization to be achieved through what is called in MS-DOS jargon an "autoexec.bat" file, which contains the daily computer start-up routine. ("Autoexec" for automatic execution—no user intervention needed, "bat" for batch.) The following programs are commonly part of the startup batch file:

- A clock program to read date and time from the system or network clock.

- Device drivers for hard disk.

- The network control program.

- Network device drivers.

- The network configuration activation program.

Normally, all the programs required for system start-up will need to be on the one disk. Network commands usually are the last operations performed before the system is ready.

Installation Hazards

Theoretically, installing the various pieces of hardware and configuring the network is routine. As in any installation of add-on boards, you (or a technician) open the microcomputer, insert the new cards, close the micro, and plug in the cables. Then you turn on the network, and all runs smoothly.

Be forewarned: in reality, installation and configuration present more potential problems than any other part of the LAN installation process. Given the large number of options available for most microcomputers, the few pages devoted to configuration in the documentation, and the short history of local network use, it is easy to underestimate the magnitude of the job.

- First potential complication: Documentation. First rate, step-by-step documentation for the configuration process does not exist. Most of it jumps casually from step to step, skipping a few points along the way, or does not bother to divide the process into distinct steps. In either case, you are guaranteed to become lost and hopelessly confused more than once.

- Second potential complication: During system configuration every piece of equipment—each workstation, drive, printer, and so forth—must be identified for the network operating system. Software and parameters need to be sent to the network interfaces of individual workstations. Copies of the network operating system often must be made for each workstation and distributed. The process is lengthy, tedious, and very prone to error. The chance of misidentifying a component is high. If you make a mistake or forget one piece, the network may not work. Tracking such problems can be difficult.

- Third potential complication: Third-party equipment may conflict with servers and user workstations. Add-on memory boards do not necessarily work with the network interface boards. There can be contention for interrupt channels and direct memory access. Extra care must be taken when installing device drivers and system software to get the various programs in the proper order. This is the dark side of networking that vendors do not like to mention, and users would just as soon forget.

- Fourth potential complication: Although network configuration programs are included with the operating system, many are only minimally user-friendly. Instructions tend to range from fair to poor to unusable. Get your local scholar of arcane computer knowledge to help.

- Fifth complication: This one is bound to cause difficulties even if you've successfully avoided all other pitfalls. You never know what is going to cause problems.

It may be any of the above, none of the above, or something brand new that no one else ever saw before. Remember Murphy's Law: If anything can go wrong, it will.

Solution: Be prepared. Read and reread the documentation before beginning configuration. Set aside adequate time and resources to get the system up and running. If nothing else, the trials of configuration are a strong reason to insist on a reliable system from a vendor who has wide experience with networks.

Configuration Evaluation Factors

Given that configuration can be one of the more difficult aspects of LAN setup, the configuration process deserves a hard look before a purchase decision is made.

Points to look at include the following details:

- Are directions clear, step-by-step, in English, not technical jargon?

- Is there a configuration program?

  — How detailed is it?

  — Are the questions asked listed in the documentation?

  — Does it use icons or other graphics?

- What pre-configuration aids are provided?

  — Worksheets

  — Planning charts

- How much configuration information is required?

• How are workstations and users identified?

— In English?

— By the Network Interface Unit serial number?

— Other?

• Is workstation ID user-selectable?

Troubleshooting

Errors and failures are a fact of life in local area networks, as they are in all data communications and computer systems. Many different conditions may cause network problems: failed disk drives, dead CRTs, stuck keys on keyboards, and all the ills which plague microcomputers are only the beginning of potential hardware problems. Malfunction of network interfaces is more common than most vendors like to acknowledge. Cables may be damaged during installation or afterwards. Every hardware problem must be identified before it can be repaired.

If many different end user applications are run on the network, discovering the cause of problems becomes exceedingly complex. Failure may be caused by a particular program or by the conflict of two programs attempting to access the same file. Applications which directly address the workstation's internal memory may interfere with the network operating system. Single user software may not work on a LAN, even when being used by only one person at a time, as the program is not designed to allot memory to the network interface software. Programs which refer explicitly to a particular disk drive may need to be rewritten when the files they need to access reside on the file server.

Whatever the problem, the objective is to solve it with minimal disturbance to the user. Often the biggest challenge is discovering what went wrong. Before network troubles can be solved, they must be identified and located. The coordinator must be able to detect a problem, help determine where it is located—the particular segment of the network or piece of equipment—and start the process of getting the users back on line.

How much disruption users will tolerate often depends on the importance of the task being performed on the LAN and the frequency with which the LAN fails. Users' perception of the LAN is also important. If users feel, rightly or wrongly, that the technical coordinator is responsive to their concerns, they are more likely to accept problems with good humor.

Problem Reporting

The first step in solving a problem is knowing that you have one. This knowledge implies a regular mechanism for reporting problems and someone to respond to user's calls for help. Not all user-identified problems are true network problems. They may be user problems stemming from inadequate training and lack of thorough documentation, or from other shortcomings. The designated problem-recorder/ solver needs to distinguish the source and respond appropriately.

For most small microcomputer LANs, a simple notebook recording date, time, person reporting the problem, and a brief problem description normally will suffice. Include the resolution: what was done, time service restored, and so forth. For a larger LAN, more formal procedures, such as problem reporting forms, may be necessary. In general, if your established computer problem reporting system works, it can be extended to cover network problems. If there is no prior routine, devise one. (See Figure 11.2 for a sample troubleshooting report form.)

Reporting a problem naturally raises the issue of who is responsible for network maintenance and repair. The vendor? An in-house technician? A third-party repair service? It is important for someone to be readily available, and that the network coordinator can get repair service when it is needed. Remember, the objective is to maintain a functioning network for the greatest possible time.

Date: _____   Time: _____

Name: _____

Location: _____

Phone: _____

Equipment: _____

Problem: _____

_____

_____

Disposition: _____

_____

Additional action needed: _____

_____

Time full service restored: _____

Figure 11.2 Troubleshooting Report Form

Network Monitoring

Large LAN or small, you do need to know how well the network is performing. If you don't know objectively (that is, by sources other than user complaints or raves) how a system is working, how can you know whether it is or isn't doing the job?

You will need diagnostic software and hardware to provide a picture of what is happening on the network. The network operating system should include utilities capable of diagnosing problems, testing how the LAN works under various conditions, and monitoring traffic on the network.

Test equipment may be required to monitor the critical components of the network, report incipient problems or failures, and help identify the source of problems when they do occur.

The Network Control Center

Most LANs can profit from the presence of a network control center, a station from which performance of the whole network, including transmission media and workstations, can be monitored, failures can be identified, and initialization and configuration can be accomplished. It may be part of the network server or a separate workstation with appropriate test equipment.

The testing and monitoring system should be capable of performing the following:

- *Monitoring*: observing the critical components of the network and reporting problems as they occur.

- *Testing*: when problems occur, checking the various parts of the network with the aim of identifying and locating the problem.

- *Recording*: making a record of the traffic flow. The system should be able to begin recording traffic automatically at a certain time of day or have recording initiated by a specified event. Ideally, traffic flow data could be displayed immediately, stored for later display, or printed.

- *Statistics collection*: statistics concerning network activity should be collected on a regular basis. Activities covered include utilization, errors, packet counts, and message or packet length, among others. Results may be presented as graphs, tables, or diagrams.

- *Traffic analysis*: analysis utilities should help understand what is happening on the network and where system variables may need adjusting. As part of analysis, the coordinator may need to select out a substream of network traffic.

- *Modeling*: the capability to generate traffic at user-specified rates to observe network behavior, much like financial modeling using a spreadsheet.

Problem diagnosis will need to be instituted as soon as a problem is reported. Modeling and non-time critical tests may be made on-line during normal operation or with the test center off-line, operating independently. In some networks, it is crucial that testing does not interfere with normal daily operation. In these cases, test data must be taken in a non-disruptive manner and analyzed off-line.

Many of the activities listed above will be useful in fine tuning daily operation and in planning for expansion. The more accurate the observations, the more useful the information will be for planning. Test results should be clearly presented so that valid conclusions can be drawn and action taken.

12

Network Security

A paradox: the underlying goal of a LAN is to make resources, particularly data, more available to users. But to protect corporate data from misuse, access to that data and the equipment on which it is used must be restricted. Before local microcomputer networks are a fully viable solution to information management requirements, a balance must be achieved between open access and security. The issue has two facets:

- Security: the protection of network and organizational resources against unauthorized and/or accidental use, modification, destruction, theft, or disclosure.

- Privacy: the right of individuals to determine for themselves who has access to personal information, under what circumstances that information should be available to others, how the information is made known, and how much information is revealed.

As corporate reliance on computer systems grows, security and privacy of data become increasingly critical. All information important enough to be included in the corporate database for analysis and retrieval is important enough to need protecting.

A small, self-contained LAN will have security problems that are different from those faced on a large, multi-departmental network. But small LAN or large, security measures are mandatory.

Security Versus Microcomputer Technology

Information stored on a floppy disk is inherently not secure, because of the small size of disks, the ease of copying, and the fragility of the media. Even with measures such as physically locking up disks every night and handing out blank disks one at a time, the proliferation of floppy disks is difficult to control. Disks are too readily available, obtainable everywhere, for those measures to work.

Microcomputers containing both a Winchester drive and a floppy disk drive are equally insecure. Given the ease of copying from hard disk to floppy disk and the convenience of having all data in one place, such a system actually may present more of a security risk.

Attempting to control not one or two microcomputers, but an office full of interconnected machines is even more difficult. How can you monitor the millions of bits of data that are daily transmitted from one workstation to another? There are just far too many opportunities for data stored on a network to be copied, tampered with, or to stray.

Computer technology is ahead of computer security technology. The very technology that makes microcomputer networks desirable just as easily can be used to destroy the system and thereby the company.

Becoming Security Conscious

If corporate health is to be maintained, information on the network must not be lost, stolen, or damaged. Programs and data need to be protected from equipment failure, program errors, catastrophe, and human misuse, whether deliberate, such as theft and vandalism, or unintentional. Despite the difficulties, network security is possible.

Granted, *absolute* security is impossible to achieve. But the difficulty of preventing all unauthorized and undesirable actions must not serve as an excuse for foregoing all security measures. (Nor should the need for security result in measures so restrictive that work is hampered.)

Adequate security, sufficient for most organizations, is achievable. You should feel insecure if ordinary and reasonable precautions are not being taken to protect the equipment which constitutes your local area network and the information on it. (See the chart in Figure 12.1.) Steps towards designing an adequate security plan encompass:

- Assessing the security risks in a particular situation, factoring in the size of the LAN, the types of information on it, and the business of the organization as a whole.

- Identifying means to minimize the threats.

- Selecting actions based on the trade-off between the cost and seriousness of possible damage and the cost of prevention.

A secure network requires controls and a person to institute and oversee the measures necessary to insure the proper use of the network. It doesn't matter who—the departmental manager, the network coordinator, the corporate security officer. The important point is to have someone responsible and a plan from which he or she can work.

Areas to be assessed for appropriate preventive measures include personnel practices; backing up of data and equipment; controlling access to data on the network; physical security measures; environmental control; encryption; and disaster planning. Implementing security begins with the people who manage and use the local area network.

LAN Security

1. Security cannot exist without a
    management policy.

2. LAN users should be positively identifiable
    before they have access to network
    resources.

    Prevention: passwords, passkeys,
    authorization measures.

3. Data, hardware, and software should be
    protected from unauthorized and/or
    accidental use, modification, destruction,
    theft, or disclosure.

    Prevention: locks.

4. Data should be reconstructible.

    Prevention: frequent, regular backup of files.

5. Equipment must be protected from fire,
    dirt, and natural disasters.

    Prevention: smoke detectors, sprinklers, air
    conditioning.

Figure 12.1 Essentials of LAN Security

Personnel Practices

The most serious threat to a local network is from misuse
by insiders. Unintentional errors and omissions are the
greatest danger: outright ignorance of the proper use of the

network accounts for a high percentage of disruptions, particularly when the network is first installed. Deliberate malicious acts—dishonest or disgruntled employees attempting to "get even" or to get rich at your expense—can create havoc and even destroy your company. A small, but very real, threat is posed by bored programmers out to beat the system.

Attitude is a crucial part of combating security problems. While some users understand from the first that security is vital and welcome reasonable security measures, others see little or no value in security and therefore are unwilling to adhere to preventive measures, or even may view security as a challenge to be beaten. Employees must be encouraged to develop a positive attitude. Security briefings, identifying areas of potential loss and the consequence of such losses for the organization and for the employee, are helpful.

Training users in security measures is important. Training them in how the LAN operating system works is equally vital. Ignorance causes as much havoc as deliberate mischief. The most elaborate security controls are worthless if your users are trained improperly.

Personnel practices must be designed to enhance security. Special care should be taken in hiring staff who will have access to critical data. Drug, alcohol, and gambling abuse programs can prevent incipient security problems. Termination of staff is always a sensitive issue: particular caution should be used in firing workers who have been part of the network or who have had access to sensitive data.

A *corporate code of conduct* defining what is acceptable behavior can serve as a deterrent as long as the code is visibly practiced and promoted by management. Violations of the code must be dealt with fairly and decisively.

Users respect the need for security most when they feel that they are a valued part of the company. Workers who know that a good job will be acknowledged and achievement rewarded are more willing to look after the company's interests.

Controlling Access to Data

Restricting who has access to the information on the network, how that access is gained, and what each user may do are vital steps. Network users should be positively identifiable before use of the system. Access to specific data on the network should be authorized and, when particularly sensitive data are involved, monitored. (See Figure 12.2 for an illustration of the layers of data security.) Access control can be accomplished through passwords, pass cards and pass keys, and the operating system software.

- Passwords are the simplest control techniques. Users must know the appropriate password or passwords to log on to the network and possibly to gain access to particular files. To be effective, passwords must be assigned randomly and changed frequently. Several microcomputer networks have built-in password protection schemes. If the LAN you favor does not, add-on access-control boards which provide password control are available.

- Pass cards and pass keys are cards containing a microprocessor plus small amounts of memory. The microprocessor contains a unique ID and a series of authorization algorithms. When the network user inserts the card into a pass reader attached to the workstation, the computer checks the ID for validity. If the card is valid, the computer begins the authorization process. The large number of possible combinations prevents accidental discovery of the correct authorization. Any attempt to compromise the pass physically or electronically will render the card useless.

- Operating system software controls the sharing of data, programs, and computer resources. It is a standard defense for large mainframe systems. Such built-in protection should be provided for LANs. Under such an operating system, use tables are established, which define which users are authorized and what access rights they possess. Access may be read only, write, modify, and execute. Each time a user requests data, the request first is checked against the authorization table before either the data is supplied or access is denied.

- As well as assigning levels of clearance to users, the system may assign varying levels of classification to the data files. Clearances and classification are matched for each request.

Access control schemes should be only one part of a security system. Remember that no scheme is foolproof. The larger and more complex the local area network, the more vulnerable the network is to exploitation. Therefore, additional steps should be taken to protect your resources.

- Monitoring changes to the network, particularly programming changes, is mandatory. No single person should have the authority to alter system software or circumvent system security features without specific clearance for each instance. No one person should have free access all files.

- Audit programs are appropriate in systems demanding very tight security. The program is run after a change or on a regular basis to verify that any changes to the network are appropriate, have not bypassed controls, and do not compromise security.

- A positive call back system or similar barrier to intrusion may be necessary. Controlling outside access is often ignored, but very necessary, to the network. Modems and gateways to remote computers offer easy entry to unwanted callers. The use of outside communication should be discouraged where practical. It may be wise to restrict incoming modem access to a dedicated microcomputer not connected to the network, which contains no important data.

- Isolating sensitive data on a separate network and severely limiting access is recommended for situations requiring strict security. Networks containing company private and/or government classified information should severely restrict outside access.

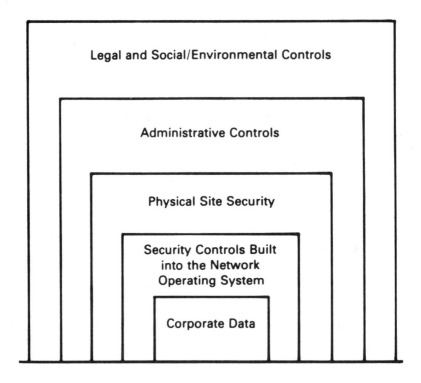

Figure 12.2 Layers of Data Security

Encryption

In encryption, the value of each character in a file is encoded, that is, changed so that it is not understood easily. The new values are generated by an algorithm (formula). The result is a page or file of seemingly meaningless gibberish, which is therefore worthless to intruders.

Most encryption involves a key, consisting of a password or random numbers, used to initiate encoding and decoding of the data. Once a user-defined key is entered, the block of data undergoes a series of transformations and substitutions. While it is possible to crack most codes, anyone without the proper key is faced with an enormous number of possible combinations. If a key is lost, encoded data usually cannot be decoded.

Many products employ algorithms which conform to the Data Encryption Standard (DES) developed by IBM and subsequently adopted by the National Bureau of Standards. The algorithm which controls these transformations is on public record. Products which do not use DES employ a vendor's proprietary algorithm. While such products may not be able to generate as many key combinations, some users prefer an algorithm which is not public knowledge.

One or two keys may be required. Single, or private key systems, are the most common. In private key systems, the same key is used to both code and decode data. In two (public) key systems, pairs of keys are used. One key only encodes data. This key is freely made public. The second key only decodes data and is controlled closely. Since separate keys are required, public key encryption is usually considered to offer more absolute security.

Careful key management is a must for both private and public key encryption. The need to communicate the key to others is a point of weakness. Keys must be kept secure from potential intruders. Less obviously, but equally important, keys must be protected within the organization. To be effective, the user must be able to change the cipher at will.

The Necessity of Encryption

Recently, local area networks have begun to include encryption facilities. The encryption may be performed by a chip on the network interface board, by special encryption hardware attached to the communications lines, or by software within the workstation.

Is encryption really necessary? The verdict is still out. Several factors influence the decision in a particular case.

- Sensitivity of data: The more sensitive the data used within the organization, the more necessary is encryption.

- Cost: While software encryption products are not very expensive, they do require a sizable piece of computer memory, usually 200K or more. Traditionally, hardware encryption products have been quite expensive. With microcomputer memory and add on devices rapidly decreasing in price, cost will be less of a factor in the future.

- Performance: Software encryption tends to be slow, resulting in a decline in system performance. Hardware devices can perform the encryption several times faster than software. But both are exceedingly complex and put a barrier between users and their work.

- Communication: Transmitting encrypted files on the LAN should present no problems. Telecommunications is a different story. Most encryption schemes transform text files into non-text files. Not all telecommunications programs can transmit non-text files. This eliminates encrypted files, as well as graphics and/or spreadsheet data. If users of the local area network have a high need to communicate with other users not on the LAN, the telecommunications program must be able to transmit encrypted files.

Backing Up Data and Equipment

Backup of all data on a regular basis is mandatory for all workstations whether networked or not. Hard disks will need tape backup: floppy disk backup is unwieldy and therefore easily postponed or botched. For particularly critical data, multiple duplicate copies should be kept at different locations, including one in an environmentally controlled off-site location. Taking the critical backup data home is not advisable, nor should it be permitted.

In addition to backing up data, you need to back up hardware. A private stock of replacement parts, particularly network interface units, is needed for the local microcomputer network. Then when one fails, your in-house technician can replace the defective unit immediately. If you have to wait for an outside technician or for replacement parts to arrive from the vendor, you may find yourself without a network for several days.

If the network is larger than a half dozen workstations, it should be possible to provide secondary resources so that the network is not crippled by a single machine failure. One method is to set task priorities: if a workstation performing a vital task fails, its workload may be assigned to a workstation performing a task of lesser importance. Despite the relatively low cost, it is rarely practical to stock a spare microcomputer.

Large networks and organizations which maintain mainframes as well as microcomputers, will need a strategy to back up or replace all data processing capabilities.

Environmental Control

Remember the central computer room with mainframes isolated behind locked doors in air conditioned splendor? Physical safety wasn't the only reason. Dust, dirt, and heat are major enemies of hardware. People and equipment work best where the air is comfortably clean, cool, and free from excess moisture. Air conditioning is no longer a luxury: it is a necessity for all areas where microcomputers and workstations are located.

You may need to pay special attention to environmental threats such as dust from nearby construction or metal shavings on the factory floor. Subtle hazards abound. IBM has discovered that chemicals used by humidifiers can be fatal to disk drives. Microwave/radar radiation and excessive vibration from traffic or nearby construction also may cause disruptions.

Do not forget that people are a potential source of environmental trouble. One spilled soft drink can blow circuits

Figure 12.3 Computer + Food = Disaster

on the machine. Cookie crumbs can clog the keyboard. Computers like smoke no better than lungs do. Cigarette ash can disrupt disk drive heads and cause scratches on floppy disks. Protective plastic covers help. Restricting smoking and food help even more. Keep the site clean.

Fire and Water

Fire prevention measures can save dollars and lives. Even if not mandated by law, smoke detection equipment is a wise investment. Computer environments require a highly sensitive fire detection system. Electrical fires in equipment tend to be too localized to raise room air temperature sufficiently to trigger heat detectors, even though the fire itself burns quite intensely.

Properly rated fire extinguishers throughout the whole building—and employees who know how to use them—are advisable. Sprinkler systems designed for computer environments further help control the extent of fire damage.

Water creates more data processing installation claims than any other hazard. Storms, broken water or sewer lines, roof leaks, sprinkler discharge: whatever the source, water damage is hard to recover from.

Physical Security

Safeguarding the physical security of your site is mandatory. I am constantly amazed at the number of companies that leave side doors wide open and do not have a receptionist in constant attendance at the main entrance. Is it any wonder that microcomputers "disappear" so often? The market for used micros is large and active: don't let your company's machines join it.

Locks are needed. Outside doors should be locked at all times. (But do have them openable from inside for fire safety.) Windows and doors should be protected by burglar alarms which send an immediate alarm message to a security control center or to the police, as well as sounding a warning. Visitors should be required to sign in before entering and sign out upon leaving.

Information, software, and equipment should be kept in locked rooms. Open plan offices and movable walls may be fine for atmosphere, but they offer an open door to theft. Individual workstations should be secured further by using a desk anchor or an alarm pad. Floppy disks should be locked in a desk drawer or cabinet every night.

Report all missing components to a central location. Often, microcomputer components may be "borrowed" internally, and no one will notice until long after the fact. Such practice should be emphatically discouraged.

Disaster Planning

Despite careful maintenance, equipment failure is inevitable. Despite the best precautions, accidents do happen. We are not talking about just major disasters. Without a plan, the loss of even part of your processing capabilities can be devastating.

Disaster planning can be seen as having three aspects:

1. Minimizing the probability of disaster.

2. Minimizing the damage if disaster does occur.

3. Recovering from damage caused by the disaster.

The extent of the recovery plan depends on your situation. Before a plan can be devised, you will need to identify where your vulnerabilities lie. Which applications, processes, or data are vital to keeping the company operating? What measures are needed to compensate for loss? Where, for instance, would extra staff help, or are alternative processing sites required? How much time can elapse between disaster and recovery? It may be useful to keep this rule of thumb in mind: you must be able to recover from disaster quickly enough to keep your business running.

Security
Evaluation Factors

Security evaluation factors refer to the provisions inherent in the network operating system, not to conditions that exist within your organization.

Does the LAN provide the following?

- Passwords

- User ID's

- Access rights assignable by individual

- Encryption

- Is the available security appropriate to the needs of your organization?

13

Communicating with the World

Not all the information used by an organization originates within that organization. Some extremely valuable data comes from outside: from a sales office in another city; from government economic forecasts; from stock market reports; from commercial data libraries and services, such as Dialog, D.R.I., Lexis; from almost any source that you can name.

Even when needed data does originate in-house, it may not be available on the LAN. Perhaps you need the graphics capabilities of the mainframe or get sales figures from the mini in marketing. Or maybe your organization has two local area networks, and the data you need are on the other one. In any case, the need for communication outside the immediate local area network tends to increase over time, as use of the LAN increases.

Before connections can be made with devices off the LAN, all the problems that plague communications between two dissimilar machines (such as addressing, differing message formats, error control) must be solved for the network as a whole. Two categories of communications service are required:

1. Basic functions: services that must always be provided, even when the networks desiring to communicate are of identical types. These include routing of messages from one network to another and addressing messages across network boundaries.

2. Extended functions: services that must be provided when the networks requesting interconnection do not provide the same services. Examples are improved error detection, protocol conversion, and packet resequencing.

The level of interconnection services that must be provided depends on the situation:

- A modem if the needed resources are remote and infrequently accessed.

- A communications server for networks with high demand for outside communications.

- Bridges and/or gateways for connecting two networks.

- A micro-mainframe link to get data from the mainframe.

Modems

The basic function of the modem is to accept data from a transmitting computer and translate the digital computer signals onto the analog voice-frequency telephone carrier wave. Conversely, the modem decodes those signals it receives from a remote computer. (See Figure 13.1.)

The more features that a modem has, the "smarter" it is considered to be. Cost of the modem is directly proportional to transmission speed and the built-in "intelligence." The speed of a modem is the maximum rate at which it can transmit or receive data.

- Low speed modems transmit at 600 bits per second or less.

- Medium speed modems transmit at 1200 to 9600 bits per second.

• High Speed modems transmit at more than 9600 bits per second.

Chart 13.1 shows modem standards and speeds.

Most serious users find 300 bits per second agonizingly slow even for relatively small quantities of data. If you needed to send a 100,000 word file to your office 20 miles away, it would be faster to copy the file to a floppy disk and send it by a messenger on bicycle.

Figure 13.1 Computer Connected to the Telephone System

Consider that the standard microcomputer screen holds 25 lines of 80 characters each, or 2000 characters. The standard double-spaced typewritten page also contains 2000 characters. At 300 bps, either takes just over a minute—66 seconds to be exact—to send. You would need over an hour to send a 50 page report, 3.2 hours to transmit an entire floppy disk containing 356,000 characters. A long novel such as *Crime and Punishment* would require almost a full 24 hour day.

At 1200 bps, one typewritten page takes under 20 seconds; our 50 page report would take about 15 minutes; and the data contained on a floppy disk would require 48 minutes to transmit. Our theoretical long novel would take 5 hours and 45 minutes to transmit.

Speed	Standard
300 bps	AT&T 103
1200 bps	AT&T 212A
2400 bps	CCITT V.22
4800 bps	none
9600 bps	none (CCITT V.32 under development)

Chart 13.1: Modem Standards and Speeds

Modem Capabilities

Most modems have at least some intelligence: some new modems contain the equivalent of a small microcomputer and buffer memory. Almost all come with software designed to enhance functionality. Overall modem capabilities may include the following features:

- Memory: to store telephone numbers which the modem can dial automatically when requested by the user or the workstation.

- Autodial: permits the user to dial a telephone number through the workstation keyboard, or through software access of a telephone number and associated information stored in a disk file, rather than using the telephone dial.

- Autoanswer: gives the workstation the ability to respond to an incoming call without human intervention. Autoanswer capability frequently is associated with the ability to store any messages received.

- Autocall: allows the user to preset messages for delivery at a specific time and date to a specific place, and/or in response to specific callers or events.

- Callback: when the modem answers a call, the caller's identity is checked against a previously stored permission list. If the caller is authorized, the modem calls the user back at the telephone number also contained on the list. Thus, while unauthorized callers may have a valid code, they will not connect with the computer unless they have gained access to the telephone actually associated with that code.

- Status reporting: informs users of the progress of the call they have placed. Identifies if the line is busy, ringing, or answered.

- Autoredial: redials the last number called, without requiring the user to start all over.

- Autologon: automatically enters the password and other signals needed to identify a user to a remote computer.

- Self-test: diagnostics to recognize a problem within the modem itself.

Communications Servers

Communications servers (Figure 13.2) are designed to relieve the network of data communications tasks. In effect, the server acts like a telephone switchboard, performing for workstations and digital data many of the same functions that a standard PABX performs for telephones and voice, such as message routing and data encoding/decoding.

Figure 13.2 Communications Server

Through the communications server, a workstation may call another resource (local or remote), search an internal directory for available resources, or wait on a line for a particular resource to become available. The communications server also may be employed to connect incompatible devices to a network.

While a communications server duplicates the services of a modem, particularly in providing access to long-haul telephone networks, there are differences. Most modems are connected to one workstation and can be used by only that workstation; communications servers are connected to the network and thus are available to all workstations. Most communications servers can manage multiple requests. In addition, the communications server offers more functions, such as multiplexing and switching capabilities; higher error-free speed; and greater flexibility.

Large-scale systems may use a communications server rather than developing network-specific hardware interfaces. The LAN's communications abilities are restricted to the functions supplied by the specific communications server.

Gateways

Between any two networks, major barriers to communications may be present. Typical difficulties include the following:

- One network may allow a larger maximum packet size than the other. Packets may have to be broken up into smaller pieces for another, a process called *fragmentation*.

- A network's methods of handling errors may range from no error recovery to highly reliable end-to-end service within the network. Internetwork service should not depend on, nor be interfered with, by the nature of an individual network's error recovery capability.

- Each network will have its own user access control protocol. The internetwork facility must be able to interface with it as needed. Furthermore, a separate internetwork access control technique may be required.

A gateway serves as the means of communicating between networks and is designed to reduce the problems of interfacing a large number of different networks and/or devices. The networks involved may be two local networks, which employ different higher level protocols, or a local network and a long-haul network. Some gateways can accommodate multiple networks. (Figure 13.3 illustrates a gateway connecting two networks.)

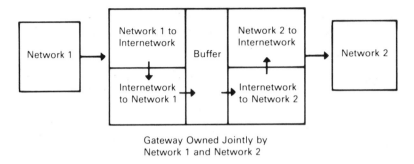

Gateway Owned Jointly by
Network 1 and Network 2

Figure 13.3 Gateway

The gateway provides the necessary translation of data from the form used by one network into the form used by another, much as a United Nations interpreter who can accept Portugese input and produce Chinese output.

Technically, the gateway does the following:

• Accepts messages from any device on the LAN;

• Reformats the data for acceptability to the distant network;

• Adds the necessary control, addressing, and routing data;

• Transmits the message through to its destination.

When a gateway receives data, it converts the data to the protocols used by the local network for delivery to the destination node.

To perform its task, the gateway uses a combination of hardware interfaces, software protocols, and specialized network control applications packages. In addition to intelligence, the gateway contains a generous amount of buffer memory. Buffering is essential: when the gateway receives a message to be transmitted from one network to another, it must wait for an opportunity to transmit on the connecting media. Furthermore, the buffer capabilities allow the gateway to perform speed-matching, and other required protocol conversions.

In a gateway connecting only two networks, as many as four translation processes may occur:

1. Network 1 protocol to internetwork protocol.

2. Internetwork protocol to network 1 protocol.

3. Network 2 protocol to internetwork protocol.

4. Internetwork protocol to network 2 protocol.

Translation to and from internetwork protocol is not always necessary. In a gateway connecting multiple networks, similar translation processes are provided for all attached networks.

Additionally, the gateway may gather network statistics to assist in error detection and recovery; monitoring utilization, throughput, and delay; and status reporting.

Bridges

As networks increase in size and complexity, an orderly means of handling the demand for service is required. In general, the larger a network, the more diverse the requirements of the users. Rather than attempting to satisfy all users, it may be desirable to divide the network into subnetworks.

A bridge (Figure 13.4) connects two subnetworks, which normally are located near each other. Because the subnetworks are segments of what was once a single system, networks connected by a bridge use the same internal protocol for medium access and the same interface to attached devices.

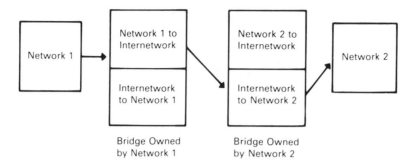

Figure 13.4 Bridge

The major task of the bridge is to selectively pass messages from one subnetwork to the other and to provide any necessary buffering. While the two subnetworks may be connected by long-haul facilities, the bridge gives LAN users no access to the wider capabilities of the long-haul system. Thus, even if the bridge uses telephone lines to join the subnetworks, users would not be able to place calls to other locations. The bridge has minimal impact on the key characteristics of the network.

Like a gateway, a bridge contains two network-specific interfaces, one for each subnetwork it connects; a limited amount of buffer memory; and sufficient intelligence and control to identify which messages need to be transmitted to a destination on another subnetwork. The bridge buffer serves two purposes: first, to hold messages while waiting for a chance to pass them between the two subnetworks. Second, it allows differing data rates to be employed on a single local network.

It is possible for the bridge to know the locations of all workstations on all networks. It then will be capable of passing packets through in appropriate cases. To do so, station addresses must be unique across the whole set of linked networks, implying a large address field. For large networks, or those which are changing rapidly, the overhead associated with this system becomes insupportable.

The main difference between a bridge and a gateway is the networks involved. Bridges connect similar networks, which tend to be local in relation to one another. Gateways connect dissimilar networks and interconnect local area and long-haul networks. As a result of the different interconnect requirements, while a gateway performs protocol conversion, the bridge does not.

Subnetworks

At what point does it become desirable to operate two related networks rather than just one? Although the problem sounds difficult, it's not much more complex than the decision to buy two copies of a best-selling novel for the library rather than one.

The following factors encourage establishing subnetworks:

- Performance: Performance in a local area network declines as the demand for service increases. In a network with a high traffic volume, overall load (and hence delays in response) can be reduced by partitioning the network into self-contained subnetworks, each with a low demand for the resources of another subnetwork.

- Security: Some data on the network, such as accounting or personnel files, is important enough that access to it should be restricted and supervised closely. Isolating sensitive data in a subnetwork makes it considerably easier to safeguard.

- Reliability: The hidden danger in joining all the workstations in an organization into a single network is that a fault on the network may disable all communications. Dividing a network into semi-autonomous clusters can minimize problems associated with total network failure.

- Growth: Realistically, there is no way to provide for an unknown number of potential users with widely varying needs that change over time. Subnetworks offer a way to keep size and services manageable.

- Cost effectiveness: On scattered locations, such as between buildings in an industrial park, establishing separate subnetworks at each location may be easier and more cost effective.

- User requirements: When users' demands vary greatly, particularly when some users have a demand for augmented services not required by a majority of users, two networks with different resources may better satisfy users' needs.

The logical way to divide an existing network into subnetworks is along natural divisions within the organization, such as by department or by groups with shared interest and requirements. In this way, traffic across the bridge can be minimized.

The architecture of the subnetworks determines the complexity of the bridge. A long-distance bridge, comprised of two half-bridges at either end of a point-to-point communication channel is possible. Each half-bridge consists of a network-specific interface, a controller, and sufficient buffers to handle the traffic over the link.

Micro-Mainframe Links

There are two major reasons for users to link microcomputers with the mainframe: time and cost. Much of the data used by managers is already available on the mainframe. Why retype data that can be downloaded? As for cost, the mainframe provides more cost-effective storage than a micro.

The purpose of micro-mainframe links is to allow workstation users to download files for local use and storage. Conversely, microcomputer files should be able to be uploaded quickly for batch processing and/or storage on the mainframe. Ideally, the process should be transparent to the user and not necessitate complex procedures.

Most micro-mainframe linkage involves terminal emulation, in which the microcomputer mimics a terminal on the
host network. In such a link, the microcomputer relin-
quishes control, and performs to the dictates of the mainframe, just as if it were a terminal. Basic terminal emulation
can be achieved through software and/or hardware.

The communications software may be run from the
microcomputer, or the mainframe, or it may require complementary programs on both machines. Terminal emulation
hardware comes in the form of add on communications
boards installed in the micro workstation.

The earliest terminal emulators simulated dumb-
terminals and were so primitive as to be barely functional.
Current basic terminal emulation products offer batch file
transfer, and, while they are not interactive, do offer the
ability to download a whole file at a time, as opposed to
earlier screen-by-screen downloading. The workstation then
can manipulate the data or create a new file using microcomputer applications programs, before passing the file back to
the mainframe.

A second level of micro-mainframe linkage is provided
by terminal emulators with file transfer and file conversion
capabilities. A task defined on the workstation is executed on
the mainframe, much as in traditional distributed data
processing. The micro has the ability to execute main-
frame-dependent applications.

More sophisticated emulators permit file-access, allowing users to specify parts of a file or to specify pre-
processing operations, such as summaries and averages. Such
programs require some knowledge of how the data is stored
on the mainframe. Quite complex interaction is possible,
depending on the hardware and software used.

Transparent service, in which information can be created, manipulated, and transferred between machines with
minimal user intervention, is the goal of all micro-mainframe
links. True transparent interactive service is easier to accomplish when the same database exists on both the micro and

the mainframe. With a single database, it is not necessary for the link to handle data format conversion or translation of queries.

Before selecting any micro-mainframe link, the user needs to consider the following points:

- *Functionality*: What level of service does the hardware/software provide? Not all necessary features are provided by one product. Be sure that the one you select contains the functions that your users need.

- *Ease of use*: How much training will users need to be efficient? Pay particular attention to the user interface and to documentation as indicators of complexity. The easier a product is to use, the greater the acceptance and use of it will be. Nontechnical end users need a simple, familiar interface. At the same time, experienced and/or technically oriented users need the ability to get where they want in a minimum of actions. All users need detailed information on the cause of problems.

- *Support*: Who will install and configure the product? Who will solve users' problems?

14

Taking Stock

Before you can install a LAN, you need to make the following assessments:

1. Know what resources—hardware, software, information—exist within your organization and how those resources are used.

2. Identify your requirements, factoring in constraints such as the type of equipment to be interconnected, time, budget, and level of security necessary, which will affect your decision.

3. Set your priorities.

4. Evaluate current LAN products, either by yourself or by talking to vendors.

Charts in this chapter are designed to help identify the available resources which will be part of your LAN.

Hardware Inventory

The object of the hardware inventory is to develop a comprehensive list of equipment. The larger your organization is, the more microcomputers you wish to connect with a network, the more important it is to be thorough. Be warned: it may take quite a lot of work to obtain accurate information about the resources which exist in your organization. But effort expended now does pay off. All the information gathered will be usable for better management of company resources, networked or not.

Once each device has been identified, a summary sheet should be prepared to provide an overview. It should show the number of devices of each type, the distribution of the traffic load over the hours of each day in the month, and the peak hours of usage in a day, week, and month. This summary sheet will be used when you set priorities and when you begin to define your purchases. Drawing a map showing locations of the equipment will be necessary before actual network installation.

MICROCOMPUTER INVENTORY

For each microcomputer in use in the organization:

1. Micro: _____
    Model number: _____
    Serial number: _____

2. Manufacturer: _____
    Address: _____
    City, State, Zip: _____
    Telephone: _____

3. Description: _____
    Memory: _____
    Number and type of drives: _____
    Graphic capabilities: _____
    Special boards installed: _____
    Special functions, abilities: _____

4. Attached peripherals: _____
    Hard disk: _____
    Printer, plotter: _____
    Modem: _____
    Other: _____

5. Location: _____

6. Installation date: _____

7. Average traffic volume: _____
    Hours of use: _____
    Number of users: _____
    Peak activity hours: _____

8. Where/how data was collected: _____

HARD DISK INVENTORY

For each hard disk to be attached to a workstation on the network:

1. Device: _____
    Model number: _____
    Serial number: _____

2. Manufacturer: _____
    Address: _____
    City, State, Zip: _____
    Telephone: _____

3. Description: _____
    Size: _____
    Backup method in use: _____

4. Location: _____

5. Installation date: _____

6. Average monthly usage: _____
    Hours of use: _____
    Number of users: _____
    Peak activity hours: _____

7. Where/how data was collected: _____

PRINTER AND PLOTTER INVENTORY

For each printer or plotter to be attached to a workstation on the network:

1. Device: _____
      Model number: _____
      Serial number: _____

2. Manufacturer: _____
      Address: _____
      City, State, Zip: _____
      Telephone: _____

3. Description: _____
      Type: _____
      Speed: _____
      Special abilities: _____

4. Location: _____

5. Installation date: _____

6. Average monthly usage: _____
      Hours of use: _____
      Number of users: _____
      Pages of output: _____
      Peak activity hours: _____

7. Where/how data was collected: _____

MODEM INVENTORY

For each modem:

1. Device: _____
      Model number: _____
      Serial number: _____

2. Manufacturer: _____
      Address: _____
      City, State, Zip: _____
      Telephone: _____

3. Description: _____
      Type: _____
      Speed: _____
      Special abilities: _____

4. Location: _____

5. Installation date: _____

6. Average monthly usage: _____
      Hours of use: _____
      Number of users: _____
      Peak activity hours: _____

7. Where/how data was collected: _____

OTHER PERIPHERALS INVENTORY

For each peripheral which will be attached to a workstation on the network, but is not inventoried elsewhere:

1. Device: _____
   Model number: _____
   Serial number: _____

2. Manufacturer: _____
   Address: _____
   City, State, Zip: _____
   Telephone: _____

3. Description: _____
   Speed: _____
   Special abilities: _____

4. Location: _____

5. Installation date: _____

6. Average monthly usage: _____
   Hours of use: _____
   Number of users: _____
   Peak activity hours: _____

7. Where/how data was collected: _____

HARDWARE SUMMARY

1. Microcomputers: _____
   Type: _____
   Number: _____

2. Hard disks: _____
   Type: _____
   Number: _____

3. Printers and plotters: _____
   Type: _____
   Number: _____

4. Other peripherals: _____
   Type: _____
   Number: _____

5. Programs: _____
   Function: _____

Software Inventory

Do you know what software is available in your organization? How many copies of how many different programs? Have you worried about illegal copies of programs? Most microcomputer programs restrict use to a single user on a single microcomputer. Network use, with several people sharing one copy of a program, does not fall within routine licensing restrictions. To be strictly legal, each user must have his or her own program, or, where available, you must obtain a site license from the vendor, allowing duplicate copies of a program. Sharing software designed specifically for network use is legal. Right now, while you are taking inventory, is a good time to make sure your organization is "clean."

Applications software and software tools—utilities, programming languages, development programs, application generators—should be included.

APPLICATION PROGRAM INVENTORY

For each program, or distinct version:

1. Program name: _____
    Version number: _____
    Number of copies owned: _____
    Serial number(s): _____
    License (single CPU, site): _____

2. Manufacturer: _____
    Address: _____
    City, State, Zip: _____
    Telephone: _____

3. Description: _____
    Major functions: _____
    Information generated: _____

4. Location: _____

5. Purchase date: _____

6. Average monthly usage: _____
    Hours of use: _____
    Number of users: _____
    Peak activity hours: _____

7. Where/how data was collected: _____

SOFTWARE TOOL INVENTORY

For each program, or distinct version:

1. Program name: _____
   Version number: _____
   Number of copies owned: _____
   Serial number(s): _____
   License (single CPU, site): _____

2. Manufacturer: _____
   Address: _____
   City, State, Zip: _____
   Telephone: _____

3. Description: _____
   Major functions: _____

4. Location: _____

5. Purchase date: _____

6. Average monthly usage: _____
   Hours of use: _____
   Number of users: _____
   Peak activity hours: _____

7. Where/how data was collected: _____

Information Use Inventory

Now that you have identified the tools used to handle information, you need to define who uses it and how. (Do not be surprised if this survey reveals masses of information being circulated from one employee to another, but never used productively. There's a lot of worthless paper in any system.)

Undoubtedly, this phase of the inventory will take more effort than the hardware and software inventories. Users will be asked to respond to questions on information received, information processed or generated, and information passed on to others. The quality of the answers received is largely dependent on the willing participation of the users. Interviewers must be particularly sensitive to the users' needs in order to receive full answers to their questions. The aim is to get an overview, not exact statistics. Remember that knowing where and how your staff get their information is a crucial part of the evaluation process.

INFORMATION RECEIVED SURVEY

1. Item: _____

2. Description: _____
   Content: _____
   Type: _____
   Form: _____
   Quantity: _____

3. Source: _____

4. Regularity of exchange: _____

5. Response time: _____

6. Action required: _____

7. Where/how data was collected: _____

TASK SURVEY

For each type of information worked with on a regular basis:

1. Task: _____

2. Description: _____

3. Frequency: _____

4. Input: _____
   Source: _____
   Quantity: _____
   Action required: _____
   Resources used: _____

5. Output: _____
   Destination: _____
   Quantity: _____
   Form: _____

6. Time required: _____

7. Where/how data was collected: _____

INFORMATION DISTRIBUTED
SURVEY

1. Item: _____

2. Description: _____
    Content: _____
    Type: _____
    Form: _____
    Quantity: _____

3. Destination: _____

4. Regularity of exchange: _____

5. Storage format: _____

6. Where/how data was collected: _____

INFORMATION USE OVERVIEW

1. Most important information: _____

2. Source: _____

3. Busy time: _____

4. Daily telephone calls: _____
   Initiated: _____
   Received: _____

5. In the past six months, have you noticed any change in the quantity of information that crosses your desk? __
   _____

6. Do you expect this information load to increase in the next six months? _____

7. In the next year? _____

8. In the next two years? _____

9. Have you noticed any changes in the types of information you receive? _____

10. In the types of information you use? _____

11. Do you anticipate any changes? _____

12. What information or tools would help you perform your job better? _____

13. What concerns you most about possible changes in your job? _____

14. Where/how data was collected: _____

15

Evaluating Current Local Area Networks

By now, you should have a good idea of the resources already available within your organization. The next step is looking at your requirements. Requirements have two facets:

- Social, encompassing users with their differing responsibilities and needs.

- Technical, encompassing the numerous devices to be interconnected and the services to be provided by the proposed system.

Careful definition of your requirements is crucial: if your requirements are developed haphazardly, are based on insufficient information, or are disorganized, the resulting network will be unsatisfactory. Without a clear understanding of your expectations and requirements, the wrong network probably will be installed. Practical concerns, such as the microcomputers and peripherals to be interconnected, the services to be provided, and site considerations will be the major factors influencing the network you select.

Realistically, no one network will satisfy all (or even most) of the needs of all the users. Therefore, the decision process becomes one of setting priorities and making trade-offs. Remember, your object is to find the network that will satisfy your needs for the next few years, not to select a LAN that will permanently solve your communications problems.

Ultimately, your choice of LANs is influenced by the following factors:

- The types of equipment already installed in your organization.

- The services your users need.

- Available products.

- Your budget.

Consideration Points

The questions and issues presented below are designed to help you think about your requirements and to provide broad guidelines toward LAN selection. Some questions will need to be asked again when you evaluate specific LANs. Unlike the inventory questionnaires, it is not necessary to answer all the questions asked, nor to address all the issues. It is important, however, to identify those issues which are of importance to your organization.

The User Community

Who will use the LAN? Is the intended audience a small, homogeneous community, with similar user requirements and similar tasks? Or are the network users a large group, with differing requirements and many diverse demands? The more diverse the user community, the harder it will be to satisfy all the users' needs. For microcomputer networks, the optimum plan seems to be multiple work-area networks, each of which provides information and resources to a group of people performing related tasks.

Who will have access to the network? Will data, programs, and resources be available to anyone in the company regardless of the physical location of the user and the resource? Or will access be restricted to specific groups?

What tasks do your users perform? Which of these tasks will be performed on the network? What services are needed to support your users? As a minimum, the network should be able to support word processing, data base management (data entry, report generation, and so on), and calendar management. The network operating system should provide record and file locking, electronic mail, and print spooling. Consider services not yet in demand, then factor sufficient flexibility into your plan to add these services at the appropriate time.

Usability

From the end users' point of view, how easy and convenient is working through the network? Is network operation invisible to the user? Usability is influenced by the interface between the user and the network. Menu driven systems are the easiest to use, while command driven systems are more efficient for experienced users and can provide more functions. Examine the network software, documentation, and training aides for a rough estimate of usability.

If communication over the network is troublesome, the network will never realize its potential. The usability of a network is damaged by a complex, difficult, or lengthy interface. Signing on should be accomplished with minimum user effort. By the same token, signing off from the network should require little effort and must not disrupt other operations on the network.

Once the user is connected to the network, tasks should be performed almost as if they were performed on a standalone workstation. Dialog with the network should be fast, and easily initiated. Direct physical interaction between the user and the network should be minimal, except for unusual occurrences, such as failure.

Network Capacity

How many workstations will you be connecting? Six? Twenty? One hundred and twenty? More? For two to four microcomputers, a low-end network using the microcomputers' communication ports may be sufficient. Most CSMA/CD networks using twisted pair wire can accommodate thirty-two microcomputers. Installations of more than one hundred workstations will require a broadband network.

Are you connecting a single type of microcomputer, compatible microcomputers, or diverse microcomputers with different operating systems? Is there a mainframe or mini that you would like to include in the network? Interconnecting microcomputers and equipment from different manufacturers is difficult on most networks. Newer microcomputer LANs permit multiple operating systems to share the same resources. Few, however, permit the diverse systems to interchange data.

Where are the users located? Adjacent to each other on one floor of a building, on different floors, or in separate buildings? Is there a demand for inter-site communication? How far apart are the sites? Finding a LAN which meets your requirements is simplest if just one site is involved. If several locations must be supported, the network will, of necessity, be more complex. Distance between sites is important: if, for instance, the sites are ten miles apart, networks which cannot go that far are eliminated automatically. (See Figure 15.1.)

	Small	Medium	Large	Very Large
Topology:				
Bus	X————————X			
Ring			X————X	
Star		X————X		
Media:				
Twisted Pair	X————X			
Baseband Coaxial	X————X			
Broadband Coaxial		X————X		
Fiber Optic			X————X	

Figure 15.1 Distance Compared by Topology and Media

What types of traffic will use the network—data, voice, video? Must these services be integrated? If your network will support data only, baseband media—twisted pair, or baseband coaxial—is sufficient. Broadband coaxial and/or fiber optic are necessary when you include voice and video transmission.

How heavily will the network be used? The LANs ability to deal satisfactorily with the load is influenced by protocol. Contention protocols, optimized for networks with low traffic volume, tend to become unstable under heavy load, with service rapidly degenerating. Polling networks can support moderate to heavy traffic volume, but perform best with a moderate load. As traffic increases, transmission delays may become unacceptably long. Polling is inefficient for light loads: most of the burden on the network is overhead. Token passing networks cope well through the entire traffic spectrum and do not degrade markedly as the demand for service increases. (See Figure 15.2.)

	Low	Moderate	High	Very High
Media:				
Twisted Pair	X			
Baseband Coaxial	X———X			
Broadband Coaxial		X———X		
Fiber Optic			X———X	
Protocol:				
Contention	X			
Token Passing			X	
Polling		X		

Figure 15.2 Network Traffic Capacity by Media and Protocol

Traffic patterns are not random. Workstations acting as servers will bear far more traffic than user workstations. Within a large network, certain local groups will naturally form centers of activity and interaction. These groups are prime candidates for subnetworking.

Surveys of existing mainframe networks suggest that the peak traffic load is approximately two to two-and-one-half times the average daily traffic. The network selected must have sufficient capacity to meet the expected peak traffic load.

Expandability

How expandable and/or flexible should the network be? How much do you expect your organization to change in the next few years? Take your best estimate and double or triple it. It is far easier to ignore excess capacity than to operate with a system that is too small.

In most situations, expandability and flexibility are vital. Organizations grow and change; the technology is also changing, maturing. The network installed must be able to accommodate evolution. Some networks are inherently more flexible than others.

There are two facets of expandability: the innate ability of a system to accommodate additional nodes and cover larger distances and the increase in size dictated by the growth of your organization. Without a doubt, growth will take place. Any LAN selected must be able to support increases. A modular design is best, one in which additional cable can be laid and new workstations connected without rewiring the whole network. (See Figure 15.3.) Bus and ring networks can accommodate change readily. Growth of a star network is restricted by the number of available ports on the central server.

Expansion of token passing and polling networks is more complex than expansion of a contention network. Token passing networks require that the token circulation pattern is revised each time an addition is made. Polling networks also require a new order of precedence. In contrast, addition of workstations to a contention network is relatively easy, as the new workstation must simply recognize its own unique address.

	Easy	Moderate	Difficult
Topology:			
Bus	X		
Ring		X	
Star			X
Media:			
Twisted Pair	X		
Baseband Coaxial	X		
Broadband Coaxial		X	
Fiber Optic			X
Protocol:			
Contention	X		
Token Passing		X	
Polling		X	

Figure 15.3 Expandability by Topology, Media, and Protocol

The growth of the network must be planned; it should not be allowed just to evolve. Evolution results in unidentified nodes, unauthorized users, and possibly obscure links between sites which are not functional for proper use.

Environment

What operations are taking place in-house? Is all the activity office work, or is there manufacturing? What special requirements are imposed by the operations? Is there electrical interference from heavy machinery, dust, metal filings, excess heat or moisture, other hazards?

What special requirements are imposed by your location? Is your area subject to flooding, earthquake, tornado, violent storms? Is there nearby major construction or industry which affects air quality?

Environmental hazards can cause major limitations. Of all the media, fiber optic is most resistant to interference and the environment. The fiber optic cable is thin, light weight, very flexible, and extremely resistant to ordinary transmission hazards. At the very least, presence of special environmental considerations will affect the degree of duplication and backup necessary.

Reliability

Reliability is of utmost importance. The cost of unreliability is high, including lost productivity, overtime to make up downtime, and possibly lost business. How dependent are you on the proper working of the network? How much extra is it worth to provide duplication of services and equipment for backup in case of failure?

On many systems, extremely high reliability of equipment is vital. (Some authorities suggest more than 99 percent reliability as a minimum.) The network must be available to users for a high percentage of the time. Malfunction or failure of one element should not disable the entire system.

How susceptible is the network to failure? To damage? How interference-prone is the network? While bus networks are vulnerable to failure from damage to the main cable, failure of any one workstation rarely affects the network. In a ring network, failure of a node can disrupt service on the whole net unless a bypass mechanism is provided. Star networks are vulnerable to failure of the central server. On all networks, locating a failed component may be difficult: in a system with wide geographical distribution, it may not be possible immediately to repair or circumvent the problem.

All media share a susceptibility to damage from improper installation, sharp bends, and contact with rough surfaces. Fiber optic cable is particularly demanding to install: cables must be spliced precisely. In exchange, properly installed fiber optic cable can tolerate a wider range of environments than any other media.

Inter-network connections to distant sites are generally the least reliable, least predictable element of a network. If you have a high need for communications to other sites, then multiple routes between sites is necessary. If even brief periods of network failure are unacceptable, the backup facilities must be invoked automatically, without human intervention.

Security

How high a security level is appropriate to your organization? Unfortunately, most current microcomputer LANs have minimal provision for security. Some networks have better security features than others and should be investigated for that purpose. Network users should keep in mind, however, that there are no perfectly secure computer systems of any size, with microcomputers being the most inherently insecure. Information that requires heavy security is far safer on a mainframe or on a stand-alone micro.

If you are concerned about wiretapping, fiber optic is the only choice. Because of the lack of shielding, signals on a twisted pair cable may be intercepted by stations not actually connected to the network. Baseband coaxial cable also can broadcast the signal further than you wish it to travel, thus permitting unauthorized tapping. Although broadband coaxial cable does not broadcast the electrical signals it carries, it can be tapped easily by anyone who can gain physical access to the cable.

Budget

How much can you afford to spend for a LAN? Define your answer in dollars, time, and resources. What will that much money buy you—how much equipment, how many applications, what type of network, how much training? How much are you willing to pay to obtain a specific resource or service? How long can implementation take? When will equipment need to be ordered? When do you want the network to be installed? With a modular network, you can spread out purchases over several budget periods, rather than your having to buy everything at once. (See Figure 15.4.)

	Low	Moderate	High	Very High
Cable:				
Twisted Pair	X			
Baseband Coaxial	X			
Broadband Coaxial		X		
Fiber Optic		X————X		
Installation:				
Twisted Pair	X			
Baseband Coaxial	X			
Broadband Coaxial		X		
Fiber Optic			X	

Figure 15.4 Media Cost Comparison

Installation of cabling and associated equipment is one of the two great hidden cost of networking. (Training is the second.) For all media, the cost of installation easily exceeds that of the cost of the wire itself. Remember, also, that installation and hardware are only part of the cost of a LAN. Training can equal the cost of hardware.

How much do you expect to save from increased productivity? If the cost of the network exceeds the expected savings achieved through increased productivity, the system isn't worth the price.

Politics

Of all considerations, office politics is often the hardest to deal with. Politics enters at every step, from convincing upper management that a LAN is desirable, to appointing people to plan the network, to deciding on one product over another. Politics continue after the purchase, influencing how technical and administrative responsibilities are assigned.

The questions of who (and how much of the organization) has access to the local area network and of which department will benefit first from LAN installation are both technical and political issues. How many connection points will your department be allocated? How will workstations, hard disks, printers, and other network devices be allocated? Because these questions involve politics, they may well be extremely difficult to solve.

If a local area network is to be implemented successfully rather than just endlessly debated, you must prevent, insofar as humanly possible, the technical and managerial decision process from becoming an arena for political contests. When user or managerial factions wrestle for control of the project, everyone loses.

Evaluating Specific Networks

LAN technology is advancing rapidly: the minimalist boards and wires of 1984 and early 1985 are on their way to becoming multifunctional networks complete with operating system and utilities. When you begin evaluating products, you do not have to evaluate every one. Learn enough to be able to ask intelligent questions and to not feel overwhelmed by the vendor's claims. Ultimately, the whole evaluation process is designed to answer one question: Will this product do the job I need it to do?

If you are installing a moderate sized LAN, you may want to have a consultant help make decisions and formulate a proposal for installing a local area network at your site.

Paying a consultant's fees is not automatically detrimental: the consultant's greater familiarity with the market can save you money in the long run and will help you reach a conclusion much more quickly.

Appendix A contains a list of LAN vendors and products. Although I have made an effort to be inclusive, some LANs undoubtedly have escaped my notice. You might begin by defining those vendors and products you will evaluate first. Do check the various computer publications for additional vendors.

Vendor Information

By vendor, I mean both the manufacturer of a network and your local source. If you are working with a consultant, be sure to fill out a vendor statement for each of the alternative networks proposed.

The temptation to be exhaustive in listing vendors, even local vendors, should be resisted, because it wastes time for both sides. Ask colleagues at other companies who they recommend locally. If their answers all point to one particular source out of the several local possibilities, make that vendor your prime candidate. A reliable, knowledgeable vendor is your best guarantee.

VENDOR INFORMATION SHEET

1. Name: _____
    Address: _____
    Telephone: _____
    Date founded: _____

2. Local representative: _____
    Address: _____
    Telephone: _____
    Contact: _____
    Date founded: _____

3. Who recommended the local vendor/consultant? ____
    _____

4. Responsiveness of the local vendor/consultant: ____
    _____

Product Information

Information in this section changes frequently. Upgrades and new products are announced weekly. Remember my earlier caution: Do not buy a newly released system unless you have little other choice. I would add to that the advice: never buy a system that you have not seen up and running at an actual user site. Vendor demonstrations are very useful, but do not reflect true performance. Talking to current users of a network is one of the best methods of learning how a network really works.

There is no "best" architecture, only the combination of technologies that seems to offer the services you need.

PRODUCT INFORMATION SHEET

1. Product Name: _____

2. Installation history: _____
   Date first offered: _____
   Date first system installed: _____
   Number of installed systems: _____
   Size of largest installation: _____
   Names of local user(s) where operation can be observed: _____
   Equipment availability: _____

3. Architecture: _____
   Control protocol: _____
   Topology: _____
   Transmission medium: _____
   Data rate: _____
   Maximum network length: _____
   Maximum number of workstations supported: _____

4. Interconnections: _____
   Gateway(s): _____
   Bridges: _____
   Modems: _____

5. Compatibility: _____
   Which microcomputers: _____
   Mainframe link: _____
   Links multiple operating systems: _____

6. Operating system: _____
   Vendor: _____
   Menu or command driven: _____
   Complexity: _____
   Disk sharing: _____
   Data sharing: _____
   Boot from network server: _____

7. Operating system functions: _____

   File locking: _____

   Record locking: _____

   Caching: _____

   Print spooler: _____

   Electronic mail: _____

   Other: _____

8. Monitoring and testing aids: _____

   Statistics and/or management information provided by monitoring: _____

   Configuration aids: _____

9. Security provisions: _____

   Passwords: _____

   User IDs: _____

   Encryption: _____

   Other: _____

10. Documentation: _____

    User manual: _____

    Technical reference: _____

    Quick reference card: _____

    Training materials: _____

11. Manufacturer support: _____

    Hotline: _____

    Bulletin board: _____

    800 number: _____

    Local service depot: _____

12. Vendor/consultant support: _____

    Hotline: _____

    Bulletin board: _____

    Local service depot: _____

Acquisition Information

All the information gathered to this point has focused on the local area network. This section changes the focus to address the details of a specific proposal.

ACQUISITION INFORMATION SHEET

1. New workstations and servers: _____
    Type: _____
    Number: _____
    Unit price: _____
    Multi-unit price: _____
    Function: _____
    Availability: _____

2. Additional hard disk storage: _____
    Type: _____
    Number: _____
    Unit price: _____
    Multi-unit price: _____
    Function: _____
    Availability: _____

3. Additional peripherals: _____
    Type: _____
    Number: _____
    Unit price: _____
    Multi-unit price: _____
    Function: _____
    Availability: _____

4. Network interfaces: _____
    Number required: _____
    Description: _____
    Failure rate of network interfaces: _____
    Under what circumstances do interfaces tend to fail?

    _____

    What is the effect of interface failure? _____

    _____

Number of spares and duplicates required: _____
Availability of the equipment: _____

5. Cabling: _____
    Type: _____
    Approximate length of cable: _____
    Cost: _____
    General layout: _____
    Where installed: _____
    Connectors: _____
    Repeaters/transceivers/amplifiers/etc.: _____
    Cost for each device: _____

6. Service and support: _____
    Who will install the system? _____
    System installation cost: _____
    Who will maintain the system? _____
    Maintenence cost: _____
    Who will install the cabling? _____
    Cable installation cost: _____
    Network maintenance equipment: _____
    Can routine repair be carried out by our staff? ____

7. Training: _____
    Materials available: _____
    Materials cost: _____
    Who will train the users? _____
    Training cost: _____

8. Installation timetable: _____
    Equipment delivery date: _____
    Time required for installation: _____
    Installation strategy: _____

9. What do you feel is the strongest point of the proposed
    LAN? _____

10. What is its weakest point? _____

11. What, in your view, are the critical considerations for a
    company planning to install a LAN? _____
    _____

12. What new products or changes in LAN technology do
    you foresee within the next two to five years? _____
    _____

Conclusion

You are about to embark on a project that can change your whole organization. One quick way to get to the heart of the question: If you find that one local vendor is consistently praised for the quality of service and responsiveness, then strongly consider accepting that proposal, even if it is not the lowest cost. For when all the technical factors are juggled, it all comes down to four simple questions:

1. Does the system work? (Does it do the job we need it to do?)

2. Can we afford it? (Can we afford *not* to buy it?)

3. Who will solve my problems, both during installation and later?

4. How soon will the system be repaired when it fails?

Good luck!

Appendices

Local Area Network Vendors

Altos Computer System
2641 Orchard Parkway
San Jose, CA 95134
(408) 946-6700

WorkNet II: CSMA/CA, bus, twisted pair

Apple Computer, Inc.
20525 Mariani Ave.
Cupertino, CA 95014
(408) 996-1010

Applenet: CSMA/CD, bus, twisted pair

Applitek Corp
107 Audubon Road
Wakefield, MA 01880
(617) 246-4500

NI10/E, NI10/T: CSMA/CD, bus, coaxial, fiber optic

AST Research, Inc.
2121 Alton Ave.
Irvine, CA 92714
(714) 863-1333

AST-PCnet: CSMA/CD, bus, coaxial baseband

AT&T Information Systems
1 Speedwell Avenue
Morristown, NJ 07960
(201) 898-2000

STARLAN: CSMA/CD, star, daisy chain, twisted pair

Autocontrol, Inc.
11400 Dorsett Road
St. Louis, MO 63043
(314) 739-0055

Soft/Net: CSMA/CA/CD, bus, coaxial baseband

B-Komp Inc.
5949 Sherry Lane, Suite 1535
Dallas, TX 75225
(214) 750-5667

Net-worker: token passing, tree, twisted pair

Bridge Communications, Inc.
1345 Shorebird Way
Mountain View, CA 94043
(415) 969-4400

EtherSeries: XNS, bus, baseband coaxial

Complexx Systems, Inc.
4930 Research Dr.
Huntsville, AL 35805
(205) 830-4310

XLAN: CSMA, bus, coaxial, twisted pair

Concord Data Systems, Inc.
303 Bear Hill Rd.
Waltham, MA 02154
(617) 890-1394

Token/Net: token passing, bus, broadband coaxial

Corvus Systems, Inc.
2029 O'Toole Ave.
San Jose, CA 95131
(408) 946-7700

Omninet: CSMA/CA, bus, twisted pair

Crowntek Networks Inc.
249 Tempo Avenue
Willowdale, Ontario, Canada
(416) 499-5552

MicroProd/Net: token passing, tree, baseband coaxial, fiber optic

Datapoint Corp.
9725 Datapoint Dr.
San Antonio, TX 78284
(512) 699-7000

ARCnet: polling, bus, star, baseband coaxial

Davong Systems, Inc.
217 Humbolt Court Drive
Sunnyvale, CA 94086
(408) 734-4900

MultiLink: token passing, mesh, broadband coaxial

The Destek Group
830 E. Evelyn Avenue
Sunnyvale, CA 94086
(408) 737-7211

Desnet: CSMA/CA, bus, baseband coaxial

Digital Microsystems, Inc.
1755 Embarcadero
Oakland, CA 94606
(415) 532-3686

HiNet: SDLC, bus, twisted pair, fiber optic

Digital Products Inc.
600 Pleasant Street
Watertown, MA 02172
(800) 243-2333

NetCommander: star, RS-232

Excelan, Inc.
2180 Fortune Drive
San Jose, CA 95131
(408) 945-9526

EXOS Series: CSMA/CD, bus, baseband coaxial

Fox Research, Inc.
7005 Corporate Way
Dayton, OH 45459
(513) 433-2238

10-NET: CSMA/CD, bus, twisted pair

Gamma Productions, Inc
817 Tenth Street
Santa Monica, CA 90403
(213) 451-9507

Gamma-Net 3.1: CSMA/CD/CA, bus, shielded twisted pair

Gandalf Data, Inc.
1019 S. Noel Avenue
Wheeling, IL 60090
(312) 541-6060

PACXNET: contention, star, ring, twisted pair, coaxial

Gateway Communications, Inc.
16782 Redhill Avenue
Irvine, CA 92714
(714) 261-0762

G/NET: CSMA/CD, bus, baseband coaxial

Hewlett-Packard Corporation
1820 Embarcadero Road
Palo Alto, CA 94303
(415) 857-1501

Office-Share Network: CSMA/CD, bus, baseband coaxial

IBM Entry Systems Group
P.O. Box 1328
Boca Raton, FL 33432
(305) 998-6048

PC Lan: CSMA/CD, bus, baseband coaxial

Token Ring: token passing, ring, star, twisted pair

IDEAssociates, Inc.
35 Dunham Road
Billerica, MA 01821
(800) 257-5027

IDEAnet: CSMA/CD, bus, baseband coaxial

Interactive Systems, 3M Corp.
3M Center
St. Paul, MN 55144
(612) 733-1100

LAN/1: token passing, bus, coaxial broadband

Kantek, Inc.
13730 N.E. 20th Street, Suite J
Bellevue, WA 98005
(206) 285-7266

KANnet: token passing, ring, baseband coaxial

Magnolia Microsystems Inc.
4039 21st Avenue West
Seattle, WA 98199
(206) 285-7266

MAGnet: token passing, bus—logical ring, twisted pair

MICOM Systems, Inc
4100 Los Angeles Avenue, P.O. Box 8100
Simi Valley, CA 93062
(805) 583-8600

NI5010 Ethernet Controller: CSMA/CD, bus, twisted pair

NBI, Inc.
P.O. Box 9001
Boulder, CO 80301
(303) 444-5710

Multinet: Polling, bus, star, twisted pair

NCR Corporation
1700 South Patterson Boulevard
Dayton, OH 45479
(513) 445-5000

PC2PC: CSMA/CA, bus, twisted pair

Nestar Systems, Inc.
2582 Bayshore Rd.
Palo Alto, CA 94303
(415) 493-2223

PLAN 3000: token passing, tree, twisted pair, fiber optic

Network Development Corp.
81 Great Valley Parkway
Malvern, PA 19355
(215) 296-7420

DNA (Device Net Architecture): polling, star, twisted pair

Novell, Inc.
1170 N. Industrial Pk. Drive
Orem, UT 84057
(801) 226-8202

NETWARE/ Omninet: CSMA/CA, bus, twisted pair

Orchid Technology, Inc.
47790 Westinghouse Dr.
Fremont, CA 94539
(415) 490-8586

PCnet: CSMA/CD, bus, baseband coaxial

PC LAN Technologies
106 Londonderry Office Park
5780 Lincoln Drive
Minneapolis, MN 55436
(612) 935-7509

LT LAN: CSMA/CD, bus, twisted pair, baseband coaxial

Proteon Inc.
4 Tech Circle
Natick, MA 01760
(617) 655-3340

ProNet: token passing, ring, coaxial, fiber optic

Quadram
4355 International Blvd.
Norcross, GA 30093
(404) 923-6666

Quadnet VI: CSMA/CA/CD, bus, baseband coaxial

Radio Shack, Division of Tandy Corporation
1700 One Tandy Center
Fort Worth, TX 76102
(817) 390-3011

ViaNet: token passing, tree, baseband coaxial

Santa Clara Systems
1860 Hartog Drive
San Jose, CA 95131
(408) 729-6700

SCS PCnet: CSMA/CD, bus, baseband coaxial

The Software Link Inc
8601 Dunwoody Place, Number 632
Atlanta, GA 30338
(404) 998-0700

LanLink: proprietary, star, tree, twisted pair

Standard Data Corp.
3040 S.W. 10th Street
Pompano Beach, FL 33069
(800) 327-5567

StandardNET: CSMA/CD, bus, baseband coaxial

Sunol Systems
1187 Quarry Lane
Pleasanton, CA 94566
(415) 484-3322

Sun Net: multiplexing, star, flat ribbon cable

Sytek, Inc.
1225 Charleston Rd.
Mountain View, CA 94043
(415) 966-7346

LocalNET: CSMA/CD,FDM, bus, broadband coaxial

Tangent Technologies
5720 Peachtree Parkway
Norcross, GA 30092
(404) 662-0366

Think Link System: SDLC, star, twisted pair

Tecmar, Inc.
6225 Cochran Rd.
Solon, OH 44139
(216) 349-0600

ComNet: CSMA/CD, bus, broadband coaxial

TeleVideo Systems Inc
550 East Brokaw Road
San Jose, CA 95112
(415) 363-2418

Personal Mini: proprietary, star, twisted pair

Texas Instruments, Data Systems Group
P.O.Box 809063
Dallas, TX 75380
(800) 527-3500

EtherSeries: CSMA/CD, bus, baseband coaxial

3Com
1390 Shorebird Way
Mountain View, CA 94043
(415) 961-9602

EtherSeries: CSMA/CD Ethernet, bus, coaxial baseband

TIENET, Inc.
2300 Central Avenue, Suite F
Boulder, CO 80301
(415) 444-2600

TIENET: CSMA/CD, bus, twisted pair

Ungermann-Bass, Inc.
2560 Mission College Blvd.
Santa Clara, CA 95050
(408) 496-0111

Net/One: CSMA/CD, bus, baseband, broadband coaxial

Wang Laboratories, Inc.
1 Industrial Avenue
Lowell, MA 01851
(617) 459-5000

Wang Net: CSMA/CD, bus (physical ring), broadband coaxial

Xerox
800 Long Ridge Road, P.O. Box 1600
Stamford, CT 06904
(203) 329-8700

Ethernet: CSMA/CD, bus, baseband coaxial

Xyplex Inc.
100 Domino Drive
Concord, MA 01742
(617) 317-1400

XYPLEX System: CSMA/CA, bus, coaxial, fiber optic

Local Area Network Software Vendors

Applied Intelligence
1043 Stierlin Road
Mountain View, CA 94043
(415) 967-3512

PC/NOS

Banyan Systems
135 Flanders Road
Westboro, MA 01581
(617) 366-6081

Vines

Novell, Inc.
1170 N. Industrial Pk. Drive
Orem, UT 84057
(801) 226-8202

Advanced Netware

Torus Systems Inc
485 Seaport Court, Suite 103
Redwood City, CA 94063
(415) 363-2418

Tapestry

ViaNetix
5766 Central Avenue
Boulder, CO 80301
(303) 440-0700

ViaNet

Waterloo Microsystems
175 Columbia Street West
Waterloo, Ontario, Canada
N2L 5Z5
(519) 884-3141

Port

Glossary

A

Algorithm: a well-defined set of rules or processes (usually mathematical) used to arrive at a solution to a problem.

Applications software: provides functionality for the user so that work can be done.

Architecture: the overall design of a network. Includes hardware and protocols.

ASCII code: American Standard Code for Information Interchange.

B

Bandwidth: the information carrying capacity of a communications channel.

Bit: binary digit, the smallest unit of information manipulated by a computer.

Bps: bits per second. The basic unit of data communications measurement.

Branch: a cable that carries the network to the general area of the user.

Bridge: connects two networks using the same internal protocols or segments of a large network.

Broadcast: the ability to send messages or communicate with many or all points on a circuit simultaneously.

Buffer: storage area for a block of data.

Burst: a group of events occurring together in time.

Bus topology: all workstations are connected to a single shared communications link.

Byte: a group of bits.

C

Cable taps: connect the transceiver to the main cable.

Cache memory: readily accessed computer memory which contains the next most likely sequence of instructions or frequently used data.

Carrier: a fixed frequency signal which is combined with an information-bearing signal during the modulation process to produce a signal suitable for transmission.

Carrier Sense Multiple Access (CSMA): contention protocol in which workstations monitor the transmission channel for traffic before transmitting.

Carrier Sense Multiple Access with Collision Avoidance, (CSMA/CA): in addition to monitoring the transmission channel, workstations signal their intent to transmit. In case of multiple requests to transmit, the order of precedence is predetermined.

Carrier Sense Multiple Access with Collision Detection (CSMA/CD): in addition to sensing whether the transmission channel is in use before beginning to transmit, workstations monitor the link during transmission and can sense when a message must be retransmitted.

Centralized control: access to the network and allocation of channel is determined by one node.

Channel: a data communications path.

Communications medium: the physical link which carries information from one microcomputer or peripheral to another. Normally, provided by a piece of cable.

Communications port: a connection to the data receiving and transmitting abilities of a system.

Communications processing: the collective term for all the activities which help to ensure the successful entry, transmission, and delivery of information.

Communications servers: provides communications for the network.

Compound star: network in which a workstation on one network may act as server and/or controller for a secondary network.

Configuration: process of formatting disks, copying network software, and identifying the installed equipment for the network operating system before a network can be used.

Contention: competition by users for access to a common transmission channel and network resources.

Control characters: special characters used to give the computer instructions.

D

Data: the raw numbers or text used by a computer.

Data communications: the active process of transporting data from one point to another.

Directional couplers: insure that signals transmitted by any network device will be transmitted only toward the head end of a baseband network.

Distortion: the unwanted modification of signals by interference or some characteristic of the line and/or equipment being used for transmission.

Distributed control: workstations can access the network channels independently, according to a shared set of protocols.

Drop: cable which connects the user outlet to the branch.

E

Electronic mail: a computerized version of a post office.

Emulation: the act of imitating a different device or program.

Encryption: modifying known information so that to an unauthorized observer it appears to be a random sequence of data.

Ethernet: a CSMA/CD network using baseband cable.

F

File locking: data protection scheme which restricts use of a whole file to one user at a time.

Flag: a bit field or character used to set apart the data on either side of itself.

G

Gateway: the means of communicating between two different networks or different devices. Provides the necessary translation of data from the form used by one network or device into the form used by another.

Guardband: in a broadband system, the unused frequencies between subchannels used to prevent interference.

H

Head end: the point of origin of all radio frequency signals and the collection point for all signals being generated on a broadband network.

I

Information: data converted into human-usable form.

Interface board: device which connects the microcomputer to the network and allows it to interact with other microcomputers and peripherals.

Interference: unwanted noises and/or signals on a communications channel.

Institute of Electrical and Electronic Engineers' (IEEE) Project 802: committee defining local area network standards.

International Standards Organization (ISO): creator of a reference model for mainframe wide area network communications which defines the exchange of information among terminal devices, computers, people, networks, and processes.

L

LAN (Local Area Network): a communications network designed to interconnect a variety of computer-based equipment within a small area. Includes both hardware and software.

Logical connection: implies that workstations are able to communicate, whether or not a direct physical connection actually exists between them.

Long-haul network: a communications network encompassing a large area, such as the telephone system.

Loop: a ring network using centralized control.

M

Message: a specific piece of information.

Modem: device which accepts data from a transmitting computer and translates the digital computer signals onto the analog voice-frequency telephone carrier wave and vice versa.

Monitor: a program or device used to observe an operation without interfering with it.

Multipoint connection: a single cable which connects more than two workstations.

N

Network: a communications system designed to convey information from a point of origin to a point of destination.

Network Control Center: workstation from which performance of the whole network can be monitored; failures can be identified; and initialization and configuration can be accomplished.

Network Interface Unit: a microprocessor based device containing hardware and software which supplies the intelligence to control access to and communications across the network, and to perform all communications processing. It is the means by which the workstations are functionally and physically connected to the network.

Network operating system: the software which controls the operation of the network.

Network utilities: programs which handle routine procedures like troubleshooting.

Node: the beginning, intersection, or end of the communications link or the device located at that point.

Noise: interference on a communications line caused by the line itself or induced by transient bursts of energy.

O

Overhead: the additional information that must be transmitted through the network in order to facilitate the proper transmission and delivery of messages.

P

Packet: a block of data containing both a message (or part of a long message) and addressing information.

Point-to-point connection: joining two, and only two, adjacent workstations, without passing through an intermediary workstation.

Polling: protocol involving the central control of all workstations in a network.

Print server: a workstation with an attached printer, a spooler, and software to process and manage printing tasks.

Propagation delay: the length of time required for a signal to travel the channel.

Protocols: the formal rules and conventions governing the exchange of information between computers, defined to provide reliable and efficient transfer of information.

Q

Queuing: operating a waiting line for items requiring attention, such as requests to print various files.

R

Record locking: data protection scheme which restricts use of a particular record in a file to one user at a time.

Repeaters: boost the strength of the signal as the messages pass from one cable section to another.

Response time: time elapsed between a request for service and the performing of that process by the computer.

Ring: an unbroken circle of point-to-point connections of adjacent workstations. Messages travel from workstation to workstation in a round robin fashion.

ROM: Read Only Memory. Permanent memory storage within the computer.

S

Servers: workstations which perform a service to other workstations on the network.

Star: network in which each workstation is connected to a central server through a dedicated point-to-point channel.

Star-shaped ring: ring network in which the cable between workstations passes through a central wire center.

T

Telecommunications: the technology and science of communications through electronic transmission.

Teleprocessing: the use of telecommunications in order to access a central computer.

Token: contains network information, comprised of a header, a data field, and a trailer.

Token passing: protocol in which the network continuously circulates a special bit pattern known as a token. Only the workstation holding the token can put a message onto the network.

Topology: the physical pattern of interconnection between nodes.

Transceivers: network interface units, used on baseband networks. Provide the intelligence for reading message addresses, and for other network-oriented communication functions.

Tree: a bus network comprised of a main cable which connects floors in a building (or several buildings) and branches which connect individual workstations in a more limited area.

Trunk: the main network cable, which transports radio-frequency signals between amplifiers.

U

User workstations: microcomputers on the network which have a primary responsibility to an individual user.

Utility program: program used for computer housekeeping functions such as providing a sorted list of files on a disk.

V

Voice mail: delayed delivery of a spoken message.

W

Workstation: a microcomputer and its attached peripheral(s).

Inventory Sheets

MICROCOMPUTER INVENTORY

For each microcomputer in use in the organization:

1. Micro: _____
   Model number: _____
   Serial number: _____

2. Manufacturer: _____
   Address: _____
   City, State, Zip: _____
   Telephone: _____

3. Description: _____
   Memory: _____
   Number and type of drives: _____
   Graphic capabilities: _____
   Special boards installed: _____
   Special functions, abilities: _____

4. Attached peripherals: _____
   Hard disk: _____
   Printer, plotter: _____
   Modem: _____
   Other: _____

5. Location: _____

6. Installation date: _____

7. Average traffic volume: _____
   Hours of use: _____
   Number of users: _____
   Peak activity hours: _____

8. Where/how data was collected: _____
   _____

HARD DISK INVENTORY

For each hard disk to be attached to a workstation on the network:

1. Device: _____
    Model number: _____
    Serial number: _____

2. Manufacturer: _____
    Address: _____
    City, State, Zip: _____
    Telephone: _____

3. Description: _____
    Size: _____
    Backup method in use: _____

4. Location: _____

5. Installation date: _____

6. Average monthly usage: _____
    Hours of use: _____
    Number of users: _____
    Peak activity hours: _____

7. Where/how data was collected: _____
    _____

PRINTER AND PLOTTER INVENTORY

For each printer or plotter to be attached to a workstation on the network:

1. Device: _____
    Model number: _____
    Serial number: _____

2. Manufacturer: _____
    Address: _____
    City, State, Zip: _____
    Telephone: _____

3. Description: _____
    Type: _____
    Speed: _____
    Special abilities: _____

4. Location: _____

5. Installation date: _____

6. Average monthly usage: _____
    Hours of use: _____
    Number of users: _____
    Pages of output: _____
    Peak activity hours: _____

7. Where/how data was collected: _____
    _____

MODEM INVENTORY

For each modem:

1. Device: _____
    Model number: _____
    Serial number: _____

2. Manufacturer: _____
    Address: _____
    City, State, Zip: _____
    Telephone: _____

3. Description: _____
    Type: _____
    Speed: _____
    Special abilities: _____

4. Location: _____

5. Installation date: _____

6. Average monthly usage: _____
    Hours of use: _____
    Number of users: _____
    Peak activity hours: _____

7. Where/how data was collected: _____
    _____

OTHER PERIPHERALS INVENTORY

For each peripheral which will be attached to a workstation on the network but is not inventoried elsewhere:

1. Device: _____
   Model number: _____
   Serial number: _____

2. Manufacturer: _____
   Address: _____
   City, State, Zip: _____
   Telephone: _____

3. Description: _____
   Speed: _____
   Special abilities: _____

4. Location: _____

5. Installation date: _____

6. Average monthly usage: _____
   Hours of use: _____
   Number of users: _____
   Peak activity hours: _____

7. Where/how data was collected: _____
   _____

HARDWARE SUMMARY

1. Microcomputers: _____
    Type: _____
    Number: _____

2. Hard disks: _____
    Type: _____
    Number: _____

3. Printers and plotters: _____
    Type: _____
    Number: _____

4. Other peripherals: _____
    Type: _____
    Number: _____

5. Programs: _____
    Function: _____

APPLICATION PROGRAM
INVENTORY

For each program or distinct version:

1. Program name: _____
   Version number: _____
   Number of copies owned: _____
   Serial number(s): _____
   License (single CPU, site): _____

2. Manufacturer: _____
   Address: _____
   City, State, Zip: _____
   Telephone: _____

3. Description: _____
   Major functions: _____
   Information generated: _____

4. Location: _____

5. Purchase date: _____

6. Average monthly usage: _____
   Hours of use: _____
   Number of users: _____
   Peak activity hours: _____

7. Where/how data was collected: _____
   _____

SOFTWARE TOOL INVENTORY

For each program or distinct version:

1. Program name: —————————————
    Version number: —————————————
    Number of copies owned: —————————
    Serial number(s): ————————————
    License (single CPU, site): ——————

2. Manufacturer: ——————————————
    Address: ———————————————
    City, State, Zip: ————————————
    Telephone: ————————————————

3. Description: ——————————————
    Major functions: —————————————

4. Location: ————————————————

5. Purchase date: ——————————————

6. Average monthly usage: ————————
    Hours of use: ————————————
    Number of users: —————————————
    Peak activity hours: ————————————

7. Where/how data was collected: ——————
    ——————————————————

INFORMATION RECEIVED SURVEY

1. Item: _____

2. Description: _____
   Content: _____
   Type: _____
   Form: _____
   Quantity: _____

3. Source: _____

4. Regularity of exchange: _____

5. Response time: _____

6. Action required: _____

7. Where/how data was collected: _____
   _____

TASK SURVEY

For each type of information worked with on a regular basis:

1. Task: _____

2. Description: _____

3. Frequency: _____

4. Input: _____
   Source: _____
   Quantity: _____
   Action required: _____
   Resources used: _____

5. Output: _____
   Destination: _____
   Quantity: _____
   Form: _____

6. Time required: _____

7. Where/how data was collected: _____
   _____

INFORMATION DISTRIBUTED
SURVEY

1. Item: _____

2. Description: _____
   Content: _____
   Type: _____
   Form: _____
   Quantity: _____

3. Destination: _____

4. Regularity of exchange: _____

5. Storage format: _____

6. Where/how data was collected: _____

   _____

INFORMATION USE OVERVIEW

1. Most important information: _____

2. Source: _____

3. Busy time: _____

4. Daily telephone calls: _____
    Initiated: _____
    Received: _____

5. In the past six months, have you noticed any change in
    the quantity of information that crosses your desk? __
    _____

6. Do you expect this information load to increase in the
    next six months? _____

7. In the next year? _____

8. The next two years? _____

9. Have you noticed any changes in the types of informa-
    tion you receive? _____
    _____

10. In the types of information you use? _____

11. Do you anticipate any changes? _____
    _____

12. What would help you perform your job better? _____
    _____

13. What concerns you most about possible changes in your
    job? _____

14. Where/how data was collected: _____
    _____

VENDOR INFORMATION SHEET

1. Name: _____
    Address: _____
    Telephone: _____
    Date founded: _____

2. Local representative: _____
    Address: _____
    Telephone: _____
    Contact: _____
    Date founded: _____

3. Who recommended the local vendor/consultant? ____
    _____

4. Responsiveness of the local vendor/consultant: _____
    _____

PRODUCT INFORMATION SHEET

1. Product Name: _____

2. Installation history: _____
    Date first offered: _____
    Date first system installed: _____
    Number of installed systems: _____
    Size of largest installation: _____
    Names of local user(s) where operation can be
    observed: _____
    Equipment availability: _____
    _____

3. Architecture: _____
    Control Protocol: _____
    Topology: _____
    Transmission Medium: _____
    Data Rate: _____
    Maximum network length: _____
    Maximum number of workstations supported: _____
    _____

4. Interconnections: _____
    Gateway(s): _____
    Bridges: _____
    Modems: _____

5. Compatibility: _____
    Which microcomputers: _____
    Mainframe link: _____
    Links multiple operating systems: _____
    _____

6. Operating system: _____
    Vendor: _____
    Menu or command driven: _____
    Complexity: _____
    Disk sharing: _____
    Data sharing: _____

7. Operating system functions: _____
    File locking: _____
    Record locking: _____
    Caching: _____
    Print spooler: _____
    Electronic mail: _____
    Boot from network server: _____
    Other: _____

8. Monitoring and testing aids: _____
    Statistics and/or management information provided
    by monitoring: _____
    Configuration aids: _____

9. Security provisions: _____
    Passwords: _____
    User IDs: _____
    Encryption: _____
    Other: _____

10. Documentation: _____
    User manual: _____
    Technical reference: _____
    Quick reference card: _____
    Training materials: _____

11. Manufacturer support: _____
    Hotline: _____
    Bulletin board: _____
    800 number: _____
    Local service depot: _____

12. Vendor/consultant support: _____
    Hotline: _____
    Bulletin board: _____
    Local service depot: _____

ACQUISITION INFORMATION SHEET

1. New workstations and servers: _____
   Type: _____
   Number: _____
   Unit price: _____
   Multi-unit price: _____
   Function: _____
   Availability: _____

2. Additional hard disk storage: _____
   Type: _____
   Number: _____
   Unit price: _____
   Multi-unit price: _____
   Function: _____
   Availability: _____

3. Additional peripherals: _____
   Type: _____
   Number: _____
   Unit price: _____
   Multi-unit price: _____
   Function: _____
   Availability: _____

4. Network interfaces: _____
   Number required: _____
   Description: _____
   Failure rate of network interfaces: _____
   _____
   Under what circumstances do interfaces tend to fail?
   _____
   What is the effect of interface failure? _____
   _____
   Number of spares and duplicates required: _____
   _____
   Availability of the equipment: _____
   _____

5. Cabling: _____
   Type: _____
   Approximate length of cable: _____
   Cost: _____
   General layout: _____
   Where installed: _____
   Connectors: _____
   Repeaters/transceivers/amplifiers/etc.: _____

   _____
   Cost for each device: _____

   _____

6. Service and support: _____
   Who will install the system? _____
   System installation cost: _____
   Who will maintain the system? _____
   Maintenence cost: _____
   Who will install the cabling? _____
   Cable installation cost: _____
   Network maintenance equipment: _____
   Can routine repair be carried out by our staff? ____

   _____

7. Training: _____
   Materials available: _____
   Materials cost: _____
   Who will train the users? _____
   Training cost: _____

8. Installation timetable: _____
   Equipment delivery date: _____
   Time required for installation: _____
   Installation strategy: _____

9. What do you feel is the strongest point of the proposed
   LAN? _____

10. What is its weakest point? _____

11. What, in your view, are the critical considerations for a
    company planning to install a LAN? _____

    _____

12. What new products or changes in LAN technology do
    you forsee within the next two to five years? _____

    _____

Index

W

Wiring center 45
Workstation 26, 35

ergonomics 132
ID 139
primary 92
secondary 92
user 35

Ethics in Nursing

Ethics in Nursing
THIRD EDITION

Martin Benjamin   Joy Curtis

New York   Oxford
OXFORD UNIVERSITY PRESS
1992

Oxford University Press

Oxford   New York   Toronto
Delhi   Bombay   Calcutta   Madras   Karachi
Petaling Jaya   Singapore   Hong Kong   Tokyo
Nairobi   Dar es Salaam   Cape Town
Melbourne   Auckland

and associated companies in
Berlin   Ibadan

Published by Oxford University Press, Inc.,
200 Madison Avenue, New York, New York 10016

Oxford is a registered trademark of Oxford University Press.

Library of Congress Cataloging-in-Publication Data
Benjamin, Martin.
Ethics in nursing / Martin Benjamin, Joy Curtis. — 3rd ed.
p.   cm. Includes bibliographical references and index.
ISBN 0-19-506747-9.
ISBN 0-19-506748-7
1. Nursing ethics.   I. Curtis, Joy.   II. Title.
[DNLM: 1. Ethics, Nursing.   WY 85 B468e]
RT85.B39   1992   174'.2—dc20   DNLM/DLC
for Library of Congress   91-3785

9 8 7 6 5

Printed in the United States of America
on acid-free paper

For our parents

Ruth Hilleary
Julius Hilleary
Dorothy Benjamin (1914–65)
Louis Benjamin

Preface

The changes in this edition reflect important developments in nursing and nursing ethics. First, facts, figures, and references have been updated throughout. Second, two new cases concerning the care of AIDS patients have been added. The analysis of these cases includes an entirely new section (in Chapter 3) on the connection between personal risk and professional obligation, and an additional discussion (in Chapter 5) on the response of nursing administrators to nurses reluctant to care for AIDS patients. Third, we have added a new chapter (7) on cost containment, justice, and rationing in the health care system. As the question of limited resources becomes even more urgent, the focus of nursing ethics is expanding accordingly. Nurses have an ethical duty, based on their obligations to individual clients, to be informed about and participate in ongoing debates about justice and the allocation of limited resources—including nursing care—in the health care system. Chapter 7 provides relevant background information, illustrated through five cases, and develops an ethical framework for assessing proposals for allocating health care. Despite these changes and additions, the principal aim of the book remains the same: to provide practicing and student nurses with an introduction to the identification and analysis of ethical issues that reflects both the special perspective of nursing and the value of systematic philosophical inquiry.

A number of people have contributed to this edition. Students in our Ethical Issues in Nursing course have provided useful suggestions and continuing inspiration for updating and improving the book. In addition, nurses in a number of workshops organized by hospitals, colleges of nursing, and professional organizations in various parts of the country have helped us to identify new topics and issues. We have benefited, too, from discussions with several colleagues affiliated with Michigan State University's Center for Ethics and the Humanities in the Life Sciences. Special thanks are due to Howard Brody, Maureen O'Higgins, Leonard Fleck, Kenneth Howe, Bruce L. Miller, and James Nelson.

We are also grateful to Crystal Lange, director of the Saginaw Valley State University School of Nursing, for her critical reading of our work-in-progress, and to Susan Ecklund, whose careful copy editing saved us from a number of errors and infelicities. For invaluable assistance in proofreading we are indebted to Bruce Curtis and David Benjamin. Finally, the suggestions, encouragement, and accommodation of editors Jeffrey House and Henry Krawitz at Oxford University Press were most helpful in preparing this edition.

East Lansing, Mich.   M.B.
February 1991   J.C.

Preface to the First Edition

The aim of this book is to provide practicing and student nurses with an introduction to the identification and analysis of ethical issues that reflects both the special perspective of nursing and the value of systematic philosophical inquiry. Discussions of general and theoretical points are, wherever possible, grounded in and illustrated by their application to specific nursing situations. The text includes thirty actual cases, which are discussed in some detail. In addition, Appendix D contains a set of eleven case studies for further practice in ethical analysis and reasoning.

The book begins with an account of the nature of moral dilemmas and outlines the philosophical skills and understanding necessary for addressing them systematically. Next, Chapter 2 provides an introduction to basic ethical principles and the complex relationships between ethical, legal, and religious considerations in the nursing context. Then, through a series of ten case studies, Chapter 3 focuses upon ethical issues involving nurses and clients. Chapter 4 discusses complications that arise due to the unclear nature of the relationship between nurses and physicians. In Chapter 5 we turn to ethical dilemmas involving relationships among nurses. Finally, Chapter 6 examines the extent to which nurses ought to be concerned with the nature and direction of institutional and public policy.

Throughout the book our emphasis in discussing individual cases is to illustrate the application of ethical analysis and reasoning and the importance of thinking for oneself. Where we come to conclusions on particular points, therefore, we do not intend readers to accept them without carefully examining our reasoning. The importance of critically analyzing the reasons given for various positions applies to our arguments no less than to those of others. Readers may or may not agree with our analyses of particular cases, but if they come to their conclusions by applying some of the methods, principles, and distinctions that we have stressed, our purpose will have been fulfilled. As a recent report on *The Teaching of Ethics in Higher Education* put it: "The test of the teaching of ethics is not whether students end by sharing the convictions of their teachers, but whether they have come to those convictions by means of the use of skills that might have led in other directions and may do so in the future" (Hastings-on-Hudson, The Hastings Center, 1980, p. 61).

Unless otherwise noted, all cases presented in the text were obtained from practicing nurses as part of a 1978 research study on nurses' perceptions of ethical dilemmas. The study was based upon one-hour, structured, tape-recorded interviews with a sample of forty practicing baccalaureate-educated nurses in Michigan's lower peninsula. The distribution of the principal employment settings of the nurses who participated in the study closely approximated the percentage distribution of all active registered nurses in Michigan whose highest degree was in baccalaureate nursing: there were 28 hospital nurses, 5 community health nurses, 3 nursing school faculty, 2 school nurses, 1 nursing home nurse, 1 office nurse, and no private duty, occupational health, or self-employed nurses. While the cases developed from these interviews do not raise all possible ethical issues in nursing, they offer a fair sampling of the ethical dilemmas that frequently recur in nursing practice. Names and places have been changed to insure confidentiality but, wherever possible, the nurses' actual words have been retained.

We want to express our gratitude to the nurses who participated in this study as well as to a number of others who helped us in preparing this book. Isabelle K. Payne, Dean of the College of Nursing at Michigan State University, and Suzanne Brouse, Maureen Chojnacki, Marilyn Rothert, and Linda Beth Tiedje read the manuscript and made suggestions about the nursing aspects. Lewis Zerby and Thomas Tomlinson, of the Department of Philosophy, suggested helpful changes with regard to the philosophical aspects. Linda Henlotter, a graduate assistant in the College of Nursing, helped conduct the interviews of practicing nurses, and Stanley Werne, a graduate assistant in the Department of Philosophy, helped compile the list of further readings and made suggestions about the manuscript. Though they are too numerous to mention by name, we also want to express our thanks to students in our team-taught course in Ethics in Nursing who helped us evaluate the clarity and relevance of the manuscript and encouraged us to complete it.

We are grateful, too, to Michigan State University for an M.S.U. Foundation Grant, which supported the survey of nurses, and an All-University Research Grant, which helped in the preparation of the manuscript. Finally, thanks are due to three people who provided special assistance. JoAnn Wittick, of the Medical Humanities Program, cheerfully and skillfully typed the manuscript. Bruce Curtis, of the Department of American Thought and Language, made line by line stylistic improvements. And Jeffrey House, of Oxford University Press, offered detailed criticisms and useful suggestions which helped us strengthen some of our arguments and made certain sections clearer and more concise.

East Lansing, Mich.   M.B.
January 1981   J.C.

Contents

Cases

Ethics in Nursing

1

Moral Dilemmas and Ethical Inquiry

1. Moral dilemmas in nursing

Advances in medical knowledge and technology, together with social and political changes, have raised a number of well-publicized moral dilemmas for patients and physicians. Less well publicized, but no less important, are the troubling conflicts of value that arise for nurses in these changing circumstances. As an example of the sort of dilemma created by the special role and responsibilities of nursing, consider the following case.

1.1 Withholding the prognosis

Kim Holt, a new staff nurse with more than three years of oncological experience in another hospital, was assigned primary responsibility for Ann Hernandez, a recent divorcée in her mid-forties who had just been diagnosed as having cancer of the colon with metastasis involving lymph nodes, a cancer for which there is no proven effective treatment. Ms. Holt had cared for Mrs. Hernandez for three days preoperatively and had established good rapport with her. Mrs. Hernandez's being heavily sedated immediately after surgery plus Kim Holt's being off duty the next day prevented communication between the two until the second postoperative day.

That day it soon became apparent to Ms. Holt that, while Mrs. Hernandez had been informed that she had cancer, she had not been informed about the seriousness of her condition or of her very poor prognosis. Thus, her initial response to the patient's inquiries about details of treatment and when she would be able to return to work was judiciously vague. Shortly thereafter, one of Mrs. Hernandez's daughters approached Ms. Holt and

3

urged her to assure her mother that everything was going to be all right. Mrs. Hernandez had just gone through a long and unpleasant divorce, she explained, and she and her sister wanted their mother spared the further pain of learning that she was terminally ill and that no proven, effective treatment was available.

Deeply troubled, Kim Holt discussed this situation with her head nurse, who suggested she pursue the matter with Mrs. Hernandez's physician as soon as possible. When she found Dr. Schaeffer at the nurses' station, Ms. Holt indicated that she was caring for Mrs. Hernandez and said that she wanted to know what Mrs. Hernandez had been told about her condition so that she might be more open and supportive with her. She also mentioned the patient's request for information about her treatment and prognosis and intimated that, based on her knowledge of the patient, she thought that Mrs. Hernandez's request was authentic and that she could handle the truth.

In response, Dr. Schaeffer, who was not Mrs. Hernandez's long-standing physician, said that he had informed Mrs. Hernandez that she had cancer, but, to spare her unnecessary anxiety, he had allowed her to maintain her belief that it could be effectively treated, a belief not supported by the facts in her case. Moreover, he added, any act of disclosure on the nurse's part would have to be considered inconsistent with the well-being of the patient and inconsistent with her role as a nurse. The general tone of Dr. Schaeffer's response, though not hostile, was self-assured and disapproving.

Kim Holt then related this to the head nurse and sought her counsel. After acknowledging that Dr. Schaeffer's position presented Ms. Holt with a serious dilemma, the head nurse advised her to comply with Dr. Schaeffer's directions in order to avoid a messy confrontation. If this sort of thing really bothered Ms. Holt, the head nurse added, she would in the future do what she could to reduce the number of times Ms. Holt was assigned to care for one of Dr. Schaeffer's patients.[1]

In this case a nurse faces a difficult moral dilemma. Strictly speaking, a *dilemma* is a situation requiring a choice between what seem to be two equally desirable or undesirable alternatives. Students sometimes find themselves in a dilemma when they have to choose between two highly rated, interesting courses that are scheduled for the same time. Or one might face a dilemma in deciding whether to go out in the rain to bring in a bicycle or to let it become a bit more rusty: neither alternative, getting wet or the bike's getting rusty, is desirable, but there is no way to avoid both. These, however, are not *moral* dilemmas. In a moral dilemma, *each* alternative course of action can be justified by fundamental moral rules or principles. The nurse who believes that she is duty-bound *both* to preserve life and to reduce suffering may be confronted with a dilemma when preserving life involves prolonging suffering or when suffering cannot be reduced without increasing the likelihood of shortening life. Choosing either seems to violate an ethical principle, yet the choice must be made.

The moral dilemma in "Withholding the prognosis" centers on the choice Kim Holt must make between responding in a supportive but nonetheless truthful way to Mrs. Hernandez's questions about her condition or continuing to deflect these questions and assuring her that there is nothing to worry about. On the face of it, each course of action could be grounded on fundamental principles.

A truthful response could be defended by appealing to Mrs. Hernandez's right, as a competent adult, to an honest answer to her questions. This right, it may be argued, is based on the right to self-determination, which is itself based on the respect owed to all persons by virtue of their capacity for choice and reflection. The violation of this right would therefore constitute a significant assault on Mrs. Hernandez's freedom and dignity as a person. Moreover, Kim Holt could also maintain that her participation in the deception seriously compromises the integrity of the relationship between her and the patient, thus diminishing her personhood as well as Mrs. Hernandez's.

On the other hand, acting in accord with the wishes of the family and the physician could also be supported by an appeal to moral principle. Mrs. Hernandez's daughters argue that deception is necessary to spare their mother further pain, and Dr. Schaeffer says that he wants to spare Mrs. Hernandez unnecessary anxiety. The reduction of pain and suffering is not only a general moral imperative; it has long been a cornerstone of both medical and nursing morality. Perhaps this is what Dr. Schaeffer had in mind when he said that any act of disclosure on Ms. Holt's part would be inconsistent with her role as a nurse. This, too, can be construed as a moral appeal if we assume that Ms. Holt has some sort of moral obligation to the profession and the hospital, as well as to the patient, to act in accord with the special role she has voluntarily assumed.

How, then, should the nurse resolve the dilemma? Perhaps her initial inclination to answer the patient's questions truthfully can no longer be defended. After all, can she disregard the wishes of both the family and the physician? They seem as concerned with the patient's well-being as she is. If she still has some reservations, perhaps the wise thing to do is to take the head nurse's advice and try to avoid such situations in the future, but to go along in this instance. But what if she is right, after all, and they, though well intentioned, are wrong? If so, wouldn't it be either immoral or cowardly of a nurse not to fulfill her moral obligation to Mrs. Hernandez?

What can Kim Holt appeal to in making her decision? Many people think that codes of medical or nursing ethics should be able to resolve such problems. In the next section we will see to what extent this is so.

2. Ethical codes: uses and limitations

Codes of professional ethics are often a mixture of creeds and commandments. As creeds, they affirm professional regard for high ideals of conduct and personally commit members of the profession to honor them, thus constituting a sort of oath of professional office. The opening sentence of the 1973 Code for Nurses of the International Council of Nurses (Appendix A) states that "the fundamental responsibility of the nurse is fourfold: to promote health, to prevent illness, to restore health and to alleviate suffering." This is a statement of creed. As commandments, codes of professional ethics provide a set of prescriptions designed to regulate conduct in more specific situations. For example, the same International Council of Nurses (ICN) Code states that "the nurse holds in confidence personal information and uses judgment in sharing this information."

As creeds, codes of nursing ethics provide a valuable reminder of the special responsibilities incumbent upon those who tend the sick. Nurses often deal with people who, because of their illness or injury, are especially vulnerable and must depend upon the professional's special knowledge and skills. Hence, it is important that the nursing profession formulate and adhere to high ideals of conduct in order to assure the public that individual nurses will not exploit their advantaged position.

As sets of commandments, codes of professional ethics have two principal functions. First, they provide an enforceable standard of minimally decent conduct that allows the profession to discipline those who clearly fall below the minimal standard. For example, in 1978 the *New Yorker* reported that some nurses were being paid by antiabortion groups for the names of women who had had abortions. Members of these groups then proceeded to harass the women with abusive phone calls when they returned home from the hospital.[2] Such conduct on the part of the nurses, regardless of the strength or correctness of their views on abortion, clearly violates both the provision of the Code stating that "the nurse holds in confidence personal information and uses judgment in sharing this information" and Point 2 of the 1976 American Nurses' Association (ANA) Code for Nurses (Appendix B), which holds that "the nurse safeguards the client's right to privacy by judiciously protecting information of a confidential nature."

A second function of the commandments in codes of professional ethics is to indicate in general terms some of the ethical considerations professionals must take into account in deciding on conduct. Thus, as indicated above, privacy and confidentiality are important considerations. So too are maintaining one's own professional competence and safeguarding patients from the incompetent, unethical, or illegal practice of others.

It is a mistake to think that all a conscientious nurse needs in order to deal with the moral dilemmas that arise in nursing is an adequate code of ethics coupled with a healthy measure of common sense. To demonstrate the limitations of ethical codes we need only to try to resolve Kim Holt's moral dilemma in "Withholding the prognosis" by appealing to the ICN Code and the American Nurses' Association Code.

Parts of the ICN Code for Nurses can be cited to support each alternative in Kim Holt's dilemma. For example, a decision to respond honestly to Mrs. Hernandez's questions can be based on the provisions of the Code which hold that "inherent in nursing is respect for . . . dignity"; "the nurse's primary responsibility is to those people who require nursing care"; "the nurse, in providing care, promotes an environment in which the values, customs and spiritual beliefs of the individual are respected"; and "the nurse carries personal responsibility for nursing practice . . ." Thus, it could be argued that the Code requires Kim Holt to be truthful with Mrs. Hernandez in order to respect the patient's dignity, beliefs, and values, and because her primary responsibility is to the patient and not to the patient's daughters or to the physician. Moreover, because Ms. Holt carries personal responsibility for what she does, she, and not the head nurse or the doctor, must make the final decision.

On the other hand, one can also cite provisions of the ICN Code to support the opposing position. For example, the Code also states that one of the "fundamental responsibilities" of the nurse is "to alleviate suffering"; "the nurse holds in confidence personal information and uses judgment in sharing this information"; and "the nurse sustains a cooperative relationship with co-workers in nursing and other fields." It could, therefore, be argued that the Code requires that Kim Holt not inform Mrs. Hernandez of the nature and seriousness of her condition, since this would create needless suffering, exhibit poor judgment in sharing confidential information, and seriously strain the cooperative relationship she is supposed to sustain with the physician.

To interpret this Code in a way that supports one or the other of Kim Holt's choices would be controversial and would require a considerable amount of supporting argument. Moreover, the usefulness of the Code as a straightforward guide to the resolution of moral dilemmas is significantly diminished by the need for such interpretations.

The source of the difficulty is not so much this particular code but the very idea of attempting to codify, in a simple yet consistent and comprehensive way, all of the precepts one needs to resolve dilemmas in a field as morally complex as nursing. Any such attempt will be caught on one of the horns of a difficult dilemma. If the code is to be simple, comprehensive, and acceptable to all nurses, it will be so abstract and general that it cannot, without significant interpretation, be applied to many specific problems. Such codes may gain widespread acceptance before their use in actual situations, but only because their vagueness allows people holding opposing views to mask their differences by silently interpreting the code in accord with their favored position on various issues. When the code is then appealed to in dilemmas like that facing Kim Holt, the hitherto submerged differences in interpretation rise to the surface and those who are engaged in the dispute must go beyond the code itself in order to resolve them. If, on the other hand, one tries to draft a very specific code aimed at anticipating all of the moral problems that can arise, one encounters three significant problems. First, the code will not be able to avoid controversial precepts and hence will be unlikely to win widespread acceptance. Second, it will probably fill many thick volumes, and thus lose the advantages of brevity and simplicity. And third, no matter how detailed it is, such a code will always be incomplete if its aim is to give unambiguous guidance in all possible situations. Therefore, neither a brief, simple code nor a long, detailed one will both offer clear guidance and attain widespread acceptance.

Before accepting this argument about the limitations of codes of professional ethics, let us briefly examine the 1976 ANA Code for Nurses. As the editors of the *Encyclopedia of Bioethics* have pointed out, this eleven-point Code, together with the interspersed Interpretive Statements that go with it, is distinctive among codes of ethics because

(1) it identifies the values and beliefs which undergird the ethical standards; (2) it shows a remarkable breadth of social and professional concerns; (3) it manifests an awareness of the ethical implications of shifting professional roles and of the complexity of modern health care; and (4) it goes beyond prescriptive statements regarding personal and professional conduct by advocating a sense of accountability to the client.[3]

Unlike the ICN Code, the ANA Code, together with the set of Interpretive Statements issued in 1985,[4] seems to provide clear guidance to a nurse in Kim Holt's position. Section 1.1 of the Interpretive Statements, "Respect for Human Dignity," says that "truth telling and the process of reaching informed choice underlie the exercise of self-determination, which is basic to respect for persons. Clients should be as fully involved as possible in the planning and implementation of their own health care." Additional sentences along these lines seem to support a decision to inform Mrs. Hernandez of her prognosis, and there is little in the remainder of the Code or Interpretive Statements that would appear to neutralize this directive.

But a significant problem remains unresolved. Although the Code may provide unambiguous guidance to Kim Holt, what it directs her to do runs contrary to the inclinations of both Dr. Schaeffer and Mrs. Hernandez's daughters. They, too, are motivated by ethical considerations. Why, therefore, should they now alter their positions? The ANA Code is not *their* code. They are not nurses and are not bound by it. Why, then, should they agree that certain provisions of a nursing code should settle the matter?

If Kim Holt is unable to do more in this situation than simply recite the relevant sections of her professional code of ethics, she will make little headway in bringing the issue to a satisfactory resolution. She must also be able to set out the *reasoning* or *arguments* underlying these provisions. And they are not part of the Code itself; all that can be found in the Code are the *conclusions* of those who had a hand in drafting it. Furthermore, as Robert M. Veatch has cogently argued, neither nurses nor doctors can reasonably expect a code of ethics drafted by members of their respective professions to be the last word on ethical issues in health care. Most of these issues involve and affect patients, their families, and the public as well as doctors and nurses. And it is hard to see why patients and families should feel themselves bound, ethically, to courses of action devised solely by health professionals. "An ethic that professionals base on their own consensus of what their role entails has no ethical force," Veatch writes, "at least with nonprofessionals. It is doubtful such a standard can be called an ethic at all."[5] Ethical disagreements in nursing often involve parties who have no special obligation to uphold the rules or ideals of nursing. And the ANA Code has no purchase on doctors, or patients and their families if their views run contrary to those embedded in the Code.

We might also note that, although the ANA Code provides reasonably direct guidance in the case under consideration, it will, in other instances, offer conflicting directives. Consider, for example, a mentally competent, adult, lifelong Jehovah's Witness who refuses a lifesaving blood transfusion. With the transfusion he will be able to lead a comparatively healthy, normal life; without it he will die. Exercising his right to autonomy, he elects the latter. A nurse who turns to the following paragraph in Interpretive Statement 1.1 of the ANA Code for guidance will, we believe, not have her doubts resolved:

The fundamental principle of nursing practice is respect for the inherent dignity and worth of every client. Nurses are morally obligated to respect human existence and the individuality of all persons who are the recipients of nursing actions. Nurses therefore must take all reasonable means to protect and preserve human life when there is hope of recovery or reasonable hope of benefit from lifesaving treatment.

To respect the "dignity" and "individuality" of the client in the above example seems to require that his autonomous refusal be honored. But to "preserve human life when there is hope of recovery or reasonable hope of benefit from lifesaving treatment" seems to require that his refusal be overridden. Which should it be? The Code reminds us of relevant values but gives us little indication of how to resolve conflicts of values, which are the very stuff of moral dilemmas.

Our aim has not been to denigrate the ANA Code and its most recent set of Interpretive Statements—indeed, as codes of professional ethics go, it is among the best—but rather to demonstrate the limitations of any code of professional ethics as a resource for resolving difficult moral dilemmas in health care. That any code will be limited in this way can be explained in part by an examination of the most basic question of philosophical ethics.

3. The fundamental question of morality

Ethics, understood here as a discipline whose roots go back to Socrates, is an attempt to formulate and justify systematic responses to the following question: What, *all things considered*, ought to be done in a given situation? It is the unrestricted frame of reference indicated by the phrase "all things considered" that limits the usefulness of ethical codes and makes ethics such a difficult subject.

Many questions about what a person ought to do raise no ethical questions because they are limited to a certain context where a definite framework establishes various rules and roles that provide unambiguous direction. Thus, suppose that a person is playing checkers. At various points in the game she may ask herself, What should I do? Assuming that the question is bounded by the rules of the game and motivated by a desire to win, it is not an ethical one. The answer will be determined solely by appeal to the rules and strategies of checkers. Similar questions that arise *within* various clearly defined occupational or familial roles may be answered in the same way. But now suppose that we expand the account of the circumstances of our checker-player to include that her opponent is her five-year-old son, who is just learning the game. Here the question of what move she ought to make in a given situation is more complex. Of course, if she wants to disregard the fact that her opponent is a beginner and her child, she may proceed as before. But if she considers that her opponent is her son and that he is just learning the game, she will want to play with much less competitive vigor than if he were someone like herself. Her task here is a ticklish one. Because she presumably wants to help develop her son's skills and knowledge without crushing his spirit, she must play reasonably well (otherwise he would never learn to play well himself) but not too well (otherwise his confidence would be dealt a severe blow). So, as this simple example shows, determining what one ought to do, *all things considered*, is more complex than determining what one ought to do within a more narrowly circumscribed frame of reference. And as with the combined roles of checker-player and parent, so too there can be tension between what one ought to do as employee, citizen, parent, spouse, and so forth, when these roles overlap.

Consider, for example, a driver who approaches an intersection at 3:00 A.M. as he is taking his pregnant wife, whose labor has begun, to the hospital. The light is red and there are no other cars in sight. Should he wait until the light turns green or proceed through the intersection? As a law-abiding citizen he has a duty to wait, but as a husband taking his wife to the hospital, it could be argued, he has a duty, after checking for traffic, to continue. Thus, the question arises as to what, all things considered, he ought to do. And this *moral* question requires that the framework of inquiry go beyond a simple appeal to the ordinary requirements of drivers and husbands, respectively.

Ethical issues about whether one ought or ought not to do something arise, then, when a question cannot be answered by appeal to the special or restricted considerations governing simple, clearly defined, and justifiable roles or practices. Here one must enlarge the frame of reference and identify and critically examine all the relevant considerations. It is this matter of a completely unrestricted frame of reference that makes ethical inquiry so difficult. The range and complexity of relevant factual and value-laden considerations often outstrip our intitial capacity to comprehend and evaluate them. This is especially true of problems that arise within the medical and nursing context. The problems are more difficult now than ever before partly because the complexities of modern medicine have required the development of health care "teams" made up of different sorts of professionals whose respective roles cannot always be precisely defined. Given the complexity of the clinical encounter and the nature of ethics (with its completely unrestricted frame of reference), no simple code—together with common sense—can relieve the thoughtful health professional of the difficult and demanding task of ethical inquiry. The reflective nurse cannot put her moral course on "automatic pilot."

4. Ethical inquiry

Even if a widely accepted code of ethics could provide unambiguous solutions to moral dilemmas in nursing, we would want to know whether these were the best or most nearly correct solutions and if this were the best code. To answer these questions, we would have to rely on conventional ethical analysis. This same sort of analysis must be applied directly to the dilemmas that resist a codified solution. The first step in this analysis is to identify ethical or other value-laden issues in nursing in a particular case, and to distinguish them from purely technical or empirical concerns. Next, we use various skills of ethical analysis and reasoning in an attempt to reach a well-grounded solution. At various points in this process, we may also have to consider the nature and limits of ethical knowledge as well as the nature and justification of basic ethical principles.

A. Identification of ethical issues

Health care professionals who are unaware of the value-laden elements of their practice may, in the name of technical expertise, impose their (often unexamined) personal values on others without adequate justification. Once it is recognized, however, that a particular question is not solely—or even mainly—a function of medical or nursing expertise, the health care professional can then try to determine who can best answer it and what, all things considered, seems to be the best-grounded solution or range of solutions.

Thus, a decision to withhold the truth cannot, like a decision to intubate, be justified by a physician's appeal to *medical* expertise. If a nurse and a physician disagree over whether a patient should be intubated, surely the presumption must be that the physician, by virtue of his or her more extensive training and knowledge, is correct. But, as Roland R. Yarling has argued:

> Because the question is nonmedical in nature, if there is a disagreement between a nurse and a physician about whether a terminal patient who requests the information should be told of his diagnosis and prognosis, the matter of whose opinion should prevail is not clear as it is in the situation where intubation is the question. There, because judgment is nonmedical, the medical expertise of the physician does not give his opinion an extraordinary value. The question whether to inform the terminal patient of his conditon is essentially a moral one, and decision on that question is a moral, rather than a medical, decision. This being so, neither the physician, as a physician, nor the nurse, as nurse, may claim a privileged position with respect to making that judgment.[6]

Once an issue is identified as basically a moral or value-laden one, those who address it should employ ethical analysis and reasoning to try to reach a well-grounded, mutually satisfactory solution.

B. Ethical analysis and reasoning

Critical reflection and inquiry in ethics involve the complex interplay of a variety of human faculties, ranging from empathy and moral imagination on the one hand to analytic precision and careful reasoning on the other. Among the more cognitive skills one employs in thinking an ethical issue through are the following:

1. Determining and obtaining relevant factual information. Although genuine moral dilemmas cannot be resolved simply by an appeal to or understanding of "the facts," certain factual matters will always be relevant to ethical inquiry. If we must reach beyond the facts in attempting to resolve a moral dilemma, we must also guard against reaching without them. Thus, for example, in "Withholding the prognosis," it is important that Kim Holt be very clear about such things as Mrs. Hernandez's prognosis, the authenticity of her request for information, and various other psychosocial and biomedical data.

Although our account of ethical analysis and reasoning begins with determining the facts, we do not want to give the impression that this can be completed at the outset. Often we cannot determine what counts as relevant factual information until we are well into an analysis. As we clarify concepts, construct and evaluate arguments, anticipate and respond to objections, identify relevant ethical principles, and so on, certain factual considerations that we initially thought to be relevant may come to seem less so, and we may perceive a need to obtain other information that, at the outset, seemed less important. In short, what counts as a relevant fact is dynamically related to the other elements of ethical analysis and reasoning. We list the determination of factual information first because it is often a good way to begin. But the list is not strictly serial; the skills of ethical reasoning are dynamically related, and we will often revise our understanding of an ethical issue and the relevant facts as we employ first one skill and then another.

2. Aiming at conceptual clarity and drawing relevant distinctions. The complexity of ethical inquiry often requires careful conceptual analysis and the recognition of important distinctions. For example, many controversies in health care involve conflicting claims of rights. These include the "right to life," the "right to die," "patients' rights," "society's rights," the "right to one's own body," the "right to health care," and numerous other "rights," all of which are often invoked to support one or another resolution of a moral dilemma. But what, exactly, is a "right"? What, we may ask, does it *mean* to say that people have a "right to life"? Does it mean that it is wrong, under any circumstances (e.g., capital punishment, war, or self-defense) to kill people? Or that killing is wrong only when it is "unjust" (and how, exactly, do we determine whether a particular killing is "unjust")? In addition, does the "right to life" require that people also be given whatever is necessary to sustain their lives (even if doing so requires enormous expenditures and forces significant reductions in other areas such as education, housing, and treatment for illness and injuries which are not life-threatening)? A satisfactory analysis of the concept of a "right" and of the various "rights" *in* and *to* health care (including the "right to life") is necessary if appeals to "rights" are to play any but a rhetorical role in the resolution of moral dilemmas in medicine and nursing. The same is true of such concepts as "health," "disease," "advocate," "death with dignity," "sanctity of life," "euthanasia," "benefit," and "mental illness." One of the reasons ethical debates often become fruitless and frustrating is that the participants fail to clarify adequately what they are talking about.

The result of a careful conceptual analysis is often the recognition of one or more distinctions that had not previously been explicitly recognized. Drawing an important distinction in ethical inquiry can be likened to using fine instruments in surgery. The surgeon needs very fine instruments to cut or suture one particular part of the body while leaving others untouched. Neither a woodsman's axe nor a kitchen knife is suited for surgical incisons because each is too crude or blunt and will cut far more than should be cut. So too, in ethical inquiry, one needs fine tools to outline a defensible position on one particular issue without thereby being committed, less defensibly, to the same position on a different kind of issue. It is one thing, for example, to argue for allowing conscious, competent, adult Jehovah's Witnesses to refuse livesaving blood transfusions for themselves and quite another to allow them to do so for their minor children. Our tools here are words; fine linguistic distinctions, like fine surgical instruments, make possible more precise analysis of complex questions.

As an example of conceptual analysis and drawing relevant distinctions, let us briefly examine the notion of a "medical decision." Patients and physicians often invoke the notion of a "medical decision" to justify the physician's authority to make one or another decision in the course of treatment. Many people, for example, might be inclined to support Dr. Schaeffer's decision to withhold Mrs. Hernandez's prognosis from her because it is a "medical decision" and he, after all, *is* the doctor. On these grounds, Kim Holt would be overstepping the bounds of her authority by even suggesting a truthful response to Mrs. Hernandez's request for information. But this line of argument reveals some confusion about the concept of "medical decision."

There are two critically different senses in which something may be a "medical decision." In the first, a medical decision is one that is based directly on medical knowledge or expertise. Such decisions are a function of a physician's special training. Let us call such decisions "medical decisions in the technical sense" and identify this use of the term "medical decision" with the subscript "t." Examples of medical decisions$_t$ are decisions about the medical diagnosis and prognosis of a particular illness, the correct dosage of various medications, and how best to perform a certain surgical procedure in a given case.

The term "medical decision" can also be used to refer to any decision made in the medical context. Such decisions, however, are not always a function of medical knowledge or expertise, though they may be informed by them. They will often turn on questions of value, and, as noted above, the physician's technical expertise does not make him or her an expert on conflicts of value. Let us call such decisions "medical decisions in the contextual sense" and identify this use of the term "medical decisions" with the subscript "c." Decisions in health care that are largely a matter of resolving a conflict of values or of other factors that are not exclusively medical will thus be called medical decisions$_c$. These include decisions about whether a patient should be informed of the diagnosis and prognosis of a certain illness; whether the costs, inconvenience, or risks of a certain medication are outweighed by the benefits; and whether, all things considered, a patient should undergo a certain surgical procedure. Having made this distinction, we can say that not all medical decisions$_c$ are medical decisions$_t$.

The decision about disclosing Mrs. Hernandez's prognosis is a medical decision in the contextual sense. The controversy turns largely on a conflict of values and not on matters of medical expertise. To attempt to cut off ethical inquiry by an appeal to the decision's medical nature is to fail to appreciate the distinction between medical decisions$_t$ and medical decisions$_c$. Although this does not show that Kim Holt's inclination to disclose the prognosis to Mrs. Hernandez is correct, it does show that she is not, in pursuing the question, mounting any sort of challenge to Dr. Schaeffer's expertise *as a physician*. She might be on considerably weaker ground, however, had Dr. Schaeffer been Mrs. Hernandez's long-standing physician.

3. Constructing and evaluating arguments. We use the word *argument* in the logician's sense, in which an argument is a set of reasons, or premises, together with a claim, or conclusion, which they are intended to support. Having identified an ethical issue, we must not only conduct factual and conceptual investigations, we must also construct and evaluate arguments for and against various positions.

In so doing, we search out reasons for or against a certain position and critically determine the extent to which the reasons, as premises, constitute good grounds for accepting the conclusion. In the case of "Withholding the prognosis," for example, Dr. Schaeffer suggests an argument for his decision to withhold the prognosis from Mrs. Hernandez. The argument, when spelled out, might have two premises, one of which is assumed to be true, although it is not explicitly stated:

1. Telling Mrs. Hernandez the truth will cause her unnecesary anxiety. (This is the stated premise.)
2. One ought to spare patients unnecessary anxiety. (This premise seems to be assumed, but is not stated.)

If Kim Holt is still inclined to question Dr. Schaeffer's conclusions, she will have to show exactly where and why these reasons fail to support the conclusion that Mrs. Hernandez should not be told the truth.

An argument must meet two principal conditions if its premises are to be regarded as good grounds for accepting the truth of the conclusion. The first has to do with the argument's *validity*. "Validity," as used in logic, is a technical term referring to the logical connection between an argument's premises and conclusion. An argument is valid if the assumption that its premises are true gives us very good grounds for supposing that its conclusion is true. Validity, then, has to do not with the *actual* truth or falsity of the premises but rather with the logical connection between the premises and the conclusion *if* we suppose that the premises are true. Thus, for example, both of the following arguments are equally valid, even though the first premise of *B* is false:

A. 1. All doctors are human.
    2. All humans are fallible.
    3. Therefore, all doctors are fallible.

B. 1. All nurses are women.
    2. All women are fallible.
    3. Therefore, all nurses are fallible.

Although both *A* and *B* are, strictly speaking, valid arguments, *B* shows that there is more to an argument's providing good grounds for accepting its conclusion than its being valid. The premises of a good argument would not only provide support for the conclusion *if they were true*, but they must also in fact *be true*. A valid argument whose premises are true is called a *sound* argument. Both arguments *A* and *B* are valid, but only *A* is sound. An argument whose premises provide good grounds for accepting its conclusion will be sound as well as valid.

Let us now examine the argument we have attributed to Dr. Schaeffer for its validity and soundness. First, the argument seems valid. If the premises are true, then the conclusion will be true. But are the premises true? Is the argument sound? It seems to us that the argument we have attributed to Dr. Schaeffer, though valid, is of questionable soundness.

One can initially challenge both premises of Dr. Schaeffer's argument. The first premise, at the very least, needs further support. Factual support is needed to show that telling the truth would cause Mrs. Hernandez *more* anxiety than the anxiety she now appears to be experiencing because of her uncertainty and, perhaps, her perception that her physician, family, and nurse are being less than forthright in responding to her queries. Here, of course, questions also arise as to which of the parties—Dr. Schaeffer, Mrs. Hernandez's daughters, or Kim Holt—is most qualified and in the best position to make this judgment. Furthermore, even if she were to experience more anxiety by being told of her prognosis, it still has to be shown that this is *unnecessary* anxiety. Perhaps, when looking at the larger scheme of things, it could be argued that this anxiety, though regrettable, is, all things considered, unavoidable if certain other important values are to be acknowledged (such as her freedom to make certain plans or decisions about how she wants to spend the remainder of her life). Thus, we need an analysis of the concept of "unnecessary anxiety" and an indication of the criteria to be used in determining whether a certain amount of anxiety is "unnecessary."

The same applies to the second (implied) premise, that "one ought to spare patients unnecesary anxiety." Like premise (1), this rule requires a careful analysis of what can be considered *unnecessary* anxiety. Given the rule's scope, any such analysis will be deeply immersed in value-laden considerations and may, if pursued thoroughly enough, involve an appeal to one's most basic beliefs about the nature and meaning of human existence. And since people's views of the nature and meaning of human existence are not uniform, it is presumptuous to think that the second premise is both clear enough to guide conduct *and* so well accepted that it needs no supporting argument itself. Insofar as it is clear enough to guide conduct in all relevant cases, it will lack widespread acceptance; insofar as it is widely accepted, it will probably be only vaguely understood and will need to be tempered by successive applications to a variety of complex cases.

Our reconstruction and evaluation of Dr. Schaeffer's argument have shown that it cannot, at this point, be accepted as sound. We have not, however, shown that his conclusion is false—only that the argument he appears to have in mind does not, in its present form, support his conclusion. It is still open to him to reformulate the argument so that the premises do, in fact, provide good grounds for accepting the conclusion. On the other hand, those who want to show not only that his argument is weak but also that his conclusion is false must now attempt to construct a sound argument whose conclusion is something like: One ought to tell Mrs. Hernandez the truth. A more thorough examination of the sorts of arguments that might be given in this case will be found in the section entitled "Deception" in Chapter 3.

We have, in this brief illustration, only scratched the surface of what is involved in constructing and evaluating arguments. Readers who want to develop their skills in this all-important activity are advised to work their way through one or more of the books listed under "Philosophical Analysis and Reasoning" in the Suggestions for Further Reading at the end of this book. Another alternative, for students, is an introductory course in logic.

4. Developing a systematic framework.   Efforts to construct and evaluate particular arguments should draw upon and be incorporated into a developing, systematic, ethical framework. The development of such a framework is important for two reasons. First, it provides a common ground for resolving moral disagreements. Insofar as we share a systematic framework, made up of principles, rules, distinctions, standards of justification, and so on we will then be able to use it to settle certain disputes. And even in those cases—so frequent in modern health care—in which such a framework gives no direct guidance, it can at least provide a common background and starting point for the development of satisfactory resolutions.

Second, the development of a systematic ethical framework is of personal as well as interpersonal value. One of the qualities most of us admire in others and try to cultivate in ourselves is personal integrity. A person of integrity, in this sense, is one whose responses to various matters are not capricious or arbitrary, but principled. Such a person attempts to respond to new situations, as far as possible, in ways that are consistent with justifiable responses to past situations. This principled continuity of conduct is part of his or her identity as a person, and the degree to which he or she is able to *integrate* responses to various situations determines the extent of his or her integrity and identity as a particular person. Thus, so far as a person wants to maintain a unitary sense of identity and an accompanying sense of personal integrity and reliability, he or she will want to adopt a systematic framework for analyzing and responding to ethical issues.

Given the open-ended nature of the fundamental question of morality ("What, all things considered, ought to be done?") and the complexity of our rapidly changing world (with the special difficulties created by the high stakes, personal intimacy, and enlarged range of possibilities that character- ize moral dilemmas in the medical context), the development and mainte- nance of a personal and interpersonal ethical framework requires continual attention. As an ethical framework is repeatedly applied, tested, refined, and revised, its adequacy is gauged by the extent to which it is consistent, coherent, and comprehensive.

An ethical framework is *consistent* to the extent that its particular judg- ments, rules, and principles are logically compatible and do not contradict one another. A particularly bald example of inconsistency in an ethical framework appears in a widely reprinted article, "Moral and Ethical Dilem- mas in the Special-Care Nursery."[7] In discussing the reluctance of special- ists in newborn intensive care to deal with issues having to do with conflict between parents and physicians over discontinuing treatment, the authors write: "Some physicians recognize that the wishes of the families went against their own, but they were resolute [about continuing treatment]. They commonly agreed that if they were the parents of very defective children, withholding treatment would be most desirable for them. How- ever, they argued aggressive management was indicated for others" (p. 892). Unless these physicians can justifiably demonstrate a morally relevant differ- ence between themselves *as parents* and the parents of their patients, their ethical frameworks are inconsistent. Other things being equal, if aggressive management is indicated for others, it is indicated for oneself; if withholding treatment is desirable for oneself as a parent, why is it not desirable for other parents?

An ethical system is *coherent* insofar as its individual judgments, rules, and principles are mutually supportive. The elements of a coherent frame- work "hang together" so that it provides a systematic basis for addressing unprecedented dilemmas. Controversy over the use of new life-prolonging medical technology, for example, might be more readily resolved by appeal to a set of rules and principles that are themselves related to widely accepted judgments about prolonging life in less controversial contexts.

It is often tempting to obtain both consistency and coherence for an ethical framework by restricting its domain or *comprehensiveness*. If consistency has to do with logical compatibility and coherence with mutual support, both will be easier to achieve and maintain within a restricted frame of reference. But to do so would be to retreat from one of the aims of systematic ethical inquiry: the development of a comprehensive framework that will provide guidance in a large number of contexts of moral choice. Other things being equal, then, the wider the range of situations in which a framework is able to provide systematic (i.e., consistent and coherent) guidance, the better the framework is.

Although consistency, coherence, and comprehensiveness are equally important criteria for the adequacy of an ethical framework, people sometimes overemphasize one at the expense of the others. They may, for instance, place a high value on consistency and coherence at the expense of comprehensiveness. Issues that either create conflicts among values or cannot neatly be integrated into the core of their value system are simply disregarded. It is thus that many in health care are tempted to ignore social, political, and economic considerations that would, if acknowledged, strain their framework's consistency and coherence. But the gain is illusory. Since the social, political, and economic dimensions of health care create new ethical dilemmas as well as aggravate more conventional ones, they cannot be ignored. Any ethical framework that cannot or does not address them is, to that extent, insufficiently comprehensive.

5. Anticipating and responding to objections. No matter how careful our ethical analysis has been, it is always possible that our reasoning was defective, that we overlooked some important factor, or that new social or biomedical developments have undermined some of our basic assumptions. We must therefore be concerned not only with critically evaluating the positions of others, but also with anticipating and responding to possible objections to our own position and arguments. As John Stuart Mill argues in his celebrated essay *On Liberty:*

He who knows only his own side of the case knows little of that. His reasons may be good, and no one may have been able to refute them. But if he is equally unable to refute the reasons on the opposite side, if he does not so much as know what they are, he has no ground for preferring either opinion. . . . Ninety-nine in a hundred of what are called educated men are in this condition, even of those who can argue fluently for their opinions. Their conclusion may be true, but it might be false for anything they know; they have never thrown themselves into a mental position of those who think differently from them, and considered what such persons may have to say; and, consequently, they do not, in any proper sense of the word, know the doctrine which they themselves profess. . . . So essential is this discipline to a real understanding of moral and human subjects that, if opponents of all-important truths do not exist, it is indispensable to imagine them and supply them with the strongest arguments which the most skillful devil's advocate can conjure up.[8]

C. Ethical principles and knowledge

In addition to skills in ethical analysis and reasoning, ethical inquiry often requires an understanding of the nature and justification of basic ethical principles, the status of knowledge in ethics, and the relationships among ethics, law, and religion. These very complex topics will be examined in the next chapter. What follows is simply a brief introduction to each area in order to complete our overview of ethical inquiry.

1. Basic ethical principles.   Suppose Kim Holt and Dr. Schaeffer agree, after some discussion, that the question of whether to tell Mrs. Hernandez the truth is a moral and not a purely medical matter. Suppose, too, that they agree on the facts (including the prediction that the longer Mrs. Hernandez remains ignorant of the true state of affairs, the happier she will be—in the ordinary sense of "happy"), and that they are using words in the same way. In these circumstances it is still possible for Ms. Holt and Dr. Schaeffer to disagree, if, for example, the principle of utility is the foundation of his ethical framework while she espouses some version of the Kantian notion of respect for personal autonomy and dignity as the basic principle of ethics.

Appealing to the utilitarian imperative to maximize the general happiness, Dr. Schaeffer may reason that not informing Mrs. Hernandez will, on balance, bring about more happiness than unhappiness and that therefore she should not be informed about her condition. Ms. Holt, on the other hand, may argue that preserving a person's autonomy and dignity is more important from a moral point of view than maximizing his or her happiness. Since withholding the truth both restricts Mrs. Hernandez's autonomy and violates her dignity as a self-determining person, Ms. Holt would argue that the patient ought to be told the truth even if this limits her happiness. If the disagreement between Ms. Holt and Dr. Schaeffer takes this form, there is no way to resolve it apart from examining the nature and justification of the principle of utility and the principle of respect for persons and attempting to determine which principle is most basic in cases in which they give conflicting direction.

2. Knowledge in ethics.   How do we determine whether one or another ethical decision or principle is better grounded than the others? Can we *know* that some position or framework is better than its rivals, or are such choices ultimately matters of personal opinion or individual taste? To answer these questions, we must say something about the extent to which ethics is a cognitive discipline. Many people believe there is no such thing as knowledge in ethics, and thus no way to know that one decision or principle is better than the others. Moral judgments and principles, they maintain, are at bottom "merely subjective" and nothing more than expressions of personal preference or taste. If this were true, our efforts to use reason, evidence, and argument to resolve moral dilemmas and disagreements would be of limited value. So it is vital to show the extent to which ethics can be regarded as a cognitive discipline and exactly what it means to have knowledge in ethics (see Chapter 2).

3. Ethics, law, and religion.   Legal and religious considerations may be relevant in various ways to the resolution of moral dilemmas. But how are they relevant and how much weight are they to be given in various contexts? To what extent, for example, can Kim Holt, Mrs. Hernandez's daughters, or Dr. Schaeffer appeal to the law to support their respective positions? If something is illegal, is it also necessarily unethical? And if something is not illegal, does it follow that it is morally permissible? Some understanding of the relationships between legal and ethical considerations is necessary for ethical inquiry.

So too is an understanding of the relationships between religious and ethical considerations. For we may ask to what extent, if any, are ethical claims grounded upon, and inseparable from, religious ones? And to what extent must an acceptable ethical framework allow for decisions based on appeals to religious conviction?

5. Ethical autonomy and institutional-hierarchical constraints

Generally speaking, individuals are autonomous to the extent that they are self-determining or able to act in accord with a plan they had either freely chosen or at least independently endorsed. In everyday life, personal autonomy is a function of the degree to which one can be regarded as *one's own person*, capable of independent action and judgment. By regarding autonomy as a matter of degree, we suggest that people can be *more* or *less* autonomous than others as well as more autonomous in one area of their lives and less in another. Thus, for example, Ann can be regarded as more autonomous than Bea, but less so than Celia; and she can be more autonomous as a teacher than she is as a wife or mother.

Ethical autonomy has a central place in the network of moral concepts and is closely related to the notions of personhood, self-respect, and moral responsibility. In fact, it is unlikely that a satisfactory analysis of any of these concepts can avoid referring to the others. Ethical autonomy involves being one's own person when one decides upon or judges conduct. To the extent that someone is not her own person, her will becomes the instrument of another or she may be a "cog in a machine." To be seen in this way is to fail to be respected as a person. Respect for persons, Kant pointed out, involves their being regarded as *ends-in-themselves*, not as mere means to someone else'e ends. To be an end-in-oneself is to be capable of independent thought and action. Thus, the choices, commitments, and projects of an end-in-herself are worthy of respect not because they produce good results but because they *are* the choices, commitments, and projects of a person. To have self-respect in this context is simply to respect oneself *as a person*, as a being capable of deliberation on ethical questions and one whose choices and decisions, when effected, will result in certain changes in the world. In the ethical sphere, then, self-respect includes holding oneself morally responsible for the results of one's choices and decisions. We may summarize this extremely brief account by stating that to respect oneself (and be respected) as a person it is necessary to cultivate one's ethical autonomy and thus increase the range of things for which one is morally responsible.

A special problem, however, arises for nurses. Put bluntly it is this: To what extent can a nurse be ethically autonomous? Consider, for example, this view of the primary role of a nurse:

In my estimation obedience is the first law and the very cornerstone of good nursing. And here is the first stumbling block for the beginner. No matter how gifted she may be, she will never become a reliable nurse until she can obey without question. The first and most helpful criticism I ever received from a doctor was when he told me that I was supposed to be simply an intelligent machine for the purpose of carrying out his orders.[9]

Good nursing and ethical autonomy are, according to this writer, incompatible.

Although the author of this passage is reported to have been "a considerable influence on nursing in her time,"[10] that time was nearly a century ago, and her position would probably be met with disbelief or scorn if propounded to contemporary nurses. Yet the behavior it urges nurses to adopt may to a large extent remain even when exhortations to practice it have become embarrassing. In 1966, for example, a study of nurse-physician relationships revealed that nurses often complied with medical directives that they knew fell short of minimally decent standards of practice.[11] The researchers structured a situation in which a doctor directed a nurse to administer a particular dose of medication. The directive was unusual because the dosage of medication was obviously excessive; the directive was transmitted by telephone, which violated hospital policy, and the voice was one with which the nurse was not familiar; and the medication was unauthorized inasmuch as it had not been placed on the ward stock list. Nonetheless, the study showed that twenty-one out of a sample of twenty-two nurses placed in this situation prepared the medication and were ready to give it to the patient when the researchers finally intervened.

This study bears on our present concerns in two ways. First, it shows that some degree of ethical autonomy is a desirable characteristic in a nurse *as a nurse*. As the authors of the study state:

In a real-life situation corresponding to the experimental one, there would in theory be two professional intelligences, the doctor's and the nurse's, working to ensure that a given procedure be undertaken in a manner beneficial to the patient or, at the very least, not detrimental to him. The experiment strongly suggests, however, that in the real-life situation one of these intelligences is, for all practical purposes, non-functioning.[12]

Secondly, the study obviously indicates that there may be a discrepancy between a nurse's professed ethical autonomy and the actual nature of her behavior in situations where its exercise involves possible conflicts with physicians, hospitals, or others presumed to have some authority. The researchers observe that

in nonstressful moments, when thinking about her performance, the average nurse tends to believe that considerations of her patient's welfare and of her own professional honor will outweigh considerations leading to automatic obedience to the doctor's orders at times when these two sets of factors come into conflict.[13]

The nursing context is characterized by a number of constraints that frequently make the exercise of autonomy problematic. In 1988 the Secretary's Commission on Nursing, a twenty-five-member public advisory panel established by Otis R. Bowen, Department of Health and Human Services (DHHS), reported that constraints on nurse decision-making contributed to problems in nurse recruitment and retention. The commission specifically recommended the following:

Employers of nurses, as well as the medical profession, should recognize the appropriate clinical decision-making authority of nurses in relationship to other health-care professionals, foster communication and collaboration among the health-care team, and ensure that the appropriate provider delivers the necessary care. Close cooperation and mutual respect between nursing and medicine are essential.[14]

More than 68 percent of nurses must contend not only with the conventional hierarchical structure of medical decision-making but also with restrictions on behavior imposed by the bureaucratic system of the hospital. Thus, the hospital nurse finds herself constrained in various and occasionally conflicting ways by the hospital (which employs her), the physician (with whom she works), the client (for whom she provides care), and the nursing profession (to which she belongs). To what extent can she be her own person—i.e., be ethically autonomous—in these circumstances? The same kinds of difficulties, it should be noted, can arise for public health and visiting nurses, school and industrial nurses, and nurses working in extended care facilities. In these settings, the agency or organization for which nurses work places similar limits on their practice as does the hospital. In the following chapters different cases will illustrate this problem of ethical autonomy, which is so basic to the consideration of ethics in nursing and so difficult to resolve.

We conclude this section with two important reminders about the notion of autonomy. First, autonomy does not mean unconditional freedom that would allow us to will or do anything. We are all aware of the formative influence of genes, culture, and social environment. Long before we were able to think for ourselves, each of us was provided with a set of emotions, beliefs, desires, principles, and so on. Nonetheless, how we use our natural, cultural, and social endowments in responding to the environment is, to varying degrees, up to us. As Gerald Dworkin has put it: "If the autonomous man cannot adopt his motivations *de novo*, he can still judge them after the fact. The autonomous individual is able to step back and formulate an attitude towards the factors that influence his behavior."[15] Autonomy, therefore, is compatible with a view of the world that includes a great deal of causal determination and constraints on our behavior.

Second, ethical autonomy involves thinking *for* oneself, not *of* oneself or *by* oneself. To think of oneself identifies the object and not the manner of one's thinking. Thinking by oneself, like "thinking for oneself," does designate a manner of thinking, but in ethics this manner of thinking is unlikely to yield the best results. Given the unrestricted frame of reference and complexity of ethical inquiry, thinking *for* oneself is usually more successful if it includes at least some thinking *with* others who can call one's attention to relevant considerations that one might otherwise have overlooked or misunderstood. This is why discussion with people of various relevant backgrounds is vital to sound ethical inquiry. Thus, we may conclude, being one's own person or ethically autonomous implies neither selfishness nor isolation. One may perfectly well think *for* oneself and still think *about* and *with* others.[16]

Notes

1. This case has been adapted from one examined in Roland R. Yarling, "Ethical Analysis of a Nursing Problem: The Scope of Nursing Practice in Disclosing the Truth to Terminal Patients," *Supervisor Nurse* Part 1 (May 1978):40. For a detailed analysis of this case that applies many of the points made in this chapter, see the remainder of this article as well as Part 2 (June 1978). Whereas Yarling emphasizes dilemmas associated with withholding a diagnosis of cancer, this practice is no longer as prevalent as it once was. The issue raised in "Withholding the prognosis," however, is still quite common; see John M. Lincourt and Alex F. Sanchez, "Benevolent Deception in Family Medicine," *Family Medicine* 16 (March/April 1984):47–49.

2. Talk of the Town, *New Yorker*, 3 July 1978, p. 19.

3. Warren T. Reich, editor-in-chief, *Encyclopedia of Bioethics*, vol. 4 (New York: Free Press, 1978), p. 1789.

4. American Nurses' Association, *Code for Nurses with Interpretive Statements* (Kansas City, Mo.: American Nurses' Association, 1985). All subsequent references to the Code's Interpretive Statements are to this edition.

5. Robert M. Veatch, *A Theory of Medical Ethics* (New York: Basic Books, 1981), p. 107. For the entire argument against the legitimacy of professional codes for adjudicating most ethical disagreements in health care, see pp. 79–107.

6. Yarling, "Ethical Analysis of a Nursing Problem" (Part 1), p. 49.

7. Raymond S. Duff and A. G. M. Campbell, "Moral and Ethical Dilemmas in the Special-Care Nursery," *New England Journal of Medicine* 289 (25 October 1973):890–94.

8. John Stuart Mill, *On Liberty* (New York: Liberal Arts Press, 1956), p. 45.

9. Sarah Dock, "The Relation of the Nurse to the Doctor and the Doctor to the Nurse," *American Journal of Nursing* 17 (1917):394. Cited in Marjorie J. Stenberg, "The Search for a Conceptual Framework as a Philosophic Basis for Nursing Ethics: An Examination of Code, Contract, Context, and Covenant," *Military Medicine* 144 (January 1979):10.

10. Stenberg, "Search for a Conceptual Framework," p. 8.

11. C. K. Hofling et al., "An Experimental Study in Nurse-Physician Relationships," *Journal of Nervous and Mental Disease* 143 (1966):171–80.

12. Ibid., p. 176.

13. Ibid., p. 177.

14. "Executive Summary of Secretary's Commission on Nursing Report," *Nursing Economic$* 7 (January–February 1989):57–58.

15. Gerald Dworkin, "Autonomy and Behavior Control," *Hastings Center Report* 6 (February 1976):24.

16. For two accounts of the concept of and format for ethics rounds as a way of institutionalizing ethical inquiry for nurses in the clinical context, see Kathleen A. Mahon and Sally J. Everson, "Moral Outrage—Nurses' Right or Responsibility: Ethical Rounds for Nurses," *Journal of Continuing Education in Nursing* 10 (no. 3, 1979):4–7; and Anne J. Davis, "Helping Your Staff Address Ethical Dilemmas," *Journal of Nursing Administration* 12 (February 1982):9–11.

2

Unavoidable Topics in Ethical Theory

1. Introduction

Ethical inquiry in everyday life and in health care often proceeds without formal recourse to ethical theory. Questions may be clarified, distinctions drawn, arguments examined, and solutions found without appealing to theoretical considerations about the nature and justification of basic moral principles. Thus, the fact that two people have different foundations for their ethical views is sometimes irrelevant to the resolution of a particular problem.

Suppose, for example, a question arises over whether everything possible should be done to prolong the life of an elderly man in a nursing home. Suppose, too, that he has no known family and that the decision must be made by the staff. One person, *A*, might argue that the man should be treated because not to do so would be to violate the duty to preserve and prolong life. Another person, *B*, might also argue that the man should be treated, but for different reasons. *B* may argue that the man is not in severe pain and that even though his mental capacities are significantly impaired, he seems to be reasonably content. Since it is *B*'s view that one ought, above all, to do what will maximize happiness, she believes that efforts to prolong the man's life should continue. So the issue in this case can be resolved despite the fact that *A* and *B* hold different basic principles and, perhaps, different conceptions of how they are known and justified.

Yet things do not always work out this way. Sometimes different positions on a particular ethical issue are a direct function of the parties' holding different ethical principles. In this event, the issue cannot be resolved without some discussion of the nature and justification of the ethical principles underlying the differing positions. Suppose, for example, that the facts in the case sketched above were altered so that the patient was experiencing unmitigable pain and distress. In this case, *B*, with her basic commitment to maximizing happiness, would have to revise her particular judgment and say that efforts to extend the man's life should no longer be as strenuous. The change in facts, however, would not be relevant to *A*, and her judgment that the patient's life should be prolonged would be the same. Here the resulting disagreement is rooted firmly in the difference between their basic principles. If they pursue the matter further, they will encounter questions about the nature and justification of ethical principles that have long been the subject of ethical theory.[1]

This chapter is a bare-bones introduction to three topics in theoretical ethics that cannot be avoided by anyone who seeks to develop systematic responses to ethical issues in nursing. First, we will make a brief survey of *basic* ethical principles and how they constrain or engender *secondary* principles. Then we will discuss knowledge in ethics and, in particular, the kinds of considerations that are relevant to determining whether one basic principle is more securely grounded than another. Finally, we will turn to the important question of the relationships and relative priority of ethical, legal, and religious considerations in a pluralistic society.

2. Basic ethical principles

Persons holding different ethical principles might well come to different conclusions about what ought to be done in the following case, which raises questions about how nursing care should be distributed when conditions are less than ideal.

2.1 Priorities: baby or parents?

Martha Schwartz, one of the most senior staff nurses in the neonatal intensive care unit, works only part time because of her own children. Baby Daniel Ingerman has coded, and Martha, with a recently graduated RN at her side, is quickly and efficiently working with a house doctor to resuscitate him. It is clear, however, that the baby's chances of surviving this episode are extremely slim, and that even if he lives he will probably be severely handicapped both mentally and physically.

As she is about to help with a medication, Martha glances through the window at Elaine and Don Ingerman somberly watching the staff's frantic activity. At once she realizes that she should be in two places simultaneously. The parents need her; their child is dying. She has worked with the Ingermans during the past two critical days and believes she could be of help to them.

What should Martha Schwartz do in this case? Is it best to stay with the baby or go to the parents and let the other nurse assist in the emergency? Is the likelihood that the other nurse will be able to work less effectively than Martha with the doctor going to lessen the baby's already slim chances for survival? Is it fair to the young nurse, the doctor, or the baby to leave them in this situation? Or should Martha stay with the baby and send the new RN to be with the parents, people she's never met?

To see how basic ethical principles occupy a central role in ethical inquiry, consider the following excerpt from a fictional discussion of this case by three nurses.

DEBBIE: I definitely think that there is no problem here. There is only one thing that Martha can do. And that's to stay with the baby and do everything possible to help save its life. And the new RN, even though she may not be able to help the doctor, ought to stick around and learn how to be effective in such situations in the future.

RENEE: Why do you say this?

DEBBIE: It's simple. The most basic duty of doctors and nurses is to save life. Sure it's important to communicate with parents and other family members when you can. But when you have to choose between that and honoring the duty to preserve and protect the patient's life, there's no choice. You go with the more basic duty, and no duty is more basic for us than preserving and prolonging the patient's life.

URSULA: Boy, nothing personal Debbie, but that kind of rigid, moralistic thinking really drives me up the wall. I mean, how can you have so much confidence in an absolute rule like "Always preserve and protect life"? I can think of lots of cases where the consequences of doing that would do nothing but make everybody more miserable. I really think we've got to get away from these old-fashioned, absolute dos and don'ts and start being more realistic and flexible.

DEBBIE: Then what do you think Martha should do in this case?

URSULA: Well, I think she should do whatever would work out best for everyone. If she thinks that staying with the doctor would make more people happy, she should stay; and if going to talk with the parents would be best for everybody, then she should do that. You've got to be flexible, you know. You can't apply rigid rules without paying attention to the consequences.

RENEE: Well, what do you think would have the best consequences *in this case*?

URSULA: Mmmm, that's hard to say. I think I need more facts and time to balance things out.

DEBBIE: Martha didn't have all that much time to "balance things out."

URSULA: O.K., assuming that the baby was going to die anyway or that even if he lived, his life would create enormous unhappiness for himself and everyone else, I think she should have gone to talk with the parents. This would relieve some of their anxiety and perhaps help them prepare for the grieving process. And the new RN would have an opportunity to get some valuable experience which will be useful when she is working on a code that would have better consequences than this one.

DEBBIE: You make it all sound so heartless and mechanical. What do you think, Renee? Which of us is right?

RENEE: I don't know. Frankly I don't think I can go along a hundred percent with either of you. For me, the most important thing is to respect people's basic rights. I think lots of people have important rights in this case. The parents have a right to be supported and informed about what's going on. The baby has a right to life. The doctor has a right to the best available assistance. And the new RN has a right not to be abandoned in a situation in which she is over her head. The main problem in this case is that you can't satisfy all of these rights. So I guess you start with the most basic, which is, of course, the baby's right to life. And that means that Martha ought to stay with the baby.

URSULA: But I think your "right to life" is just as old-fashioned and rigid as Debbie's "duty to save life." As a matter of fact, it's the same thing only inside out. And what good is a "right to life" if the consequences of honoring it make everyone miserable, including the person whose life is saved?

RENEE: I don't know, Ursula, except that I think that some things are right or wrong even if they don't have the best consequences or make everyone deliriously happy. And respecting people's basic right to life is one of these.

In this admittedly contrived discussion, each participant represents an ethical outlook that is anchored by a different sort of basic principle. Debbie's basic principles take the form of duties. Her framework is what we might call duty-based.[2] It holds that there are certain basic duties that must be discharged *no matter what*. Although it does not deny the importance of maximizing happiness or respecting certain rights, these must always give way if they conflict with the performance of basic duties. Ursula, on the other hand, places the goal of maximizing the greatest general happiness at the base of her ethical framework. Everything in her framework is justified by appealing to maximizing happiness. Thus, if a conflict arises between acknowledging certain duties or rights on the one hand and maximizing happiness on the other, Ursula goes with the latter. Finally, Renee emphasizes the importance of people's basic rights. These rights occupy the same place in her framework as basic duties do in Debbie's. Although she does not deny the importance of human happiness, maximizing it is always to be constrained by respecting people's basic rights.

In the following discussion, four standard ethical frameworks will be examined more thoroughly. We begin with utilitarianism, the prevailing goal-based theory, and then turn to duty- and right-based theories, which, despite their differences, are alike in holding that at least some acts are morally required apart from the extent to which they maximize happiness or any other overall goal. Then we conclude by discussing a framework that refuses prior ranking of goals, duties, and rights. First, however, it will be helpful to say a bit more about goals, duties, and rights.

Each of the four major types of ethical framework has three elements:

overall social goals, individual duties, and individual rights. (1) *Goals* are states of affairs, considered good in themselves, that ought, morally, to be maximized. Actions may therefore be evaluated by the extent to which they further or hinder the maximization of these overall goals. People for whom the maximization of such a goal overrides all other considerations in determining what, all things considered, ought to be done, are said to have a goal-based ethical framework. And when the goal is specified as something like the greatest general happiness or social welfare, the framework is that version of goal-based theory called *utilitarianism*. In the above dialogue Ursula can be classified as a utilitarian. (2) *Duties* apply to individuals. Within a particular framework, a person has a duty to carry out or refrain from a certain action if and only if the framework includes a rule or principle requiring or forbidding that type of action. If the framework includes some duties that ought to be performed even if certain overall goals recognized by the system would not be furthered (or even if they would be compromised), the framework is duty-based. One that includes a basic duty to save or preserve life, like that held by Debbie, is such a framework. (3) *Rights* are claims or entitlements possessed by individuals which require that others not interfere with their exercise of them or, in the case of "positive" as opposed to "negative" rights,[3] that they provide the right-holder with something he or she wants or needs. As with duties, a person has a right to something within a particular framework if and only if it includes rules or principles specifying that right. If a framework includes some rights that must be respected regardless of how this will affect the pursuit of some of the framework's aggregate goals, it is right-based. Renee's position seems to be right-based.

What distinguishes the main types of ethical framework, then, is not their elements, for all include goals, duties, and rights. Rather, the critical feature is the way in which each framework *orders* these elements. Whether, in cases of moral conflict, certain goals, duties, or rights are always *basic*, as opposed to *derivative* or *subordinate*, is the crucial question in determining the structure of an ethical framework.

A. *Utilitarian theories*

Utilitarianism, in all of its forms, holds that the rightness or wrongness of an act is always a function of the extent to which its being performed or omitted will contribute to the goal of maximizing the overall good, which is construed variously as the total or average happiness or welfare. Although the consequences of the act for each affected individual must be given equal consideration, it is the aggregate or total amount of good that is decisive, not how equitably it happens to be distributed. The application of the utilitarian principle may be direct or indirect,[4] but it remains, for the utilitarian, the supreme principle of morality, the court of ultimate appeal on every moral issue.

Of course, utilitarians still talk about rights and duties, but these are always derived from the utilitarian principle. They have no independent standing. If, for example, including a right to freedom of speech would increase the chances of maximizing the overall goal, then this right would be included in the utilitarian's framework. Its status, however, would depend on its continuing to contribute to the utilitarian goal. In his celebrated defense of individual liberty, John Stuart Mill argues that "the sole end for which mankind are warranted, individually and collectively, in interfering with the liberty of action of any of their members is self-protection."[5] He adds, however, that the right to individual liberty is not basic, but rather derived from the principle of utility:

It is proper to state that I forego any advantage which could be derived to my argument from the idea of abstract right as a thing independent of utility. I regard utility as the ultimate appeal on ethical questions, but it must be utility in the largest sense, grounded on the permanent interests of man as a progressive being.[6]

In his view, then, if there were ever a clash between the claims of utility (the basic principle) and the right to freedom of speech or action (the derived principle), it would be the latter that would give way. Utilitarians like Mill, however, have argued that such an occurrence, though not impossible, is highly improbable.

Utilitarians can, in the same way, include certain duties in their framework. The connection between the goal of maximizing utility and the existence of individual rights and duties could be represented in a goal-based framework as follows:

BASIC: 1. GOAL (e.g., maximize happiness)

DERIVATIVE: 2. RIGHTS   2. DUTIES

For a utilitarian, then, both the rights of patients and the duties of nurses and physicians are determined by appeal to the utilitarian principle. Whenever there is a conflict between such a right or duty and utility, the right or duty loses its source of justification. One consequence of this view is that *in principle* the utilitarian has a solution to every moral dilemma. All such dilemmas, which are construed as conflicts among rights and duties, can, in principle, be resolved by a fresh appeal to the facts of the case and the principle of utility. Whichever course of action promises to yield the greatest net balance of utility is the one that ought (morally) to be pursued.

B. Duty-based theories

Duty-based theories take some particular duty or set of duties as fundamental. Examples of such theories are those based on a duty to obey God's will as expressed, say, in the Ten Commandments, Kantian theory (especially the first formulation of the categorical imperative: "Act only on that maxim that you can will to be a universal law"), and traditional medical morality rooted in the dos and don'ts of the Hippocratic tradition (such as "Do no harm"). In taking some duties as basic, such theories place what have been called "side-constraints"[7] on goals like the maximization of happiness. Although maximizing happiness may be regarded as an important goal in such theories, there is a limit on the means that can justifiably be employed to attain it. In particular, one cannot justify the violation of basic duties by appeals to utility because such duties are founded independently of utility and occupy a more central place in the framework in question. Frameworks in which duties to save or preserve life are basic, for example, do not allow an appeal to maximizing the total or average happiness to justify doing less than one's best to save a particular life. In such frameworks, saving or preserving life is believed to be right in itself, regardless of the consequences in terms of the greatest happiness. When conflicting duties make it impossible to uphold each one, a person has to consider the relative stringencies of the duties—supposing that they can be so ranked—or, if they are equally stringent, fairness becomes the main criterion. In extreme circumstances, one must consider utility to make the decision. Triage as a method for allocating medical and nursing resources under battlefield and other catastrophic conditions may have to be justified in this way within a duty-based theory.

Once the basic duties in such a theory have been identified, certain rights can be derived from them. Kant, for example, held that telling a lie was always a violation of a basic duty; and from this he derived the right not to be told a lie. We might, therefore, represent the structure of duty-based theories as follows:

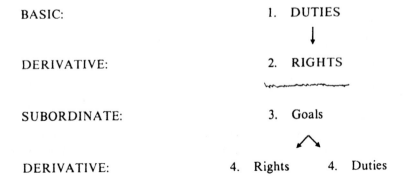

BASIC:	1. DUTIES
	↓
DERIVATIVE:	2. RIGHTS
SUBORDINATE:	3. Goals
DERIVATIVE:	4. Rights 4. Duties

Here, certain basic duties engender certain rights. Then, provided that a person does not violate these duties and rights at levels 1 and 2, he or she pursues certain goals, such as the maximization of happiness, at level 3. The wavy line emphasizes that the goals at level 3 cannot rightfully be pursued by violating the duties and rights at levels 1 and 2, which function as moral side-constraints on the pursuit of the goals at level 3. Finally, from the goals at level 3, we can derive nonbasic rights and duties at level 4. It follows that any possible conflict between the duties and rights at levels 1 and 2 and the duties and rights at level 4 are to be resolved in favor of the former, which are more basic to the overall framework. For example, suppose a nurse has a level 4 duty to obtain a patient's consent to her participation in a study. The level 4 duty is justified by appeal to the level 3 (utilitarian) value of the information sought by the study. But what if the nurse cannot obtain the patient's consent without lying to her and thus violating her level 1 Kantian duty to be truthful? Since, in this framework, the duty to be truthful is more basic than the duty to obtain the consent, the former prevails and the patient does not participate in the study.

C. Right-based theories

In many respects, a right-based theory is, just as Ursula pointed out to Renee, a duty-based theory "inside out." Its structure is as follows:

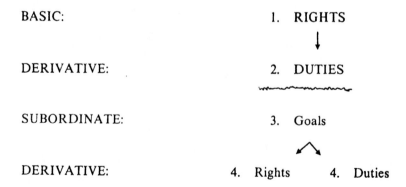

The main difference between this and a duty-based framework is that level 1 is made up of fundamental rights, which then allow for the derivation of certain corresponding duties at level 2. Examples of right-based frameworks include Thomas Paine's defense of the American Revolution, John Rawls' *A Theory of Justice*, and arguments in the context of health care that turn, ultimately, on treating or respecting "the patient as a person." A case can also be made that Kant's second formulation of the categorical imperative ("Act so as to treat all persons as ends-in-themselves and never as means only") also provides the foundation of a right-based framework.

What, then, is the difference between a duty-based and a right-based framework? Although they are alike in putting the individual at the center and in denying that the rightness or wrongness of an action is solely a function of its contribution to some overall goal, they differ in the extent to which they presuppose a relatively homogeneous set of shared values. Like goal-based theories, duty-based frameworks require significant agreement about what sorts of things are good for people. It is difficult to obtain agreement on a specific set of fundamental duties owed to others without some fairly clear conception of what is good for them or in their interest. In taking the Hippocratic oath, the physician states: "I will apply dietetic measures for the benefit of the sick according to my ability and judgment; I will keep them from harm and injustice." This assumes that the doctor and the patient will share a relatively stable set of values that will allow them to agree upon what counts as "benefit" and "harm." Societies that are characterized by a great deal of agreement on social, metaphysical, and religious beliefs may be said to provide the appropriate background conditions for a duty-based ethical framework.

Where such agreement cannot be presupposed, however—where the conception of the human condition and of human well-being is pluralistic rather than monistic—right-based frameworks may seem more plausible. For unlike duty-based frameworks, they are "concerned with the independence rather than the conformity of individual action. They presuppose and protect the value of individual thought and choice."[8] By placing the right-holder at the center, such frameworks emphasize the individual's discretion to exercise (waive or transfer) a right to do or receive something *as he or she sees fit* and in a way that flows *from his or her values and life plan*. The recent emphasis on informed consent and the patient's *right* to accept or refuse health care is based, in part, on respecting the individual patient's values and life plan. In a pluralistic society like ours, nurses and doctors can no longer be as confident as they once may have been that they know what counts as a benefit or harm for someone else. Thus it is the way a patient decides to exercise his or her rights in health care that will, in particular cases, determine the specific content of the corresponding duties of doctors and nurses.

It is interesting to note, at this point, that nurses may find themselves pulled by all three of these frameworks at the same time. The various codes of nursing ethics all seem to be duty-based. Yet the recent emphasis on informed consent, the patients' rights movement, and the Patient's Bill of Rights of the American Hospital Association seem to emanate from right-

based frameworks. Finally, the modern hospital, like all formal organizations, has a structure that is goal-based. The recent emphasis on cost-
effective care and methods of payment keyed to diagnosis-related groups
(DRGs) also presupposes a goal-based orientation. The tension between
these three sorts of outlooks in health care has in recent years become more
pronounced. And nowhere has it been felt more acutely than in nursing.

D. Intuitionist theories

There is, finally, a type of ethical theory that includes no prior ordering of
basic social goals, duties, and rights. Instead, each of these elements is
accorded the same prima facie basic status, and dilemmas or conflicts
between them are resolved on a case-by-case basis by comparing the relative
"weights" of the conflicting prima facie goals, duties, and rights. The structure of such a framework is as follows:

Someone who holds such a theory might respond to Case 2.1, "Baby or
parents," like this:

What makes this case problematic is that there is a conflict between Martha's basic
duty to help save life and the basic right of the baby to the most skilled medical and
nursing care on the one hand, and Martha's basic duty to respond to the parents'
emotional needs on the other. But, all things considered, in this particular case the
former outweigh (and not merely outnumber) the latter, so she ought to stay with the
baby. But remember, things might be different if, for example, the choice were
between staying with this baby, Daniel Ingerman, or leaving the new RN with him so
she, Martha, could help out with another baby whose chances of survival and a
normal life, if treated effectively, would be much better than Daniel's. In this case the
basic goal of maximizing happiness may tip the balance toward responding to the
baby whose chances of survival *with treatment* are significantly better than Daniel's.

If pressed as to how she "weighed" the conflicting rights, duties, and goals, the intuitionist would be unable to appeal to any more basic principles. For the conflict she is trying to resolve is *among* what she regards as a plurality of equally basic principles. Thus, her only recourse is to appeal to *intuition* or some sort of moral faculty, akin to sight as a visual faculty, that simply and directly informs her of what, on balance, is the right thing to do in this particular situation.

This completes our brief survey of the four ways of ordering the elements of an ethical framework. How are we to determine which of these four frameworks is best? To answer this question we must examine their relative strengths and weaknesses and the sense, if any, in which it is possible to know whether one framework is more firmly grounded than another.

3. Knowledge in ethics

The decision to adopt one or another basic ethical framework is extremely difficult because each has significant advantages and disadvantages. Utilitarianism, the prevailing goal-based theory, has a number of attractive features. It is highly sensitive to differences in factual circumstance and, apart from the principle of utility, has no rigid rules or principles that must be applied no matter what the consequences. As a single-principle theory it avoids the problem of conflicting basic rights or duties that can arise with other theories. For the utilitarian, then, there is in principle a solution to every moral dilemma—a way of making the best of every bad situation—by simply doing whatever is indicated by a correct application of the principle of utility. What could be more rational, one might think, than finding out which of the acts we might perform would, directly, or indirectly, produce the greatest average or total happiness, and then doing it? It might seem, therefore, that to question this theory is, as Jeremy Bentham, the father of modern utilitarianism, put it, to "deal in sounds instead of sense, in caprice instead of reason, in darkness instead of light."[9]

Bentham's rhetoric notwithstanding, there are several problems with utilitarianism. First, there are significant *difficulties of application*. These include (1) problems in defining *exactly what* each act is supposed to maximize; (2) problems in forecasting the consequences of possible courses of action quickly and accurately enough to ground decisions on utilitarian considerations; and (3) problems in comparing the happiness that a particular action will bring about in one person with the unhappiness it will bring about in another. Second, even if these difficulties of application can be overcome, there are serious questions about the apparent *implications* of utilitarianism. For example, it has been argued that the maximization of happiness may require the punishment of the innocent, the enslavement or silencing of certain minorities, or even widespread euthanasia of the elderly and unfit.[10] Such possibilities arise, it has been suggested, because, as a theory based entirely on maximizing the overall good, utilitarianism is unable to account for the independent value of justice or individual rights.[11] Although utilitarians may respond by pointing out that acts like punishing the innocent would *in fact* be likely to decrease rather than increase the overall good, they cannot rule such acts out on principle.

Duty-based frameworks, which occupy a prominent place in the history of ethics, also have a number of advantages and disadvantages. In medicine and nursing, these frameworks are reflected in the traditional emphasis on codes of ethics. Duty-based frameworks appear to give clear, specific direction and thus are easily taught and passed on from one generation to another. Another advantage of their lawlike form is the way in which duty-based frameworks readily lend themselves to enforcement. An ethical framework in the form of a set of relatively clear, specific duties makes it easier to identify immoral behavior and reduces the extent to which ignorance or slow-wittedness excuses it. Finally, duty-based frameworks make the relationship between a person's actions and his character very clear; a good person is one who does his duty. The connection between the moral worth of a person and the rightness or wrongness of his acts and judgments is not nearly so clear in other ethical frameworks.

Nevertheless, duty-based theories are subject to a number of objections. The most fundamental is that it is difficult to determine the content and justification of the basic duties. Often duty-based frameworks are versions of "divine command" theory, which maintains that the basic duties have their source in the will or law of God. But this does not solve our problem; it simply relocates it. For how are we to know what God wills or commands? If there is a disagreement about God's will or law, how do we determine whose conception is correct? Moreover, even if one could find a reasonably satisfactory account of the content and justification of the basic duties; it is unclear that any fully developed framework could be both comprehensive and consistent. If the set of basic duties is comprehensive, it is likely, given the complexity of human affairs, that situations will arise in which they would conflict; hence they would be inconsistent. If, on the other hand, efforts were made to eliminate such inconsistencies, they would probably also eliminate certain duties as basic, so that consistency would be purchased at the price of comprehensiveness. In addition, utilitarians criticize duty-based theories as overly rigid or heartless because there will invariably be instances where fulfilling a basic duty would either cause or fail to prevent considerable pain and suffering. Finally, insofar as duty-based theories, like goal-based theories, presuppose a widely shared conception of what is good for people or in their interest, they seem less at home in the emerging world community or in pluralistic nations like the United States than in small traditional societies or more homogeneous nations.

A preference for right-based theories over goal- and duty-based theories is usually grounded on their compatibility with divergent conceptions of what is good for people or in their interest as well as with divergent religious beliefs. By emphasizing the intrinsic value of individual thought and choice, a right-based theory fosters tolerance and liberty and allows various conceptions of the good life to flourish. Underlying this is a respect for the dignity and autonomy of each person or, as Kant put it, our status as "ends-in-ourselves." To the extent that we are all ends-in-ourselves or have the capacity for rational choice, each of us has a basic right not to be treated as merely a means to an end or overall goal. Thus, a right-based theory supports our intuitions about justice and the equal worth and dignity of each person. As John Rawls argues, "each person possesses an inviolability founded on justice that even the welfare of society as a whole cannot override."[12]

The first difficulty right-based theories encounter is the same that duty-based theories confront: How do we determine the content and source of the basic rights? The early right-based theories maintained that the basic rights have their source in the will or law of God. But an appeal to God can no more settle a controversy over the content and source of our basic rights than it can for basic duties. Second, problems arise in determining who possesses basic rights. If the capacity for rational choice confers such rights, it seems that not all human beings have them (e.g., infants, the severely retarded, the senile) while some animals do (e.g., chimpanzees with extensive sign-language vocabularies). But if such rights are assigned to all and only human beings, how can merely belonging to a particular biological species, regardless of one's moral nature or cognitive capacities, be a sufficient basis for possessing the rights? Third, as with basic duties, a comprehensive set of basic rights will probably lead to conflicts when applied and hence be inconsistent. One possible solution, of course, is to rank basic human rights in order of relative stringency—but what nonutilitarian criteria are to be employed in doing this? Fourth, it is argued that at times respecting one person's basic right will require others to undergo an enormous loss of human happiness. As a reductio ad absurdum, it has been said that a right-based theory may require that "justice be done though the heavens fall and the masses perish."[13] Finally, by placing so much emphasis on individuality and independent choice, a right-based theory may make it extremely difficult to preserve or develop a system of shared values and the valuable sense of community and belonging that goes with it.

Intuitionism attempts to preserve the most attractive features of the other frameworks by granting certain goals, duties, and rights a prominent place among its basic principles. In situations where these principles give conflicting guidance, persons can appeal to their moral intuition to determine which, all things considered, is overriding. With this flexibility built in, the intuitionist will never be forced into absurdity by prior commitment to a goal, duty, or right as more basic in every situation than any of the others. She will never have to sacrifice the right to life for a modest increase in overall happiness or pass up the opportunity to obtain a very large increase in happiness in order to honor a comparatively inconsequential basic duty or right.

Although in many ways a plausible and attractive framework, intuitionism raises a number of difficulties. First, insofar as it takes some goals, duties, and rights as basic, intuitionism encounters difficulties like those that attend goal-, duty-, and right-based frameworks. There will be problems in applying goal-based directives and problems in determining the content and justification of basic duties and rights. Moreover, a moment's reflection reveals that intuitionism's flexibility comes at a heavy price: it provides no criteria for resolving conflicts of intuitions. This limitation may not be very noticeable in everyday situations in a homogeneous, close-knit society where new circumstances are few and people's intuitions, because of their similar upbringings and the slow pace of social change, generally coincide. But the limitation becomes apparent in a context like that of modern health care in a pluralistic society. Issues in this context are in many ways unprecedented. They arise from recent advances in medical knowledge and technology and against the backdrop of social, cultural, and legal change. Moral intuition, for example, cannot take us very far in resolving disagreements over the use of life-sustaining technology in an era of increasingly restricted medical resources. Since our "intuitions" largely derive from lessons learned as children, they are not easily applied to this issue, especially when a solution requires that a large number of people—patients, nurses, social workers, physicians, and others—agree.[14]

This concludes our brief survey of the relative strengths and weaknesses of the four main types of ethical frameworks. The question now is whether we can determine that one is better than the others, and if so, how. This important question about the nature and justification of knowledge in ethics has been a matter of philosophical controversy for hundreds of years. Though we cannot even begin to address it adequately here, we believe that a variation of what John Rawls has called the "method of wide reflective equilibrium" provides the best way to compare and evaluate ethical frameworks.[15]

The version of wide reflective equilibrium we have in mind has three main components. Ethical frameworks are evaluated by comparing the extent to which the *ordered sets of principles* that constitute them give consistent and comprehensive guidance while cohering with two other sets of beliefs: the *pretheoretical moral judgments in which we have the greatest confidence* (e.g., torturing children is wrong) and well-grounded *background beliefs and theories about the world* (e.g., scientific and metaphysical beliefs about the nature of persons, including various capacities for autonomy, pain, suffering, etc.).[16] The three main components of the equilibrium and the relationships among them may be represented as follows:

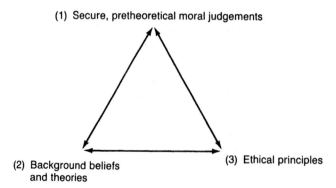

(1) Secure, pretheoretical moral judgements

(2) Background beliefs   (3) Ethical principles
     and theories

To the extent that one or another ethical theory—represented mainly by the ordered set of principles that constitutes the third corner of the triangle—satisfies the requirements of wide reflective equilibrium better than the others, it is, for the time being, the most adequate theory. The three components are said to be in *equilibrium* if they are mutually supportive. The equilibrium is said to be *reflective* if the favored set of ethical principles is based upon a continuous dialectical interplay with the other two components. This requires a willingness on our part to reopen the comparison with different sets of principles in the light of new evidence, arguments, or situations. And the equilibrium is wide, as opposed to narrow, if nonethical elements, such as our background beliefs and theories, provide a more or less independent constraint on moral judgments and ethical principles. As our analysis proceeds, none of the components enjoys privileged status. Elements of each may be modified, abandoned, or replaced in the interest of achieving a more consistent, comprehensive, and coherent equilibrium, or overall "fit," with the others. For this reason, each of the three connecting lines in our diagram points in both directions.

Once we have determined that one ethical framework initially satisfies the conditions of reflective equilibrium better than the others, we apply it to new or previously unconsidered situations or to situations in which we are unsure what our particular judgments ought to be. We then examine our new judgments in the light of our earlier, more secure judgments and our background beliefs and theories. If they conflict, we must do something to restore the initial equilibrium. This may require modifying or replacing one or more of our ethical principles, pretheoretical judgments, or background beliefs and theories. If none of these possibilities seems attractive, we may retain our equilibrium by deciding that the framework does not, at least in its present form, apply to the problematic case and therefore leave it temporarily open or unresolved.

To complete our schematic representation of the process of wide reflective equilibrium, we now include the application of our set of ordered principles to new, previously unconsidered, or problematic cases, together with tracing the implications for our secure, pretheoretical moral judgments and our background beliefs and theories:

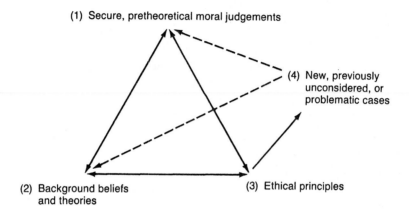

(1) Secure, pretheoretical moral judgements

(4) New, previously unconsidered, or problematic cases

(2) Background beliefs and theories

(3) Ethical principles

Once we apply our principles (3) to new, previously unconsidered, or problematic situations (4), we must trace the implications for our fairly secure pretheoretical moral judgments (1) and our background beliefs and theories (2). If these are all fairly compatible, the equilibrium is maintained. But if there is tension or inconsistency, we must try to restore the equilibrium. This may involve modifying any of the three central components or withdrawing the applications of the principles in this instance. Some examples will, perhaps, make this clearer.

Consider, first, a dilemma that arose in the late 1960s for those whose ethical frameworks included a strong commitment to a right to life or a duty to preserve (human) life. Advances in medical technology were beginning to allow doctors and nurses to maintain the lives of patients whose brains had been completely and irreversibly destroyed. In the past, such patients' hearts would have stopped within minutes and the patients would have been declared dead; modern respirators and other technology now enabled their lives to be prolonged. Sets of ethical principles anchored by a right to life or a duty to preserve life at (3) seemed to entail that treatment be continued at (4). But to many this was intuitively wrong, economically wasteful, or even silly. It clashed with other more secure judgments at (1). Two fairly obvious ways of eliminating the tension, either weakening the principles or accepting their apparent consequences, were rejected in favor of a third: the modification of one of our widely held background beliefs at (2).

An interdisciplinary committee studying the matter at Harvard Medical School suggested that, instead of regarding those whose brains were massively and irreversibly destroyed but whose hearts and lungs were functioning with the aid of machines to be living persons, to whom the right to life or the duty to prolong life was applicable, we should modify our beliefs about what constituted a living person.[17] Patients in this condition, the committee reasoned, are no longer living persons; they are actually (brain) dead. And the right to life or the duty to preserve life does not apply to those who are already dead. Thus a new situation that generated a conflict between the application of certain fundamental ethical principles and intuitive convictions was resolved by a relevant modification of background beliefs. Equilibrium was restored without either relinquishing an important principle or accepting what seemed to be a counterintuitive application of it.[18]

A second illustration of the method of wide reflective equilibrium involves the possibility that utilitarianism may require actions (such as large-scale nonvoluntary euthanasia) that conflict with certain secure, pretheoretical moral judgments (such as that nonvoluntary euthanasia is always, or almost always, wrong). Utilitarianism, as noted above, is in many ways an extremely attractive ethical theory. It squares with many of our more secure judgments at (1) and it is consistent with many of our background beliefs and theories at (2). But, as opponents of utilitarianism are fond of pointing out, its straightforward application in new or previously unconsidered situations (4) often yields conclusions that are, on their face, inconsistent with other of our moral judgments (1). For example, they argue that an unflinching application of the principle of utility might well entail nonvoluntary euthanasia of the economically unproductive elderly, sick, or retarded.[19] After all, the lives of such persons often involve extensive pain and suffering and their care frequently saddles others with considerable hardship and expense. If, then, we suppose that utilitarianism requires large-scale nonvoluntary euthanasia for this segment of the population (and many thoughtful utilitarians would argue that it does not), one who was unaware of such a requirement when initially adopting a utilitarian framework must, to retain overall equilibrium, either relinquish or significantly modify her utilitarianism at (3) or else "bite the bullet" and disown her pretheoretical rejection of large-scale nonvoluntary euthanasia for this part of the population at (1).

In proceeding in this way—going back and forth between secure pretheoretical moral judgments, background beliefs and theories, sets of ethical principles, and applications of these principles to new, previously unconsidered, or problematic cases—one is using the method of wide reflective equilibrium. Although the label may be new to the reader, the process is probably not. Many of us have frequently engaged in this process with various degrees of sophistication even if we were not explicitly aware of what we were doing.

It follows that whatever ethical framework seems to meet the conditions of reflective equilibrium better than the others does so only provisionally. As convinced as we may be of the superiority of one theory over the others, we should be prepared to reopen the matter and reexamine our position in the light of new circumstances or challenges to it. Our commitment to what appears to us, on reflection, to be the best theory available will not allow us to close the door on ethical reasoning and analysis.

There is, at present, no consensus as to what this theory is, even among those who explicitly endorse the method of wide reflective equilibrium. Each type of theory, as indicated above, has its particular strengths and weaknesses, and efforts to formulate a theory that combines all of the advantages, while avoiding the disadvantages, of the standard theories have so far been unsuccessful. Thus we leave it to the reader to partake in the lifelong personal and interpersonal task of trying to determine which ethical theory, though falling short of perfection, is best able to satisfy the conditions of reflective equilibrium. Our hope is that continued disciplined reflection of this sort among larger numbers of people will bring us closer to a well-grounded consensus. Once one makes a provisional commitment to a particular framework, one should put it to use by (1) trying to make one's position on particular moral issues reflect it; (2) continually testing it under conditions of wide reflective equilibrium and, when necessary, trying to refine it so as to reduce vagueness and inconsistency; and (3) remaining open to new or newly recognized implications or criticisms that may require significantly modifying this framework or even rejecting it in favor of another.

If what we have said about knowledge and justification in ethics is correct, there are two important consequences for ethical dilemmas in health care. First, if parties to a controversy rooted in disagreement over basic ethical principles were to recognize the limitations of all ethical frameworks, including their own, and were to engage jointly in the method of wide reflective equilibrium, they would be more likely to arrive at a satisfactory solution. As K. Danner Clouser has rightly observed:

We generally quit the discussion of values long before we have exhausted meaningful argument. We are too quick to say, "You have your values and I have mine." Further discussion can elicit much more agreement either by pursuing the *consistency* of the value in question with other values that you hold or in "unpacking" the conceptual and empirical criteria underlying the value in question. Persistent pursuit of each other's values with "why" questions will elicit a lot of hidden assumptions and reasoning, and consequently more agreement than we would initially expect.[20]

Second, even when agreement is not reached, an extended, mutually re-spectful, reflective discussion will usually convince the parties that those holding opposing positions are not thoughtless, callous, or otherwise "defec-tive" from a moral standpoint. As a result, personal acrimony will be limited and the parties may come to realize that, as thoughtful persons struggling with the limitations of the human condition and the enormous complexities involved in justifying an ethical framework, there is more that joins than divides them. And the recognition of this, in particular cases, may provide both the motivation and the groundwork for devising mutually respectful, well-grounded compromise positions that can be regarded as preserving everyone's integrity (see Chapter 4, Section 4).

Finally, let us reemphasize a point made at the outset of this chapter. In the vast majority of cases, the actions entailed by the standard ethical frameworks are the same. Those holding goal-based, duty-based, right-based, and intuitionist frameworks will all conclude, for example, that rape is morally wrong. They will differ only in the kind of ultimate reasons that they offer when pressed for an explanation as to *why* it is wrong. Therefore, it would be a mistake to assume that all ethical disagreement is a function of a conflict in basic principles. On the contrary, most ethical disagreements are rooted in misunderstandings of what is at issue, different understandings of the facts, conceptual confusion and ambiguity, faulty reasoning, and so on. Only if our analysis reveals that a particular disagreement is rooted in a conflict of basic principles need we address matters of ethical theory. And although this cannot be entirely avoided, it will arise much less often than specialists in ethical theory would have us believe.

4. Ethics, law, and religion

Legal and religious considerations often play a prominent role in discus-sions of ethical issues. But to what extent and in what manner are law and religion relevant to the resolution of moral dilemmas in nursing? We may begin our brief inquiry into this difficult question by addressing the legal and religious considerations raised by the following case.

2.2 Religious and legal considerations in conflict

Jean Lyons, employed by the county health department, provided commu-nity nursing services to a rural area, including the schools. While Jean was at the high school, Kathy Jorea, a seventeen-year-old junior student, told her that she was pregnant but that she knew her parents, especially her mother, would never "get over it" if they found out. There was, at the time, no law requiring that parents be either informed of or consent to abortions for seventeen-year-olds. A friend had told Kathy about someone who had had an abortion in a nearby city. Kathy believed that she must have an abortion, and she needed information about costs, the time it would take, and where to go.

Jean was strongly opposed to abortion on religious grounds. Appealing to the edicts of her church, she held that abortion was tantamount to murder, and she had become an active member of a "Right to Life" group shortly after the Supreme Court's Roe v. Wade *decision (1973) had invalidated her state's legal prohibition on abortion. Over the past few years she had continued to support groups working toward a constitutional amendment prohibiting abortion. The thought of Kathy, healthy and obviously intelligent, destroying her baby, angered and frustrated Jean. The thought also crossed her mind that the county had few public health nurses and, since she alone covered Kathy's township, no other professional nurse was readily available to help Kathy.*

In deciding how to respond to Kathy's request for information, how much weight should Jean give to her religiously based belief that abortion is as grave a moral wrong as murder? And to what extent does the fact that Kathy's abortion would, at present, be legal bear on her decision?

Let us begin by briefly examining the complex relationship between law and morality. The first thing to note is that, although legal and moral prohibitions often coincide, certain acts may be morally but not legally justified, and vice versa. In Chapter 1, for example, we assumed that a man taking his pregnant wife, whose labor has begun, to the hospital in the early hours of the morning is justified in cautiously driving through red lights. What he is morally obligated to do is nonetheless illegal. The circumstances may *excuse* him for violating the law, but they *do not suspend* the law. Similarly, abolitionists who violated the fugitive slave laws and civil rights activists, like Martin Luther King and his supporters, who violated certain laws as a last resort in protesting institutionalized racism, broke laws but did not act immorally. On the contrary, one may plausibly argue that what was immoral were laws that supported racism. In this case one would be saying that certain acts, though legally justified, are not morally justified.

The fact that we can identify acts that are morally justified but not legal, and vice versa, is not simply an indication of a remediable imperfection in our present legal framework. There will always be acts that are morally permissible or obligatory, but not legal, and vice versa. The former will occur because the completely unrestricted framework of ethical inquiry always allows for the possibility of new or unanticipated considerations overriding the prima facie moral obligation to obey the law. And the latter will always be with us because certain immoral acts (such as one person's falsely promising another to undertake long-term commitments solely to manipulate his or her consent to sexual relations) cannot be made illegal without resulting in either costly additions to the police force and unacceptable incursions on our liberty and privacy or an erosion of respect for the law in general. A simple appeal to an act's legal standing, therefore, is never a sufficient response to questions of ethical justification. And although a strong case can be made to show that in a reasonably just society individuals have a prima facie obligation to obey the law, it can be overridden in fulfilling a more stringent moral obligation.

How does all this bear on Jean Lyons' problem in "Religious and legal considerations in conflict"? First, Jean might correctly argue that the legality of abortion (since 1973) is no more sufficient to show that it is morally justified than its illegality (before 1973) was sufficient to show that it was not morally justified. It is still possible, she might maintain, that abortion is morally wrong, even though legal, just as slavery in this country was morally wrong even when it was legal. So, *if* (and only if) Jean can provide strong reasons to show that abortion is tantamount to murder and hence morally wrong, regardless of present legal opinion, she may not only try to dissuade Kathy from seeking an abortion but also refuse to help her, withholding relevant information and possibly even notifying Kathy's parents of her predicament and intentions. Of course, this would include a refusal to provide certain legal nursing services and a breach of confidentiality—a serious violation of most codes of nursing ethics. Therefore, Jean's case for the immorality of abortion must be extremely strong if it is to justify such drastic measures.

Jean, we are told, is strongly opposed to abortion on religious grounds. Now, to what extent can arguments resting on religious belief be used to justify judgments about conduct in ethical dilemmas?

It is widely held that all ethical decisions are ultimately grounded upon, and inseparable from, some set of religious beliefs. If this is correct, people in a religiously pluralistic society will be unable to develop a systematic framework for resolving basic ethical disagreements. Ethical differences will be regarded as a function of religious differences and ethical reasoning and discussion will be interpreted as an attempt at religious conversion.

But what does it mean to say that ethical decisions are ultimately grounded upon, and inseparable from, religious belief? For some this may mean simply that our ethical principles are *historically* rooted in one or another religious tradition. Even if this is true, however, it does not follow that the principles cannot be justified on their own terms, quite apart from the tradition from which they developed. We do not, for example, say that the validity of modern chemistry depends on the validity of Renaissance alchemy, even though the former had its origins in the latter; nor does the fact that astrology was the mother of modern astronomy imply that controversies arising in the latter cannot be resolved without appeal to the former. Similarly, even if there is a historical connection between religion and basic ethical principles, we cannot conclude that the validity of an ethical principle depends upon the validity of the religious tradition from which it emerged.

But when people claim that ethics is based on religion, they may also mean that religion alone can provide the ultimate justification of our most basic ethical principles. Many believe that an ethical principle is correct only if it has been issued by God. If this is true, a secular ethical framework will have no foundation, and basic ethical differences will be beyond the reach of reasoning and empirical evidence.

Nonetheless, we think that secular considerations offer at least as much support for basic ethical principles as religious considerations and that questions of public policy in a pluralistic society can be resolved only by appeal to secular arguments. In the previous section we suggested that the method of reflective equilibrium provides the most plausible approach to justifying ethical principles. Whatever cognitive difficulties attach to this method, they are no greater than the cognitive difficulties raised by the notion of God, or any other purely religious authority, as the ultimate source of ethical justification. Moreover, the striking similarity among the basic ethical principles held by people of widely diverse religious convictions is difficult to explain if ethical principles can be justified *only* within the context of religion. According to P. H. Nowell-Smith, this similarity

can be explained only on the hypothesis that when men think morally they think as they do when they think technologically—that is, rationally and on the basis of experience. The human needs that morality serves, nonaggression and cooperation, are everywhere the same, and it is not surprising that intelligent beings, reflecting on their own experience, have evolved broadly similar codes for meeting them.[21]

Thus, although people may attribute certain principles like the Golden Rule to religious authority, it is likely that insofar as these principles are widely accepted and presumed to be binding on believers and nonbelievers alike, they are also grounded on reason and empirical evidence.[22]

Our reasons for suggesting that questions of public policy be discussed in secular terms are mainly pragmatic. Agreement on basic policy in religiously heterogeneous societies like ours is possible only if the reasons for accepting such policies are independent of any particular religious doctrine. For example, patients and health professionals of various religious persuasions, as well as agnostics and atheists, will be able to reach agreement on recurring ethical issues in health care only if they can appeal to secular principles. Therefore, to the extent that it is important for people of differing religious convictions to adopt common basic policies, it is important that they support their views with secular arguments, even if their views had their origin in, and can also be supported by, religious arguments.

To suggest that basic ethical principles can be justified by secular considerations is not, however, to imply that people's religious beliefs, principles, and practices are irrelevant to the *content* of these principles. On the contrary, they are of central importance. To the degree that religious beliefs form a part of one's identity as a person, respecting the exercise of these beliefs is part of respecting the individual *as a person*. If a secular framework is to be acceptable to people of various religions, therefore, it should allow considerable freedom of religious observance and practice. In the context of health care, this will require that health professionals respect the importance of their clients' religious beliefs when these have bearing on decisions about their care. Thus, for example, religious holidays, dietary restrictions, and attitudes toward contraception, sterilization, autopsy, and so on, will often be important in determining a client's course of treatment. Similarly, clients and various health care organizations and agencies must, when possible, respect the religious beliefs of various health professionals.

We may now apply this brief analysis of the relationship between ethics and religion to Jean Lyons' dilemma in "Religious and legal considerations in conflict." The first thing to note is that Jean's opposition to abortion is based on her identification with particular religious ideals. This means that others, in their interactions with Jean, must, if they are to respect her, respect her personal views on abortion. But unless Jean can also provide strong, nonreligious arguments in support of her opposition to abortion, her personal, religiously grounded opposition is not sufficient to override her prima facie obligations to provide legal nursing services and to preserve the client's right to privacy. For if Jean's views are grounded in nothing more than religious teachings or conviction, any attempt to dissuade Kathy from seeking an abortion (assuming Kathy does not share Jean's religious beliefs) would amount to an imposition of the nurse's religious beliefs on the client. And although people may try to convert others to their religious beliefs, the nurse-client encounter is certainly not the proper place for it.

There are reasonably strong, nonreligious arguments to show that abortion is a serious moral wrong.[23] The problem is, however, that there appear to be equally strong, nonreligious arguments showing that abortion is not a serious moral wrong and that it is, therefore, unjustifiable to prevent a woman who wants an abortion from obtaining one.[24] Thus, even if Jean's opposition to abortion were based on secular considerations, we may hope that attempts to anticipate and respond to objections to her position would have revealed to her that decent, thoughtful people—people who are neither callous nor "moral pygmies"—can hold an opposing view. Since purely religiously based convictions are inadmissible, secular arguments are inconclusive, and abortion is not illegal, we would state our position by saying that Jean must not interfere with Kathy's efforts and probably ought to give her the information she wants. But if she can find someone else to provide this information, Jean may be able to "conscientiously refuse" to do so (see Chapter 4, Section 5) and refer Kathy to the other source.

Notes

1. A third possibility, agreement on ethical principles but disagreement on particular judgments, might arise when, for example, two people holding that one ought, above all, to maximize happiness disagree on whether treating a patient would in fact increase or decrease overall happiness.

2. The characterization of theories as duty-based, goal-based, and right-based that follows is heavily indebted to an analysis in Ronald Dworkin, *Taking Rights Seriously* (Cambridge, Mass.: Harvard University Press, 1977), pp. 169–73.

3. Rights, like the right to liberty or privacy, which require that others not interfere or otherwise encumber the right-holder's conduct, are called "negative" rights. They are contrasted with "positive" rights, like the right to an education or health care, which require not only that the right-holder not be interfered with or encumbered, but also that he or she be provided with certain goods. Generally, the case for "negative" rights is easier to make than the case for "positive" rights.

4. "Direct" or "act" utilitarianism holds that the rightness or wrongness of an action is a function of the extent to which the act itself contributes to the maximization of the good. "Indirect" or "rule" utilitarianism holds that the rightness or wrongness of an action is a function of the extent to which everyone's acting in accord with a rule contributes to the maximization of the good. Thus, act utilitarianism is *direct* insofar as it requires a fresh application of the utilitarian principle to each particular act to determine its rightness or wrongness; rule utilitarianism is *indirect* insofar as it requires that one always act in accord with certain moral rules which are, themselves, justified by an appeal to the utilitarian principle.

5. John Stuart Mill, *On Liberty* (New York: Liberal Arts Press, 1956), p. 13.

6. Ibid., p. 14.

7. That is, one's pursuit of various valuable goals is *constrained* by having to abide by certain fundamental duties (or rights). Side-constraints function in some ways like certain rules in, say, basketball, which define the permissible ways of scoring. Prohibitions against double-dribbling and walking with the ball serve as side-constraints on a team's goal of making a basket. See Robert Nozick, *Anarchy, State, and Utopia* (New York: Basic Books, 1974), pp. 28–35.

8. Dworkin, *Taking Rights Seriously*, p. 172.

9. Jeremy Bentham, *An Introduction to the Principles of Morals and Legislation*, Chapter 1, "Of the Principle of Utility," reprinted in Edwin A. Burtt, ed., *The English Philosophers from Bacon to Mill* (New York: Random House, 1939), p. 791.

10. For a powerful, disturbing argument along these lines, see Richard G. Henson, "Utilitarianism and the Wrongness of Killing," *Philosophical Review* 80 (July 1971):320–37.

11. John Rawls, *A Theory of Justice* (Cambridge, Mass.: Harvard University Press, 1971), p. 26f.

12. Ibid., p. 3.

13. See Joel Feinberg, "Rawls and Intuitionism," in Norman Daniels, ed., *Reading Rawls* (New York: Basic Books, 1975), pp. 108–24, especially pp. 108–16.

14. See R. M. Hare, *The Language of Morals* (Oxford: Oxford University Press, 1952), pp. 74–78.

15. Rawls, *A Theory of Justice*, pp. 19–22, 46–53, 577–87. See also Norman Daniels, "Wide Reflective Equilibrium and Theory Acceptance in Ethics," *Journal of Philosophy* 76 (May 1979):256–82. Versions of this method can be traced, historically, at least as far back as Aristotle, *Nicomachean Ethics*, 1094v, 12–1096a, 10, bk. 1, ch. 3–4.

16. Under the heading of "secure pretheoretical moral judgments" are those particular judgments in which, in a cool hour, we have the greatest intuitive confidence. We are, at least initially, more confident that they are correct than we are of the superiority of one of the standard ethical frameworks over the others. Although we may be unable to say with a great deal of confidence that, for example, a right-based theory is better than utilitarianism, we are confident that torturing children and rape and slavery are morally wrong. This does not mean that such judgments are necessarily or self-evidently true. They are not, in principle, immune to revision or rejection. Only if there is a conflict between one of these judgments and an equally, if not more, plausible set of background beliefs and theories or set of ethical principles will the question of rejecting or revising one of our secure, pretheoretical moral judgments even arise. Under the heading of "background beliefs and theories" come various well-grounded beliefs about the nature of the world. These include well-established scientific beliefs (from biology, psychology, etc.) as well as more metaphysical beliefs about, say, the nature and limits of free will. We cannot, for example, fully determine the nature and range of application of our ethical principles unless we know something about kleptomania and other forms of mental illness and the extent to which they compromise our capacity for self-control.

17. Ad Hoc Committee of the Harvard Medical School, "A Definition of Irreversible Coma," *Journal of the American Medical Association* 205 (August 1968):337–40.

18. For a comprehensive discussion of this topic and an introduction to the literature, see President's Commission for the Study of Ethical Problems in Medicine and Biomedical and Behavioral Research, *Defining Death* (U.S. Government Printing Office, 1981).

19. Henson, passim. For a defense of utilitarianism against this sort of criticism see, for example, L. W. Sumner, "A Matter of Life and Death," *Nous* 10 (May 1976):145–71.

20. K. Danner Clouser, "Medical Ethics: Some Uses, Abuses, and Limitations," *New England Journal of Medicine* 293 (21 August 1975):387.

21. P. H. Nowell-Smith, "Religion and Morality," in Paul Edwards, ed., *Encyclopedia of Philosophy*, vol. 7 (New York: Macmillan and Free Press, 1967), p. 153.

22. See, for example, Alan Donagan, *The Theory of Morality* (Chicago: University of Chicago Press, 1977), especially pp. 1–9, 57–66; and R. M. Hare, *Freedom and Reason* (Oxford: Oxford University Press, 1963), especially pp. 86–111, 157–85.

23. See, for example, John T. Noonan, Jr., "An Almost Absolute Value in History," in John T. Noonan, ed., *The Morality of Abortion: Legal and Historical Perspectives* (Cambridge, Mass.: Harvard University Press, 1970), pp. 51–59; and

Baruch Brody, *Abortion and the Sanctity of Life* (Cambridge, Mass.: M.I.T. Press, 1975).

24. See, for example, Judith Jarvis Thomson, "A Defense of Abortion," *Philosophy and Public Affairs* 1 (Fall 1971):47–66; and Michael Tooley, "In Defense of Abortion and Infanticide," in Joel Feinberg, ed., *The Problem of Abortion*, 2nd ed. (Belmont, Calif.: Wadsworth, 1984), pp. 120–34. The Feinberg anthology is a valuable source for strong philosophical arguments on both sides of this very difficult issue.

3

Nurses and Clients

1. Introduction

Moral dilemmas arising from encounters between nurses and clients generally raise one or more of the following questions. First, under what circumstances, if any, and for what reasons, if any, may a nurse treat an adult client as if he, or she were a child? In other words, how can what we will call "parentalism"[1] be justified? Second, under what circumstances, if any, and for what reasons, if any, is a nurse justified in deceiving a client? Modes of deception may range from nonverbal pretense to withholding relevant information to outright lying. Third, under what circumstances, if any, and for what reasons, if any, may a nurse divulge information that has been given in private under the assumption that it would be held in confidence? Fourth, what is the relationship between professional obligation and personal risk? For example, when, if ever, may a nurse refrain from caring for an AIDS patient? And fifth, how does the nurse determine to whom she owes fundamental allegiance when she cannot satisfy the interests of all those whom she has some prima facie obligation to serve? For example, how should a nurse balance the welfare of a family with the needs of individual members?

Although for the purposes of analysis we will examine each of these five kinds of questions separately, individual cases will often raise more than one of them. For example, one of the most common forms of parentalism involves deceiving patients in one way or another so that they will consent to procedures that the doctor or nurse believes to be "in their best interest" or "for their own good." The following case raises not only questions of parentalism and deception but also questions about who ought to be regarded as the principal subject of nursing care and concern.

3.1 A helpful lie?

Public health nurse Linda Stone first met Arlene Knox when she was referred to the county public health department by an emergency room nurse who was concerned that Arlene's bouts of intoxication might be harmful to her unborn child. Linda soon learned that Arlene had previously been addicted to heroin; but when her boyfriend threatened to leave her, she had stopped taking the drug. Shortly thereafter Arlene had become pregnant. Over a period of several months Arlene repeatedly told Linda that she was no longer drinking, but Linda, aware of Arlene's past need for drugs and suspicious that she had not actually stopped drinking, continually worked to educate her about the danger of alcohol to the baby.

After delivery, Arlene's doctor told her the baby had fetal alcohol syndrome. When Linda made a home visit a few days later, Arlene was still crying and distraught and asked Linda to reassure her that she had not harmed the baby, that he did not have fetal alcohol syndrome. Linda suggested they both look at him, and she was surprised by his good health and vigor. He had none of the obvious signs of the syndrome. She immediately began to suspect that the physician had lied to Arlene in an attempt to shock her into an awareness of the seriousness of her drinking. Linda did not contradict the doctor, but told Arlene to ask him again. She also calmed her by pointing out the baby's strengths and by reassuring her that she would help her learn ways to stimulate his development over the next year.

Later Linda phoned the physician and learned she was right in suspecting a ruse; any problem the baby might have from alcohol would probably be small. The doctor said he would tell Arlene the case was slight when he next saw her, but he had no intention of changing his story since it seemed to make her realize what could have happened and, as a result, seemed to have strengthened her resolve to stop drinking.

Linda knew that lying and shocking Arlene was no substitute for helping her deal with the problems underlying her drinking. However, Linda also thought that she should perhaps also lie to Arlene; she definitely did not want to see Arlene drink excessively during another pregnancy and damage a child. Telling the truth might lead Arlene to believe she had no need to worry about the amount of alcohol she could consume during another pregnancy. Linda thought that she would begin to help Arlene with some of her underlying problems whether or not she contradicted the physician's story. After several days of deliberation, Linda finally decided to go along with the deception since, she reasoned, it seemed to be in Arlene's best interest.[2]

Insofar as Linda seems ultimately to justify her complicity in deceiving Arlene by appealing to what she believes to be Arlene's best interest, the justification is parentalistic. But there may be nonparentalistic factors in Linda's mind as well. If her concern for the welfare of Arlene's baby and the children resulting from possible future pregnancies was the principal basis of her decision, the justification would no longer be parentalistic. She would not be deceiving Arlene mainly for her own good but for that of her future children. Here, of course, questions arise as to whom Linda owes fundamental allegiance: Arlene, the new baby, or possible future babies? Finally, the deception in this case, as in most others, does not involve a straightforward decision to tell a bald lie. It is more a question of withholding the truth. Of course, the situation is complicated by the fact that the deception was initiated by the physician, and a decision to unmask it could be costly to Linda's working relationship with him.

This brief discussion indicates just how complex cases of this kind can become. To attempt to analyze them, the rest of this chapter will be divided, somewhat artificially, into sections on parentalism, deception, confidentiality, personal risks and professional obligations, and conflicting claims. Discussion of the complications from the involvement of a physician will be deferred until the following chapter. The reader is reminded again, however, that in everyday life these considerations frequently overlap.

2. Parentalism

In its most general sense, parentalism means that an adult is being treated as if he or she were a child by persons acting as if they had the authority and concern of a parent.[3] Just as a parent may force an unwilling child to go to bed at a certain hour or take bitter medicine, so too, it is argued, a nurse may sometimes force an unwilling patient to get rest or receive treatment. Like the parent, the nurse will claim to be acting *on the behalf*, although *not at the behest*, of the patient; for, like the child, the patient is presumed unable to appreciate the connection between the nurse's behavior and his or her own welfare.[4]

When a parent forces or manipulates a child into doing something for his or her own good, the assumption is that the child lacks the capacity to understand, endorse, and act in accord with the parent's benevolent aims. When a child is, in fact, able to understand and appreciate the parent's reasoning, but nonetheless disagrees with it, parental force or manipulation may no longer be justified. Thus, it is one thing for a parent to force a four-year-old to brush his or her teeth; it is quite another for a parent to prevent a fourteen-year-old from going to any but "G"-rated movies. Parents are justified in coercing or manipulating children into doing things "for their own good" when (1) it is reasonably clear that the result will be in the child's interests; (2) the child is unable to understand or resists rational appeals to the connection between the act in question and his or her own (long-term) interests; and (3) it is reasonable to assume that, in the absence of special "brainwashing" or indoctrination, the child will endorse or ratify the parents' behavior at a later date when he or she can understand and appreciate the parents' aims and reasoning. It is because forcing four-year-olds to brush their teeth clearly meets all of these conditions, while preventing fourteen-year-olds from going to any "PG" movies does not, that we are inclined to think the former more justifiable than the latter.

Insofar as parentalistic coercion or manipulation of an adult involves a refusal to accept at face value the choices, wishes, or action of an individual who is presumed to be autonomous and self-determining, it bears an even heavier burden of justification. Parentalistic behavior, regardless of benevolent motives or the magnitude of the benefit to be secured or the harm to be avoided, overrides the right of an adult to be treated as a person. To be a person, as the term is used here, is to regard oneself as having the ability and right to formulate various projects and make various commitments, and then to attempt to fulfill them. A human being is identified as a particular person by the values and life plan that guide his or her conduct. To respect another as a person, then, is to take full account of his or her values and life plan and to give them as much consideration in determining the effects of one's conduct as one wants given to one's own values and life plan. Conversely, to disregard or give only perfunctory consideration to the values and life plans of others is to show contempt for them as persons. It is to regard them as mere objects or things rather than one's equals as persons, *even if one's aim is to benefit them or protect them from harm*. In Kant's terms, it is to treat them as mere means to an end, and not as ends-in-themselves.[5] And nothing is more demeaning to a person, more damaging to self-respect, than to be so treated. To deal with a sick individual as a person, then, is to place his or her values and plans, as far as possible, in the center of the picture and to attempt to preserve his or her sense of capacity for reflective choice.[6]

Nonetheless, as the following case illustrates, there may be times when an adult's capacity for reflective choice is seriously impaired.

3.2 Parentalistic restraint

Sixty-seven-year-old Henry Young had suffered a stroke and was being kept under continual restraint in the hospital at the direction of Kirsten Bennett, the supervising nurse. A locking waistbelt was used, whether Mr. Young was in bed or in a chair. The belt was a "humane" design, permitting him as much freedom as possible while assuring that he could not fall out of the bed or chair.

Mr. Young had had a fall earlier in this hospital stay, having attempted to walk while unattended. He was only slightly injured in this episode, but because of the possibility of serious injury that such a fall presents, Kirsten required him to be restrained in the waistbelt whenever he was left unattended, even for a very short period. Mr. Young vigorously protested that he was being deprived of his dignity, that he felt as if he were in prison, that he was afraid of being unable to escape in the event of a fire, and that he was perfectly competent to be left free and responsible for his own safety. In response, Kirsten repeatedly told him that the restraint was a "standard procedure" for patients in his condition and that he had no choice in the matter as long as he remained in the hospital and his condition remained unchanged.

Underlying her decision was the fact that, as is not uncommon in such cases, Mr. Young's mental capacities seemed to swing back and forth so that sometimes he was undoubtedly competent to move about at liberty, but at other times he became confused and lost some degree of motor control. It had, in fact, been during such a confused period that he had suffered his earlier fall. Another important consideration was the fact that the nursing staff did not have time to keep continual watch over him. Thus, as Kirsten explained to Mr. Young's family, the restraint was "for his own good" even though contrary to his wishes. All things considered, she maintained, it was best for him to be kept in the waistbelt, even during periods of mental clarity, in order to insure that he would not, when unattended, lapse into mental confusion and seriously hurt himself. Mr. Young's family agreed with the supervising nurse and fully supported her decision.[7]

If we assume that Kirsten's appeal to Mr. Young's best interests is not a rationalization for a more basic concern with the hospital's legal liability, the convenience of the nursing staff, or an authoritarian desire to exercise complete control over all patients, her reasons for keeping him in restraints are purely parentalistic. She believes that Mr. Young's capacity to decide for himself on this question has been seriously impaired and that because he runs a significant risk of harm from being left unrestrained while unattended, he must, for his own good, be kept in the waistbelt even if he resists and protests. The question now is whether this parentalistic intervention is justifiable.

Parentalistic behavior requires justification because it refuses to accept at face value the choices, wishes, or actions of an individual who is presumed to be autonomous and self-determining. Thus, in justifying a particular parentalistic intervention, one must show that the presumption of autonomy or self-determination no longer holds—that the choices, wishes, or actions of the individual are not genuinely autonomous or authentically self-determined.[8] Even John Stuart Mill, whose defense of individual liberty is often considered to be antiparentalistic in the extreme,[9] allowed that we may interfere with a person's acting on his or her expressed desires when we can be certain that they are not his actual desires.

If either a public officer or anyone else saw a person atempting to cross a bridge which had been ascertained to be unsafe, and there were not time to warn him of this danger, they might seize him and turn him back without any real infringement of his liberty; *for liberty consists of doing what one desires, and he does not desire to fall into the river.*[10]

Similarly, we might conclude that Mr. Young does not desire to injure himself while walking around unattended. Thus, insofar as he is prevented from doing so, the nursing staff no more violates his right as a person to do what he (genuinely) wants to do than the intervener in Mill's example violates the rights of the person crossing the bridge.

In both Mill's example and the case of Mr. Young, the defense of the intervention rests on two conditions: (1) the ignorance or impaired capacity for rational reflection of the agent, and (2) the magnitude and probability of harm that would result without parentalistic intervention. Although some would argue that only the limited autonomy of the first of these conditions is *necessary* to justify parentalistic interference, and others would maintain that the prospective harm of the second is by itself *sufficient* to justify such interference, we believe that both are necessary.[11] If a person meets condition (1) but does not thereby run an increased risk of significant harm, one cannot say that the "lesser evil" (the deprivation of liberty or choice) is justified by appeal to the avoidance of a "greater evil" (harm to the person whose liberty or choice is restricted); hence, the intervention is not clearly in the person's best interests. And if a person meets the harm condition (2) but is mentally competent and fully aware of the magnitude and probability of harm that may result from his or her action, interference cannot be justified on parentalistic grounds unless one is willing to say that autonomous people should not be free to drive racing cars, smoke cigarettes, or refuse certain forms of medical treatment.

Although a parent may be justified in making a child do things judged to *benefit* the child as well as to protect him or her from harm, we believe that generally a health care professional can override an adult client's right to self-determination *only to prevent harm*. Although the difference between preventing harm and providing a benefit is not always clear, often it is both clear and useful. The main difference between the promotion of benefit and the prevention of harm, for our purposes, is that it is much easier to obtain agreement on what constitutes a harm than on what constitutes a benefit. People may, for example, differ widely about whether public funds should be used to promote the arts, athletics, ethnic festivals, libraries, or parks, but there is usually significant agreement among the same people that such funds should be used to prevent foreign invasions, crime, and disease. The latter are regarded as harms of great magnitude by most any set of values, while whether one or another of the former is regarded as a vital benefit will vary widely from one set of values to another. Thus, unless one has a more or less explicit prior consent for interventions conceived mainly as providing a benefit rather than preventing a harm, the *presumed* benefit (which may simply reduce to the imposition of one's own values on a vulnerable patient) cannot override the *certain* infringement of a person's right to self-determination.

Underlying this emphasis on harm as opposed to benefit is an assumption that parentalistic behavior is justifiable only if the subject of the intervention in some sense consents to it. For example, a parent's forcing the child to brush his or her teeth is justified, in part, by the reasonable assumption that the child at a later date, when the parent's aims and reasoning can be understood and appreciated, will endorse or ratify the parent's behavior. As Gerald Dworkin puts it, "Parental paternalism may be thought of as a wager by the parent on the subsequent recognition of the wisdom of the restrictions. There is an emphasis on what could be called future-oriented consent—on what the child will come to welcome, rather than on what he does welcome."[12] Similarly, just as Mr. Young, the stroke victim in Case 3.2, does not want to injure himself, and the person about to walk over the bridge in Mill's example does not want to fall into the river, those who parentalistically interfere can reasonably assume that their interventions will later be ratified by the subjects of the interference.[13] Thus, we may now add a future consent condition to the two we have already provided for the justification of an act of parentalism. An act of parentalism will now be said to be justified if and only if:

1. the subject is, under the circumstances, irretrievably ignorant of relevant information, or his or her capacity for rational reflection is significantly impaired (the *autonomy* condition);
2. the subject is likely to be significantly harmed unless interfered with (the *harm* condition); and
3. it is reasonable to assume that the subject will, at a later time, with greater knowledge or the recovery of his or her capacity for rational reflection, ratify the decision to interfere by consenting to it (the *ratification* condition).[14]

Recent discussions of the justification of parentalism often distinguish two forms: "strong" and "weak." Strong parentalism emphasizes doing what is ostensibly for the patient's own good or welfare regardless of his or her capacity to consent. Weak parentalism, on the other hand, involves acting to benefit a person or limit harm when, due to irretrievable ignorance or mental impairment, the patient is substantially unable to make the decision for him- or herself. Our emphasis on the autonomy and ratification conditions indicates that we are endorsing a "weak" and not a "strong" form of parentalism. Our restriction of condition (2) to harm, and excluding benefit or welfare, indicates that ours is also among the weaker versions of "weak" parentalism. Our main reason for rejecting stronger versions of parentalism is that they are usually too quick to override the patient's autonomy in the name of a conception of the good that cannot be shown by cogent argument to be superior to the patient's own conception of the good. On the other hand, the form of weak parentalism outlined here can, in many instances, be justified in the context of health care.

Let us now become more thoroughly acquainted with our three conditions for justifiable (weak) parentalism by applying them to three more cases.

3.3 Convincing the patient

"The job of a primary nurse," in Debbie Rokken's words, "is to provide care to the patients; and that includes basic assessment, basic nursing care, bathing, and different kinds of nursing duties; also more sophisticated care, such as giving chemotherapy, blood components, IVs, and medications. If I personally cannot give the care directly, then I have an LPN or an orderly who will work along with me to see that the care gets done. I work the three-to-eleven shift, and another RN from the day shift is my associate. Between the two of us, we organize the care and provide it to the same group of patients." In the primary care system the primary nurse, being ultimately responsible for the patient's nursing needs, exercises considerable influence over the patient.[15]

Debbie and her associate cared for Mrs. Cotton, who was thought to have metastasis to the pelvic area and for whom extensive surgery was recommended. Both nurses agreed to help Mrs. Cotton decide about having surgery, which "might be radical." Mrs. Cotton was apprehensive about surgery, afraid of losing control with the anesthesia, and afraid that the procedure would be too radical. According to Debbie, Mrs. Cotton "had very little support from her husband or her children; no one talked about surgery, much less helped her decide whether or not to have it done." Debbie had seen two women recently "do very well with similar extremely radical procedures." She also thought that the other alternatives, no treatment at all or a less radical treatment, would lead to a much more rapid demise and certainly a lowered quality of life with dependence on narcotics for pain. Therefore, she attempted to convince Mrs. Cotton that such surgery might be a good idea. Debbie spent time talking about why Mrs. Cotton needed the surgery and what could happen as a result of her not having it. She spent time with Mrs. Cotton and carefully chose interpersonal relations skills that might enhance feelings of trust. She sat close to Mrs. Cotton, occasionally held her hand, and once put her arm around her shoulders to comfort her. Shortly thereafter, Mrs. Cotton decided to undergo the surgery.

Months later Debbie reconsidered her actions, not because of Mrs. Cotton, whose pelvic mass was not malignant, but because in her words, "After more experience I saw a lot of women not do so well, and suffer more from that kind of treatment. It certainly makes you ask yourself whether you're doing them a service or not." Debbie's parentalistic intervention in this case seems to meet none of the conditions we have suggested as necessary to justify such an intervention. It does not meet the first condition because there is no evidence that Mrs. Cotton's capacity for rational reflection is impaired (her fears seem to be those that most people would have about major surgery), and her ignorance of the risks of the procedure could be remedied simply by providing her with information. Debbie's intervention does not meet the second condition because, as she later learns, her belief that Mrs. Cotton is likely to be significantly harmed by not having the operation is based on insufficient evidence. Debbie's initial assessment of the risks and benefits of the surgery were based on a sample of only two cases. Finally, for the same reason, Debbie could not reasonably assume that Mrs. Cotton would later consent to her interference and hence ratify it; thus the third condition was not met. We may, therefore, conclude that Debbie's parentalistic intervention in this case was not justified.

The question of justified parentalism also arises in the following case.

3.4 Breaking the cigarette habit

Twenty-three-year-old Fred Winston had attempted suicide by shooting himself in the head. He was hospitalized with permanent brain damage, which left him largely helpless and his body deformed by muscular contractions. He required assistance for almost every activity. He was usually incontinent, though this was attributed more to a lack of concern than to physical incapacity. In addition, his speech was barely audible, and the combination of brain damage and emotional difficulties resulted in stammering, repetitious speech patterns.

Fred failed to eat well, and his primary pleasures seemed to be watching television and smoking cigarettes. After his initial period of hospitalization, those responsible for his nursing care decided to try to limit his smoking "for his own good." Thus, he was often falsely informed that his cigarettes were all gone, or that there were only one or two left and he ought to save them for later, or that no one was available to supervise him while he smoked (a safety requirement necessary because of his limited fine motor control). The nursing staff reasoned that since he did not appear to care about what was in his own best interest, they would have to take measures to limit his smoking even if he protested.

When he sensed what was happening, Fred protested as strongly as his limitations would allow. In response to the nurses' explanation that what they were doing was for his own good, he insisted that since there was little hope that his condition would improve, he was entitled to whatever gave him pleasure at the present moment. Given his condition, he maintained, smoking was "for his own good." But inasmuch as his physical debilities and difficulties with speech limited his capacity to resist or vociferously protest the nurses' behavior, their will prevailed.[16]

Before determining whether the nursing staff's conduct meets our three conditions for *justifiable* parentalism, we may want to ask whether their actions are, at bottom, parentalistically motivated. Parentalistic reasons for forcing or manipulating people to do certain things often function as rather high-minded rationalizations for conduct that is actually motivated by anger or a concern for one's own advantage or convenience. In such cases parentalistic reasoning, which we may characterize as primarily other-regarding, simply acts to conceal reasoning that is basically self-regarding, though we may be reluctant to admit this—even to ourselves. In Case 3.4, for example, it would not be surprising if the nursing staff's behavior were motivated by an underlying, unarticulated anger with Fred. After all, patients like Fred are not likely to make the nurses' already difficult job any easier. He requires a great deal of care and shows a lack of respect and consideration for the nurses by his apparently willful incontinence. His failure to eat well is also likely to frustrate the nurses and, like most people, they are probably threatened to some degree by Fred's self-destructive repudiation of society and all they hold dear, regardless of what drove him to attempt suicide. Thus, it is important in this case for the nursing staff to determine whether their conduct is actually, or only apparently, parentalistic.

Even if their plan to help Fred cut down on his smoking is intended for his own good, and not simply a rationalized expression of anger, it does not meet the conditions we have set out for justified parentalism. It does not meet the autonomy condition because, as far as we can tell from the case description, Fred is neither ignorant of the dangers of smoking nor is his capacity to reason about his decision less impaired than that of other smokers. (It should be noted that other patients in the same part of the hospital were, subject to safety rules, allowed to smoke as they wished.) The staff's parentalistic behavior fails to meet the second condition not because cigarette smoking is not harmful but rather because it has not been regarded by the society as a whole to be *so* harmful that adults, after being duly warned, are not free to decide for themselves whether the benefits outweigh the risks. Consistency demands, then, that we regard the probability and magnitude of harm to Fred from smoking at this point no greater than that to him before his hospitalization or to other people in or out of the hospital. Finally, the nurses cannot reasonably assume that Fred will, at some later date, ratify their decision by consenting to it. As he himself suggests, given his limitations, the pleasure derived from smoking has taken on a greater significance than it had before his hospitalization. As these limitations are apparently permanent, it is unlikely that he will ever be able to replace the pleasures of smoking with anything else.

If the nurses' conduct is not an instance of justified parentalism, it must be regarded as an attempt to take advantage of Fred's dependence and vulnerability to impose their values on him. Surely if he were strong enough to smoke without supervision or to protest vociferously, the nursing staff would be forced to change their treatment of him. Insofar as their force prevails, so too does their will. This, of course, is not the first time that professional dominance has violated the rights of patients to be treated as persons. But here as elsewhere, a precedent for the violation of someone's personhood ought never to be confused with an ethical justification for it.

The recent emphasis in nursing on health promotion and teaching constantly raises questions about justifiable parentalism. How far may a nurse go in trying to alter a client's way of living in the name of better health? Can one be parentalistic when the situation is very complex and the likelihood of harm cannot be reliably gauged? And if so, what form should the parentalistic interference take? Are exaggerated threats and lies acceptable if nothing else appears likely to be effective? Consider, in this connection, the following all-too-typical case.

3.5 Promoting a healthy lifestyle

Donna Boyd, staff nurse, faces the task of interpreting Alan Spencer's current health risk appraisal form to him. The appraisal, a computer print-out sheet, indicates the risks he faces from various health problems, given his age and physical condition. In Donna's professional judgment, Mr. Spencer's health risk appraisal shows that he should reduce his smoking and intake of food and alcohol, exercise more, and take his medicine with greater regularity. Although Mr. Spencer, who is fifty years old, reports that he watches his diet, has cut down on his smoking, and regularly takes his medicine, he has nevertheless gained fifteen pounds during the past year; he came into the hospital with a blood pressure of 220/140, cholesterol level of 500 mg/dl, and triglycerides level of 450 mg/dl. Donna knows that during other hospitalizations and clinic visits other nurses have tried to persuade Mr. Spencer to change his lifestyle, but he has become irritated by such efforts and what he has termed "preachy nurses." He has indicated that he wants no further discussion of his personal behavior. Donna, however, is strongly inclined to make another effort to get him to change his ways, for his own good.

Since previous discussions to this end seem to have been unsuccessful, what should Donna do? Should she simply hand Mr. Spencer the assess-

ment with no further comment? Should she try to overcome his reluctance to change by using subtle or open threats, or even lies, about the likelihood of a painful and early death? Or is there a more plausible course of action that lies between these two extremes?[17]

We leave it to the reader, at this point, to answer these questions for him- or herself. The answers, we believe, are not obvious. A good way to begin is to determine whether parentalism might be justified in this case; and, if so, whether threats or deception about the likelihood of a painful and early death can in this case be parentalistically justified. Other relevant considerations include the possibility that further efforts to alter the client's lifestyle might only increase his antagonism to medicine and nursing and thus be counterproductive, and whether or not the nurse can reasonably expect the high value she, quite understandably, places on health to be shared by the patient.

3. Deception

The foregoing case raises questions about the use of deception in trying to regulate a client's conduct. Deception is a form of manipulation, and manipulation, like coercion and rational persuasion, is a way of inducing others to do what one wants them to do. Before the forms and possible justifications of deception in the context of nursing are directly examined, it will be useful to compare and contrast manipulation with coercion and rational persuasion as ways of inducing clients to comply with various medical and nursing directives.

Rational persuasion consists of appealing to another person's rational capacities in order to influence his or her behavior. Reasons and information are provided for or against various courses of action with a view toward changing the other person's beliefs or conduct in some specific way. Ideally, rational persuasion is conceived as a dialogue in which the persons attempting to do the persuading recognize that those to whom they direct their arguments are their equals as persons. As Lawrence Stern has pointed out, "There is, in general, no point in reasoning unless the other person is capable of seeing reason, getting the point. If he can do that he can also correct *me* if I am mistaken. We are co-members of the rational community."[18] Thus, for a nurse to obtain a client's compliance with one or another directive or procedure by rational persuasion or client education is to recognize and respect his or her personhood. It is, for this reason, ethically preferable to manipulation or coercion in this interpersonal context as well as others. Despite her professional status, then, the nurse must be prepared to engage in genuine dialogue with the client, which means that the client must be allowed the same opportunity to alter the nurse's views that the nurse has to alter the client's views.

Manipulation, on the other hand, puts a premium on the results of one's intervention and less emphasis on the means. It is a mode of altering another's beliefs or behavior by subverting or bypassing his or her rational capacities. As Stern indicates, manipulation includes "such things as deceit, the deliberate by-passing of conscious processes, and various conditioning techniques (real or science fiction) which place belief or action beyond rational criticism."[19] Etymologically, the terms *management*, as in the phrase "patient management," and *manipulation* both have to do with *handling* things (*hand* is *mano* in Italian and Spanish and *main* in French). Raymond Williams, in his study of language and cultural transformation, has pointed out that "the word *manage* seems to have come into English directly from *mannegiare*, It.—to handle and especially to handle or train horses."[20] Horses are not handled or managed as if they were persons; one needn't pay attention to their capacity for rational reflection or personhood because they haven't any. To treat a person in the same manner bears a heavy burden of justification. Manipulation of persons with the aim of achieving a certain result places an overriding value on that result. The benefits of the result, in the view of the manipulator, are more important than the moral and emotional costs to the manipulated individuals from disregarding their personhood and treating them as if, say, they were horses. On the face of it, then, nurses should be reluctant to resort to manipulating their clients unless there are strong ethical grounds for doing so.

There is an interesting contrast between manipulation and *coercion*, understood here as one person's bending another to his or her will by force or the threat of harm. As Stern has pointed out:

Coercion is not dialogue. But in a sense it is closer to dialogue than is manipulation. Generally speaking, when successful, coercion achieves only unwilling compliance with the wishes of the person who uses it. There is no change of belief on the part of the coerced person; nor does he lose his capacity to do otherwise should opportunity offer. He gives in but is not convinced; and he remains an independent center of action. By contrast, manipulation brings about willing compliance or psychological incapacity to do otherwise. Coercion leaves open the possibility of dialogue; manipulation forecloses it.[21]

This suggests that coercing clients to comply with nursing directives or procedures, though needing justification and falling short of the ideal of compliance grounded on rational persuasion, is in some ways preferable to manipulating them.

Instances of rational persuasion, manipulation, and coercion can be found in the case studies we have already set out in this chapter. Linda Stone's initial response to Arlene Knox's drinking problem in Case 3.1 is an attempt to educate her about the danger of alcohol to her baby and thus rationally persuade her to stop her heavy drinking. Later, however, she also supports the doctor's decision to rely on manipulation in order to curb the drinking problem. In Case 3.2, Kirsten Bennett decides to use coercion to restrict Mr. Young's freedom of movement in the hospital. She might, however, have been able to take advantage of his lucid periods to persuade him rationally that, all things considered, being restrained in the waistbelt whenever unattended was in his best interest. Case 3.3 provides an interesting example of nondeceptive manipulation. Here Debbie Rokken uses interpersonal relations skills to manipulate Mrs. Cotton's consent to surgery. Debbie's approach to Mrs. Cotton in this instance may be no more in the subject's best interest than that of an automobile salesperson to a prospective buyer. Finally, in Case 3.4 the nursing staff first tries to manipulate Fred Winston into cutting down on his smoking, and when this effort fails, they fall back on force or coercion.

Deception is the most common form of manipulation but, as Debbie's use of "interpersonal relations skills" in Case 3.3 illustrates, it is not the only form. The clearest, most widely recognized form of deception is lying. To lie is to intentionally say what one believes to be false with the aim of having others come to believe that it is true. There are, however, a number of ways to deceive people apart from lying.[22] One may, for example, deceive people simply by one's nonverbal behavior. Pretending to be busy when you want to avoid an inveterate bore or faking left before cutting right while playing basketball are just two of many examples of nonverbal deception.

Verbal deception can also take other forms. Saying something that deliberately creates a false impression but, because it is literally true, is not a bald lie is nonetheless an act of deception. An example from a widely used logic text[23] provides a particularly apt illustration of this distinction. One night aboard a certain ship the first mate got drunk. The captain was rightly very angry at this serious offense, and despite the mate's pleas for a second chance, entered into the ship's log: "The mate was drunk last night." Smarting and eager for revenge, the mate struck back the following day by (truthfully) writing in the log: "The captain was sober last night." Now this joke trades on the distinction between saying what is literally true on the one hand and conveying a true impression on the other. When the mate writes "The captain was sober last night," what he says is literally true, but in the context it creates a false impression—namely, that the captain was drunk *every other night*. Thus, we must not allow a fastidious preoccupation with lying to blind us to the important distinction between saying what is literally true and conveying a true impression.

Other modes of verbal deception turn on negative as opposed to positive verbal acts, such as intentionally refraining or forbearing from doing something.[24] Negative acts of deception include refraining from correcting an existing mistaken belief or allowing someone to acquire a mistaken belief. Anthony Shaw, a pediatric surgeon, provides an example of the former in an account of an encounter he had with the father of a newborn infant with

Down's syndrome and an operable esophageal atresia and tracheoesopha-
geal fistula:

After explaining the nature of the surgery to the distraught father, I offered him the
operative consent. His pen hesitated briefly above the form and then as he signed, he
muttered, "I have no choice, do I?" He didn't seem to expect an answer and I gave
him none.[25]

But as Shaw admits in the next paragraph, the father's consent was not truly
informed. "The answer . . . should have been 'You *do* have a choice. You
might want to consider not signing the operative consent at all.'"[26] By
withholding this crucial bit of information, then, the surgeon had manipulated the father into signing the consent form in a manner that was no less
deceptive than if he had employed a straightforward lie.

To summarize this brief account of the various forms of deception, we
may say that deception is a form of manipulation that is aimed at controlling people's behavior by inculcating, or allowing them to retain, false
beliefs. As a form of manipulation it subverts people's rational capacities
and restricts their autonomy. Insofar as a person acts on the basis of false
beliefs that have been deliberately conveyed or uncorrected by others, his or
her freedom and dignity as a person have been compromised.

All of the standard types of ethical frameworks surveyed in Chapter 2
contain principles or strong presumptions against deception. Although the
grounds will differ from one type of framework to another, the result is the
same: deception requires justification, and the burden of proof rests on
those who wish to initiate or maintain deceptive acts.

Most duty-based frameworks include some form of basic duty against
lying or deception. St. Augustine's religiously grounded, duty-based view
held that God forbade all lies and that those who lie do so at the risk of
endangering their immortal souls:

But every liar says the opposite of what he thinks in his heart, with purpose to
deceive. Now it is evident that speech was given to man, not that men might
therewith deceive one another, but that one man might make known his thoughts to
another. To use speech, then, for the purpose of deception, and not for its appointed
end, is a sin. Nor are we to suppose that there is any lie that is not a sin, because it is
sometimes possible, by telling a lie, to do service to another.[27]

Such absolute prohibitions have also been claimed to rest on reason alone.
Kant, for example, maintained that in lying a person "throws away and, as it
were, annihilates his dignity as a man."[28] For, insofar as liars betray or
abandon reason and rationality as the proper mode of interaction among
persons, they betray or abandon the source of their moral worth. "To be
truthful (honest) in all declarations, therefore, is a sacred and absolutely
commanding decree of reason, limited by no expediency."[29] Although
neither Augustine nor Kant allows for exceptions to the duty to be truthful,

other duty-based theories may build certain exceptions into the duty. Thus, for example, a duty-based framework could hold that one has a duty to be truthful except in those situations where deception is *essential* to preserve or protect life. In this case the burden of proof would be upon the would-be deceiver to show that in this instance deception is in fact essential to preserve or protect life.

Right-based ethical frameworks ground the presumption against deception on a person's right to autonomy or self-determination. Since deception, as a type of manipulation, subverts or bypasses one's capacity to exercise rational deliberation and choice, it undermines one's personhood. As Alan Donagan puts it, the duty to be truthful rests

simply on the fact that the respect due to another as a rational creature forbids misinforming him, not only for evil ends, but even for good ones. In duping another by lying to him, you deprive him of the opportunity of exercising his judgment on the best evidence available to him. It is true that the activities of a lying busybody may sometimes bring about a desirable result; but they do it by refusing to those whom they manipulate the respect due to them.[30]

It is important to note, however, that this sort of case for truthfulness leaves open the possibility of deceiving young children, those with severe mental retardation or impairment, and others with a significantly diminished capacity for rational deliberation and choice. But even when one is justified in deceiving such persons, one must consider their capacity or potential for rational deliberation.

It is widely held that goal-based frameworks like utilitarianism allow much more leeway for deception than do either right- or duty-based frameworks. Indeed, we have echoed this bit of conventional wisdom in our use of examples in the two preceding chapters. But the issue is not so clear. Although on short-run utilitarian grounds it may appear that deception would produce a greater net balance of happiness than would truthfulness in many cases, a more long-run utilitarian outlook may indicate otherwise. As Sissela Bok has emphasized, those who engage in deception

often fail to consider the many ways in which deception can spread and give rise to practices very damaging to human communities. These practices clearly do not affect only isolated individuals. The veneer of social trust is often thin. As lies spread—by imitation, or in retaliation, or to forestall suspected deception—trust is damaged. Yet trust is a social good to be protected just as much as the air we breathe or the water we drink. When it is damaged, the community as a whole suffers; and when it is destroyed, societies falter and collapse.[31]

Thus, insofar as the consequences of each act of deception may have a corrosive effect on the sort of trust that is necessary for the preservation of essential, but fragile, social bonds, there is a strong utilitarian presumption against deception.

Given this presumption against deception common to all standard ethical frameworks, it comes as something of a surprise to learn that codes of medical and nursing ethics have traditionally been mute on the subject of truthfulness. Bok points out that, through the years, the oaths, codes, and writings of physicians have made little or no mention of being truthful.[32] Nor, for example, is a concern for truthfulness reflected in the International Council of Nurses Code for Nurses (Appendix A).

Whatever the reasons for this omission, the contemporary shift of emphasis in health care from the parentalistic dominance of professionals to the individual rights of clients is now beginning to change professional codes. The so-called Patient's Bill of Rights, approved by the American Hospital Association in 1973 (Appendix C), recognizes the patient's right to "complete current information concerning his diagnosis, treatment, and prognosis in terms that the patient can be reasonably expected to understand," and his or her right to "information necessary to give informed consent prior to the start of any procedure and/or treatment." Such information, the document continues,

should include but not necessarily be limited to the specific procedure and/or treatment, the medically significant risks involved, and the probable duration of incapacitation. Where medically significant alternatives for care or treatment exist, or when the patient requests information concerning medical alternatives, the patient has the right to such information.

This emphasis on honestly informing the patient is echoed in the most recent version of the American Nurses' Association Code for Nurses in Interpretive Statement 1.1, "Respect for Human Dignity." This shift to truthfulness places a clear burden of proof on any health care professional who decides to engage in any form of deception.

Yet this burden of proof can sometimes be met. The question is, Under what conditions and for what reasons is it permissible or obligatory to deceive a client? In what follows we will try, through a consideration of cases, to address this question.

3.6 Giving placebos

Sandra Seamans, staff nurse on a surgical unit, is caring for Dorothy Langley, whose doctor has ordered placebos to wean her off the Demerol injections that she has persistently requested since being hospitalized after a car accident. The day nurses have already given Mrs. Langley two injections of sterile water, each of which seemed to relieve her pain for several hours. Sandra does not want to give a placebo. She is worried about what she will say if Mrs. Langley should ask what medication she is giving. She has thought about warding off such questions with an "Oh, the same thing you got last time" to avoid lying; Sandra does not believe in lying to patients. Yet she acknowledges, "You can't tell the patient it's a placebo because that ruins the whole effect. I know placebos are given to help the patient—to ease off medication and to allow evaluation of pain. But it is still going behind the patient's back and I don't feel comfortable with it."

Before determining under what conditions Sandra could be considered to be participating in a justifiable act of deception, let us briefly call attention to the way in which this case illustrates the distinction between telling the literal truth and conveying a true impression.

First, since the effectiveness of the placebo requires Mrs. Langley to believe that she is receiving biochemically active medication, she is deceived even if she is never actually told a lie. Second, even if Sandra should respond to a question from Mrs. Langley about her medication by saying what is literally true ("It's the same thing that you got earlier") she nonetheless conveys a false impression. Sandra would be compounding deception with self-deception if she were to believe that there is a significant ethical difference between saying "It's Demerol" and "It's the same thing you got last time."

We turn now to the question of justification. It is, in general, much more difficult to justify administering placebos than is commonly supposed. Too often, for example, the administration of placebos reinforces the patient's mistaken belief that there is a "pill for every ill." As a result, patients often fail to understand the inevitability of certain aches and discomforts, the limitations of medical understanding and techniques, the healing power of time, the importance to health of certain patterns of living, and so on.[33] In addition, the cavalier administration of placebos involves needless expense. But most important is the corrosive effect of placebos on the trust which is an essential element in the relationships between patients and health care professionals. As Bok points out:

The practice of giving placebos is wasteful of a very precious good: the trust on which so much in the medical relationship depends. The trust of those patients who find out they have been duped is lost, sometimes irretrievably. They may then lose confidence in physicians and even in bona fide medication which they may need in the future.[34]

Finally, it is important to distinguish the placebo *effect* from the administration of placebos. The former is a way of characterizing healing that is attributable to the interaction between patient and professional, though not to any specific medication. The placebo effect adds greatly to the professional's effectiveness and requires no deception. It must be noted, however, that an indiscriminate reliance on placebos, which do require deception, will in the long run severely impair the capacity of nurses and physicians to take therapeutic advantage of the placebo effect.[35]

It follows, then, that placebos should be used with great reluctance and only when nondeceptive means to the desired end have been exhausted. For the sake of analysis we will assume that various nondeceptive attempts to reduce Mrs. Langley's dependence on Demerol have been eliminated on grounds other than convenience or expedience. Thus, we assume that Mrs. Langley has been unresponsive to attempts to educate her about the danger of addiction and to persuade her rationally to go without Demerol. Further, we assume that she is indeed running a significant risk of addiction, that in her present mental state further efforts at persuasion will be fruitless, and that her apprehension about the drug's being cut off will significantly magnify her pain and distress. If these assumptions do not hold, then we believe that the resort to placebo has been premature. But if they do hold, there is a fairly strong parentalistic justification for employing a placebo.

Recall the three conditions set out in Section 2 for justifiable parentalism. If, as we have assumed, Mrs. Langley has been unresponsive to education and rational persuasion about the dangers of addiction, we can infer that her capacity for rational reflection has been impaired (either by the drug or by her inordinate fear of the temporary pain and distress of being weaned from it); thus the first condition will have been met. The second condition will be met if significant harm is likely to result if she is not given the placebo; and it appears that it will. And the third condition will be satisfied because it is reasonable to assume that when Mrs. Langley is successfully weaned from the Demerol and informed about the way in which it was done, she will ratify or endorse the deception by retroactively consenting to it.

The following deception, although seemingly innocent, is much more difficult to justify.

3.7 "You won't feel a thing"

Amanda Adams and two other public health nurses offer an immunization clinic once each month in a conveniently located church. Amanda and her colleagues try to dispel children's fears of medical personnel by wearing pleasant, attractive clothing rather than white uniforms and by being friendly and cheerful.

One busy afternoon when the clinic was unusually crowded, David Winn, a five-year-old, was becoming apprehensive while waiting to get his rubella shot. When his turn came, David reluctantly walked with Amanda and his mother to an area behind a screen usually used to separate Sunday school classes. As Amanda picked up the syringe, David started to cry softly. Amanda noticed his distress and feared that he was building up to a long, loud scream that would upset those children who were still waiting. So, she smiled and reassuringly said, "Don't worry, you won't feel a thing." Then, as quickly as she could, she gave the injection. Although he did not cry out, David winced and emitted a little gasp as the needle entered his arm.

It is ironic that, after trying to allay the children's fears through special attention to clothing and friendliness, Amanda's panicky lie to David is likely to compound his subsequent fear of doctors and nurses with mistrust. Trust is perhaps the most important element in the nurse-client relationship, and once lost it is exceedingly difficult to regain. If what David felt was not as bad as he had anticipated, it was nonetheless worse than Amanda said it would be. The next time a nurse attempts truthfully to mitigate his fears, it would not be surprising if his response were suspicious.

To conclude this brief discussion of deception in nursing, we want to emphasize that the presumption on behalf of being truthful does not imply that clients have an obligation to learn about their illness or treatment. Although people generally have a right to such information, they may, if they wish, choose not to exercise it. Just as a right to freedom of speech does not imply an obligation to speak, so too the right to be informed about one's illness and treatment does not imply an obligation to be so informed. Clients may indicate that they would rather not know all they are entitled to know.

3.8 Deciding how much to tell

The nurses on a particular medical unit always try to sit down and talk to patients before they begin their chemotherapy. Depending on the patient's ability to understand and accept information about the side effects of chemotherapy, the information they provide is more or less detailed.

In John Coughlin's case, the nurses felt that they had a responsibility to give more instruction than he had received from the doctor. However, Mr. Coughlin, a forty-nine-year-old carpenter, was extremely anxious about receiving chemotherapy at all. He tried to keep his mind and conversation on other things and would only say, half joking, that he was sure that the chemotherapy was going to turn him into a "sniveling idiot."

After consulting with a colleague, Diane Fetterson, a staff nurse, decided that Mr. Coughlin did not want detailed information about certain side effects and possible complications. Therefore, before his chemotherapy began, Diane explained that he might become nauseated; he might lose some of his hair; he might not feel like eating; and he would need to drink many fluids. However, she did not tell everything she might have told other patients. She withheld more detailed information that she thought would be needlessly distressing to Mr. Coughlin in his present state and which he, himself, had indirectly indicated that he did not want. As Diane put it, she was sure that he did not want to know all of the "gory side effects that could occur."

Although Diane withheld certain information, we would not characterize her conduct as deceptive. Insofar as we assume that Mr. Coughlin had chosen not to exercise his right to know more about the side effects of chemotherapy, Diane was under no obligation to tell him more. To have done so in this case would have been to confuse a right to be informed with an obligation to be informed.

As nurses and doctors rightfully move away from a norm of parentalistic deception, they must be careful not to embrace a norm of parentalistic honesty. If patients clearly indicate that they do not want to know more about their illness or treatment, it is not up to the health care profession to make stronger persons of them or to bring them up to some ideal of lucid awareness. Here, as elsewhere, genuine respect for persons requires sensitivity to genuine personal differences.

4. Confidentiality

An obligation to preserve the client's privacy and hold certain information in strict confidence has long been a part of nursing and medical ethics. As Point 2 of the American Nurses' Association Code for Nurses states: "The nurse safeguards the client's right to privacy by judiciously protecting information of a confidential nature." As with deception, each of the main types of ethical framework will include a strong presumption against disclosing information about a client that has been obtained under the supposition that it will be held in confidence.

Duty-based frameworks, which underlie most codes of nursing and medical ethics, will include a duty to protect information acquired within the clinical encounter. Right-based theories will emphasize the client's right to privacy and the confidential nature of communications and records pertaining to his or her care (see Points 6 and 7 of A Patient's Bill of Rights, Appendix C). Goal-based theories like utilitarianism will base this presumption on the negative long-term effects of arbitrary disclosure of information given in confidence. Such a line of reasoning can be found in Interpretive Statement 2.1 of the American Nurses' Association Code: "The client trusts the nurse to hold all information in confidence. Thus trust could be destroyed and the client's welfare jeopardized by injudicious disclosure of information provided in confidence."

After all, if clients were afraid that certain embarrassing or incriminating information about themselves would be arbitrarily or maliciously disseminated by health care professionals, they would be disinclined to share such information, often to the detriment of their health.

Nonetheless, as with deception, there are cases in which the presumption against disclosing information obtained in the clinical encounter can be overridden. Health care professionals are required by law to report cases of venereal disease, gunshot wounds, and child abuse even though they learn of them within the clinical encounter with its presumption of confidentiality. Reporting such information to government agencies, though not uncontroversial, is frequently defended because it is designed to protect the public interest. In addition, it can be argued that such acts of disclosure do not involve a breach of confidentiality because, insofar as the relevant laws are public and knowable in advance, the health care provider does not obtain the information in question under the supposition that it will be held in confidence. More troublesome, however, are ethical dilemmas about confidentiality that do not involve a prior suspension of the principle of confidentiality. Consider, for example, the following case.

3.9 "I don't want anybody to know"

Sandy Wilson, fourteen years old, had just completed a six-month checkup for a fractured ankle. The fracture had healed completely without complications, but her hemoglobin level was in the low-normal range. As a precautionary measure she was sent to Maria Garza, a nurse practitioner, for diet counseling. Before long Sandy confided that she thought she was pregnant and that she did not want anyone else to know, especially her mother. Upon brief questioning, it became evident to Maria that Sandy had no clear idea of what she was going to do about the suspected pregnancy. Before Maria could begin to help her think the situation through, however, Mrs. Wilson came in. Mrs. Wilson said that Sandy had been nauseated and very tired lately, and she asked Maria if she had any idea of what could be causing it. As Maria prepared to respond, Sandy remained silent and glared at her.[36]

Although there is a presumption that nurses should maintain confidence, there is also a presumption against deception. Maria's dilemma in this case is due to a conflict between these presumptions.

A decision to override the presumption against deception for the sake of confidentiality could be based upon the importance of maintaining trust in the nurse-client relationship. Maria is well aware that a young pregnant girl's trust in her, as a nurse, must be preserved. Moreover, since the law in their state does not require Maria to tell parents about a fourteen-year-old's sexual activities, there is no legal ground for suspending confidentiality.

On the other hand, arguments can be made for truthfully answering Mrs. Wilson's questions. Although the presumption for maintaining confidentiality is strong, Interpretive Statement 2.1 of the American Nurses' Association Code states that information of a confidential nature must be judiciously, not absolutely, protected.

The duty of confidentiality, however, is not absolute when innocent parties are in direct jeopardy.

The rights, well-being, and safety of the individual client should be the determining factors in arriving at any professional judgment concerning the disposition of confidential information received from the client relevant to his or her treatment. The standards of nursing practice and the nursing responsibility to provide high quality health services require that relevant data be shared with members of the health team. Only information pertinent to a client's treatment and welfare is disclosed, and it is disclosed only to those directly concerned with the client's care.

This statement provides a basis for arguing that "professional judgment" in Case 3.9 dictates that the nurse should share information with the mother since it relates directly to Sandy's "well-being and safety." Teenage pregnancies pose a high risk to both mother and baby. If Sandy decides (or has already decided) not to have an abortion, obtaining good prenatal care is important and Sandy's mother may be instrumental in helping her get it. If Sandy does want an abortion, her mother could help her by arranging the abortion and, perhaps, by giving emotional support.

Another reason for being truthful with Mrs. Wilson is to refrain from reinforcing Sandy's avoidance of her problems. If Maria were to support Sandy's deception, she would undercut her own professional efforts to help Sandy develop effective ways of coping with difficult problems.

Given the limited information available to Maria, choosing between maintaining confidence and avoiding deception is very difficult. We hope that Maria would try to soften the dilemma by asking if Mrs. Wilson would leave the room for a short while so that she could talk to Sandy alone. Maria would then have time to assess Sandy's perception of family relationships. Maria could also indicate why she would like Sandy to release her from confidence so that Maria could deal more openly with Mrs. Wilson. If Sandy agreed, they could decide when and how best to tell Mrs. Wilson about the situation.

If Sandy does not release her, however, Maria would have to determine whether Mrs. Wilson's having knowledge of the suspected pregnancy would in any way jeopardize Sandy's well-being. If the knowledge would not place Sandy in jeopardy, either physically or psychologically, we believe that Maria has several reasons for telling Mrs. Wilson. First, Maria could justify breaking confidence on parentalistic grounds if Sandy seems not to appreciate the situation or is unable to deal with it, the pregnancy puts her at risk, and in the future a good chance exists that she will look back and agree that involving her mother was the right course of action. Maria could also justify breaking confidence on the grounds that, if Sandy does not choose abortion, the unborn baby's claims to health care override Sandy's claims to confidentiality. Finally, Maria could justify breaking confidence on the grounds that Mrs. Wilson's rights as a parent override Sandy's right to secrecy. The mother's responsibility for her daughter requires that she be informed of current or potential problems. To do less would be to hinder her exercise of parental responsibility.

Dilemmas of confidentiality figure prominently in debates over testing for acquired immune deficiency syndrome (AIDS). Many AIDS patients and those infected with the human immunodeficiency virus (HIV) are understandably reluctant to have others learn of their condition. Numerous persons have acquired the virus through either homosexual relationships or intravenous drug use. Each is associated with social stigma. Consequently, individuals with AIDS or those who have tested positive for the HIV virus are at increased risk for losing their jobs, housing, life and health insurance benefits, and possibly the support of friends and family. Both testing and treatment for AIDS must therefore be protected by the highest standards of confidentiality. If, for example, those at risk for AIDS cannot be assured that information about their medical condition will be held in the strictest confidence, they will very likely avoid being tested or seeking treatment. The consequences will be detrimental not only to their health but possibly also to that of the larger public. Consider the following case.

3.10 Confidential information: HIV test results

Anita Lopez, a nurse who has spent the past year working in various hospitals for several nursing pools, and who now works as a staff nurse on a substance abuse unit, wonders if she should inform co-workers that David Whitefield, a recently admitted patient, has tested HIV-positive at another hospital. When she spoke with David about the matter, he acknowledged being her former patient but denied having tested HIV-positive and refuses to be tested again.

David requires assistance and care since he is bowel incontinent. Anita is worried that David might infect someone with the human immunodeficiency virus. She has not read of a documented case of AIDS transmission from contact with feces, but she has read of a nursing home worker who failed to wear gloves and became infected from caring for a man diagnosed postmortem as having AIDS.[37]

Anita's unit nursing manager urges her staff to protect themselves against any patient (not just HIV-positive patients) if they expect to come into contact with bodily fluids. Anita always uses gloves when exposed to David's feces. However, she has seen few staff members wear gloves when cleaning David after he has been incontinent. Should Anita tell the nursing staff that David is HIV-positive? Can she do so without violating confidentiality?[38]

Before considering the question of whether or not she should tell the unit nursing manager that David has tested positive for HIV, Anita should try to persuade him to be more forthright about his condition. She may, on the one hand, have legitimate concerns about his well-being in the light of recent findings about early drug therapy. If David is in fact HIV-positive, his squarely facing up to his condition and seeking appropriate medical care may significantly improve the efficacy of subsequent treatment. For his own sake, she may maintain, it is important that he confirm the results of the earlier test and make his caregivers fully aware of his medical history. This will assure that he receives the most effective medical treatment for his condition. If, on the other hand, David appears to be in the grip of denial or genuinely unconcerned about combating the disease, perhaps Anita can appeal to his concern for others. Is he aware, she might ask him, of the risks run by his caregivers? If, in fact, he is HIV-positive, shouldn't they be so informed so as to reduce the risk of contracting the virus themselves? If out of concern for his own well-being or that of others, David agrees to be more forthcoming about his medical history, Anita will not have to consider the possibility of violating confidentiality.

Suppose now that Anita's efforts have been unsuccessful—David refuses to acknowledge his having previously tested HIV-positive. Should she inform her colleagues of his medical history? Would so doing be a justifiable breach of confidentiality? The strongest argument for Anita's revealing what she knows about David's medical condition turns on her concern for the welfare of her co-workers. Yet this is likely to be outweighed, first, by legal considerations and, second, by the utilitarian importance of strictly adhering to the rule of confidentiality.

In some states disclosing this information is prohibited by law. Although such disclosure's being illegal does not make it immoral, the burden of proof is in this case quite heavy. Underlying the legal prohibition is a rule-utilitarian argument to the effect that overall good with respect to combating AIDS will best be furthered by invariably following a rule against disclosure. Only if those who suspect they may have contracted AIDS agree to be tested for HIV will the disease possibly be contained. And such individuals will, for reasons indicated above, submit to testing only if they are assured that test results will be kept protected with the highest standards of confidentiality. Thus the long-run consequences of Anita's preserving David's confidentiality are likely to be much better, in terms of overall social welfare, than if, for the sake of securing more protection for her colleagues, she were to reveal his previous test results.

Moreover, it may be possible for her to alert her co-workers to take stricter precautions without violating David's confidentiality. Suppose, without naming any particular individual, Anita were to tell the nursing manager that she had good reason to believe that one of their patients had, on a previous occasion and at a previous hospital, tested positive for HIV. While refusing entreaties to identify this patient by name or anything else, she would strongly urge that the nursing staff scrupulously adhere to the standard precautions for minimizing the chance of infection when caring for all of their patients. In this way staff members who, for example, had previously refrained from wearing gloves when exposed to bodily fluids would now be more careful.

Staff members might at this point object that good care plans require a full knowledge of a patient's condition. Unless a nurse is fully aware of a patient's medical condition and history, she cannot provide adequate nursing care. Therefore, nurses must know about David's previous HIV test if they are to provide adequate nursing care. In response we may argue that good nursing care centers on the patient's manifest condition. In David's case nurses are able to provide high-quality care without having to have the information he is reluctant to disclose. Apart from the nurses' taking greater care to protect themselves from possible infection, little, if anything, about David's nursing care plan would be altered by this additional information. It is thus possible for Anita to alert her co-workers to take greater precautions without violating the principle of confidentiality.

5. Personal risks and professional obligations

The following case raises another ethical dilemma in nursing practice associated with AIDS: When, if ever, may a nurse refrain from caring for an AIDS patient?

3.11 Refusal to care for an AIDS patient

Mary Duncan-Keilman, a staff nurse on a medical-surgical unit, graduated from a baccalaureate nursing program two years ago. Glenn Admunson, who suffers from AIDS, has recently been readmitted to the hospital, and for the first time has been placed on Mary's unit. Glenn presents a nursing care challenge. He is very weak and has lost most of his eyesight. In addition, he forgets midsentence what he is saying, signaling a deteriorating mental status.

When Crystal Mahorn, the unit nurse manager, assigned Mary as Glenn's primary nurse, Mary immediately informed Crystal that being exposed to such a deadly disease as AIDS violated her rights. Mary told the manager that her husband does not want her to place herself at risk by caring for IV drug abusers or homosexuals who have AIDS. Mary explained to Crystal that should she have to run the risk of caring for this AIDS patient, she would leave her position "flat out," without giving notice. Mary also said that she believes her life is worth more than keeping her job.[39]

Crystal believes Mary's threat to leave her position if Crystal does not find another nurse for the assignment. Does Mary have a professional obligation to care for Glenn?[40]

Although nursing has a long history of service to others, including care of infectious patients, in 1988 nearly half of nurses surveyed in two studies believed that they had the right to refuse to care for an AIDS patient.[41] What roles should nursing tradition, estimates of personal risk, and fear play in determining a nurse's professional obligation to care for AIDS patients?

As a profession, nursing holds the traditional view that nurses are obligated to care for all persons. Point 1 of the American Nurses' Association Code for Nurses underscores this commitment: "The nurse provides services with respect for human dignity and the uniqueness of the client, unrestricted by considerations of social or economic status, personal attributes, or the nature of the health problem."

The history of nurses' commitment to care for infectious patients is underscored by Florence Nightingale's scorn of medical attendants who "take greater care of themselves than of the patient" and by her praise of "true nursing" and the "true nurse":

Perhaps the best illustration of the utter absurdity of this [cowardly] view of duty in attending on "infectious" diseases is afforded by what was very recently the practice, if it is not so even now, in some of the European lazarets—in which the plague-patient used to be condemned to the horrors of filth, overcrowding, and want of ventilation, while the medical attendant was ordered to examine the patient's tongue through an opera-glass and to toss him a lancet to open his abscesses with!

True nursing ignores infection except to prevent it. Cleanliness and fresh air from open windows, with unremitting attention to the patient, are the only defense a true nurse either asks or needs.[42]

The nursing profession's *Suggested Code* of 1926 continued to support the ideal that nurses serve others even in face of danger to themselves. The code claimed that "the most precious possession of this profession is the ideal of service, extending even to the sacrifice of life itself. . . ."[43]

More than sixty years later, nurses do not routinely support the ideal of serving others in the face of risk to their own well-being. Nurses' current concern for their well-being may indicate a shift in estimating personal risks inherent in nursing. Many contemporary nurses entered the profession believing that providing nursing care included virtually no health risk to themselves. Since the middle of the twentieth century, widespread use of antibiotics and immunizations have offered a shield of protection. Antibiotics and immunizations, however, do not completely protect health care workers against all infections. A late-twentieth-century nurse must use techniques and take precautions to control the spread of infection in her or his practice. Some nurses, believing that AIDS patients represent increased risk of infection to nurses, claim a right to refuse to care for them.

In 1986, to help nurses analyze the issue of personal risk versus responsibility to care for AIDS patients, the American Nurses' Association Committee on Ethics concluded that a nurse is obligated to care for patients, including infectious patients, if:

1. The patient is at significant risk of harm, loss, or damage if the nurse does not assist.
2. The nurse's intervention or care is directly relevant to preventing harm.
3. The nurse's care will probably prevent harm, loss, or damage to the patient.
4. The benefit the patient will gain outweighs any harm the nurse might incur and does not present more than minimal risk to the health care provider.[44]

In discussing these criteria, the Committee on Ethics concluded that in a case in which a nurse is immunosuppressed, the fourth criterion, "the most crucial," would not be met. Therefore, such a nurse would not be obligated to care for AIDS patients.

Research indicates that caring for AIDS patients does not present more than *minimal risk*, if minimal risk means an extremely low probability of contracting an HIV infection. Not only is the actual probability of nurses' contracting HIV infection from patients extremely low, but risks involved with delivering health care to such patients can also be well managed with correct infection-control measures.[45]

In addition to estimates of personal risk, a variety of fears about HIV infection may influence a nurse's refusal to care for a person with AIDS. Some writers have compared AIDS with the bubonic plague, but historian Peter Vinten-Johansen argues that AIDS more satisfactorily parallels syphilis than the plague. Although he acknowledges that some persons with AIDS have been "treated as though they were contagious plague victims," as a disease AIDS shows more similarities to syphilis than to plague. Syphilis, prior to antibiotic treatment, shared certain significant similarities to HIV infection: a person might have no visible symptoms for a protracted period, the disease could be sexually transmitted, and confidentiality and privacy were important issues.[46] In addition, syphilis, like HIV infection, could lead to dementia.

The fears of "innocent acquisition" from casual contact, associated with historical syphilis and now seen in attitudes about AIDS, reflect the same moralistic point of view from which the sufferer is seen as deserving the affliction, since the infection is "due to lack of self control or perverse sexual behavior."[47] Adding to fears of innocent acquisition is fear of homosexuality—homophobia—which is expressed in our society in discrimination against and hostility toward persons with homosexual preferences.[48] Other fears surrounding care of persons with AIDS relate to fears of and revulsion against IV drug abuse, especially since transmission of HIV infection is traced in a significant number of cases to shared use of contaminated needles. Thus, fear not only of HIV as a fatal disease may influence a nurse's refusal to provide care, but additional fears may be influential, such as those stemming from attitudes about venereal disease, homosexuality, and drug abuse.

To return to Mary Duncan-Keilman's refusal to care for an AIDS patient in Case 3.11, Mary's refusal ignores her professional obligation to provide nursing care and seems, instead, to be based upon estimates of personal risk and fear. Mary's professional obligation to care for Glenn Admunson is clear: First, according to nursing tradition and the ANA Code for Nurses, "The nurse provides services . . . unrestricted by . . . the nature of the disease." Second, since Mary is not immunosuppressed, application of the ANA Committee on Ethics criteria for analyzing personal risk and responsibility to care for AIDS patients further supports her obligation to care for Glenn Admunson. And third, since Mary accepted employment as an RN on a medical-surgical unit that provides nursing care to a variety of patients, including those with AIDS, she implicitly promised to provide service to all patients on the unit.

Mary seems to believe that she would be in mortal danger if she were to care for Glenn Admunson. Since research indicates that health care workers face an extremely low probability of contracting HIV infection through provision of care and that risks of infection can be well managed, Mary's refusal to care for this specific patient may be related to ignorance about current research concerning HIV infection and its control. Her refusal may also be related to her fear of and attitudes about venereal disease, homosexuality, and/or drug abuse. These fears and attitudes, however severe or however supported by her husband or others, do not override professional obligations inherent in her employment on a unit that provides nursing service to AIDS patients. (A discussion of Crystal Mahorn's response to Mary Duncan-Keilman's refusal to care for an AIDS patient is included in Chapter 5.)

6. Conflicting claims

In Case 3.9, the nurse had to balance her obligations among three parties: the young girl, her mother, and the potential child. Whose needs or claims are to be given priority when a nurse cannot respond to all of those to whom she has a prima facie obligation? Consider, for example, the following case.

3.12 Who is the client?

Louise Russell, staff public health nurse serving the inner city, made a home visit to Kathryn Simmons and her young baby. During the visit Kathryn told Louise that she thought she might be pregnant again. Not one to seek medical care until absolutely necessary, Kathryn had not planned to see her doctor. Louise immediately reminded Kathryn that her doctor had in-

creased her epilepsy medication just after her baby's birth, and that she would probably need to get the prescription changed to safeguard the unborn baby's development. After a short discussion about the importance of checking her medication if she were pregnant, Kathryn phoned for a doctor's appointment. When Louise left Kathryn that day, she was pleased that Kathryn had assumed responsibility for herself and her unborn child rather than letting Louise take control and call the doctor for her.

A week later Louise wondered if Kathryn had actually seen the doctor. Although Kathryn had made the phone call in her presence, she was not convinced that she would follow through. She wondered if she should call Kathryn and check if she had, but she knew that Kathryn would immediately understand the unspoken message that Louise did not entirely trust her. Or, Louise thought, she could call the doctor and find out if Kathryn had kept the appointment, which would also be an admission that Louise did not trust her client. In the past Louise had struggled with the question of whether she trusted clients to act on information she gave them, but in this situation she had to consider the unborn baby, too. She didn't know how to balance her respect for Kathryn as a person against her responsibility as a nurse to protect the health of the unborn child.

Louise's dilemma is clearly drawn: if she treats Kathryn as a responsible adult, harm may come to the fetus; if she intervenes on behalf of the fetus, she will not be treating Kathryn as a fully responsible adult. Although the case raises a number of different issues, our primary concern is this: Whose interests, Kathryn's or the unborn child's, ought to be given priority when Louise cannot, on the face of it, satisfy both?

In cases like this we would suggest applying the principle that the client who runs the greatest risk of significant harm should be the primary concern. Thus, Louise should insure that Kathryn keeps her appointment because the risk of significant harm to the unborn baby if she does not keep it is higher than the risk of significant harm to Kathryn if she is upset by Louise's intervention. An important consideration in making this judgment is that it would be much easier for Louise to repair Kathryn's wounded self-esteem than it would be to reverse the harm that might befall the fetus in the event that Kathryn neglects to have her medication changed.

The principle we have appealed to does not imply either that Kathryn has no right to be regarded as a responsible adult or that a fetus's or child's rights always outweigh those of a parent or adult. First, both Kathryn and the unborn baby have a right to Louise's respect and concern. In this case, however, the fact that the unborn baby runs a greater risk of significant harm than does Kathryn gives Louise strong grounds for overriding Kathryn's right. To say that Kathryn has a right that Louise has reluctantly overridden in the name of the unborn baby's more stringent right implies that Louise ought to do what she can to justify her act to Kathryn and indicate in other ways her respect for her as a person. Second, there may be occasions when the foregoing principle will indicate that it is a child's, and not an adult's, right to respect and concern that must be overridden. Thus, for example, if Louise makes a routine home visit to assess the development of a premature infant and discovers the mother has a badly infected cut on her leg requiring immediate treatment, her first concern should be for the mother.

Although we think it is fairly clear that Louise ought to insure that Kathryn has visited the doctor, it is not so clear whether she should do this by simply calling Kathryn or by calling the doctor. On the one hand, it may seem better to call the doctor. If the doctor indicates that Kathryn has kept the appointment, Kathryn may never learn of Louise's doubts; and the doctor's confirmation that Kathryn has kept the appointment is, perhaps, stronger evidence than Kathryn's saying that she has done so. On the other hand, making the initial call to the doctor shows less trust in Kathryn than does calling her directly; if she has in fact not visited the doctor and learns that Louise has been checking up on her "behind her back," the perceived insult and breach of trust will seem greater and the relationship between her and Louise will be more difficult to repair. We leave it to the reader to determine which of these alternatives is preferable and why. A more difficult case of competing client claims is the following:

3.13 Advocate for parents and children

As the community health nurse assigned to the city's northwest corner, Sharon Brinker believes that she is responsible to all the people on her case load. Recently, she was called into court to testify in a child abuse and neglect case involving Larry and Carolyn Trice and their three children (David, seven years old; Linda, five; and Sandra, four). Sharon found it difficult to think in terms of individual clients because she usually looks at a family as a whole. Yet the court considers a child's welfare and safety separately from a parent's wishes for the family to remain together. One option before the court is to place the Trice children in a local institution that offers therapy to whole families; children are returned to parents who successfully participate in treatment programs. Other options require more lasting separation. The judge will base his or her decision in part on the recommendations of expert witnesses—doctors, nurses, psychologists, and social workers.

Sharon first met the Trices six months ago when David was unable to stay awake in school. She thinks she has made good progress with Carolyn in that she has gained her trust and goodwill. David has been doing better since Sharon suggested that Carolyn could leave food out for him to eat before school. But many problems remain, including some relating to David's asthma. Carolyn cannot or will not keep medical appointments for David, enforce rules for the children, or keep the children on any kind of simple routine of meals or scheduled bedtimes. Larry, who works seasonally at pouring cement, usually takes little interest in the children's daily activities.

Recently, Linda has been caught stealing repeatedly from local stores on her way to and from kindergarten, with the result that Larry or Carolyn or both beat her badly enough to result in the court hearing. Sharon feels responsible for the children. She thinks that Linda especially needs her protection; if she steals again, she will probably be beaten. But Sharon also believes that the children need their parents. She thinks she must be the parents' advocate as well as the children's. She has built a positive relationship with Carolyn and thinks that, though she cannot meet all of Carolyn's many needs, Carolyn's trust in her as a professional and friend should be protected.

Sharon's problem is to determine what she could say to the court that would best preserve Carolyn's trust, protect the children, and preserve the integrity of the family.

Those, like Sharon, who consider the family or a similar social group as the unit of nursing or medical care occasionally find themselves in the following dilemma: If they do what appears best for the family as a whole, they may violate the rights or neglect basic needs of individual members; yet if they focus on the rights or needs of particular members, the result may be the weakening or disintegration of the family. Those who advocate regarding the family as the unit of care believe that what is best for the individuals and what is best for the family are generally the same or at least are not in conflict. But sometimes, as in this case, familial and individual interests do not appear to coincide. Thus, if Sharon is concerned primarily with preserving the mother's trust and the integrity of the family, she may be putting the children at significant risk. On the other hand, if her primary concern is the control of David's asthma, regularly scheduled meals and bedtimes for all the children, and an alternative to beatings as a way of dealing with Linda's stealing, her testimony in court may help weaken the integrity of the family.

This is an extremely difficult issue, and it is impossible to take a position that is beyond question or controversy. Nonetheless, we are inclined to agree with Goldstein, Freud, and Solnit that a policy of minimum coercive intervention by the state is most in accord with individual freedom, human dignity, and the intricate developmental processes of children: "So long as a child is a member of a functioning family, his paramount interest lies in the preservation of his family."[49] But where the dynamics of particular family interactions place the child at risk of serious bodily injury inflicted by the parents or the parents have repeatedly failed to prevent the child from suffering serious injury, there are grounds for intervention. One restriction on state intervention in such cases, however, is that the state must also be able to provide a better situation for the child. "If the state cannot or will not provide something better, even if it did not know this at the time the action was initiated, the least detrimental alternative would be to let the *status quo* persist, however unsatisfactory that might be."[50]

The questions in Case 3.13 are, How severe will the long-run negative consequences of the lack of regularity in their home life be to all the Trice children, and what are the special risks to David because of his asthma and to Linda because of her stealing and the subsequent beatings? If, on the basis of her knowledge of the situation, Sharon believes that one or more of these alternatives poses a significant risk of lasting harm to the children *and* if the state is able to provide something better, she should advise the court to intervene. If, on the other hand, both of these conditions are not met, she should not advise the court to intervene. Furthermore, if intervention is advisable, the less extreme alternative—placing the children in an institution that offers family therapy and the possibility of family reintegration—is, at least initially, preferable to options requiring more lasting separation.

Notes

1. By "parentalism" we mean what is conventionally referred to in the literature as "paternalism." But since women are no less capable than men of occupying the "paternal" or "father knows best" role in their dealings with others, we prefer the sexually neutral term.
2. This case was provided by Peggy Jones, BSN, Community Health Nurse, Lansing, Michigan.
3. An important distinction can be drawn between "parentalism" *as a social practice* having certain roles and expectations governing the behavior of patients and health care professionals in the total health care system and parentalism *as a justification for particular acts* of manipulation or coercion on the part of health care professionals. Unless otherwise indicated, we use the term "parentalism" in the second sense.
4. James F. Childress, "Paternalism and Health Care," in Wade L. Robison and Michael S. Pritchard, eds., *Medical Responsibility* (Clifton, N.J.: Humana Press, 1979), p. 18.
5. As Charles Fried puts it, "Even if the ends are the patient's own ends, to treat him as a means to them is to undermine his humanity insofar as humanity consists in choosing and being able to judge one's own ends, rather than being a machine which is used to serve ends, even one's own ends." Charles Fried, *Medical Experimentation: Personal Integrity and Social Policy* (Amsterdam: North Holland, 1974), p. 101.
6. Ibid., p. 95.
7. This case was provided by Bruce Walters, student in the College of Human

Medicine at Michigan State University; see also Lois K. Evans and Neville E. Strumpf, "Myths about Elder Restraint," *Image: Journal of Nursing Scholarship* 22 (Summer 1990):124–28.

8. See Bruce Miller, "Autonomy and the Refusal of Lifesaving Treatment," *Hastings Center Report* 11 (August 1981):22–28.

9. H. L. A. Hart, *Law, Liberty, and Morality* (New York: Vintage, 1966), pp. 32–34.

10. John Stuart Mill, *On Liberty* (New York: Library of Liberal Arts, 1956), p. 117. Emphasis added.

11. Childress, "Paternalism and Health Care," p. 24.

12. Gerald Dworkin, "Paternalism," *Monist* 56 (January 1972):76f.

13. Kirsten Bennett in Case 3.2 might thus be criticized for not having worked harder at obtaining consent from Mr. Young, during his lucid periods, to his being restrained, if necessary, in the future. The case, as presented, suggests that she may have been more concerned with securing his family's consent than his own.

14. Ultimately this condition must be modified to account for subjects who will never recover their capacity for rational reflection.

15. See Chapter 5, Section 1, Part B, for a further account of the role of the primary nurse.

16. This case was provided by Bruce Walters.

17. This case was provided by Dorothea Milbrandt, Vice-President for Nursing, Ingham Medical Center, Lansing, Michigan, and Marilyn Rothert, Director for Lifelong Education, College of Nursing, Michigan State University.

18. Lawrence Stern, "Freedom, Blame, and the Moral Community," *Journal of Philosophy* 71 (14 February 1974):75.

19. Ibid., p. 74.

20. Raymond Williams, *Keywords* (New York: Oxford University Press, 1976), p. 156.

21. Stern, "Freedom, Blame, and the Moral Community," p. 76.

22. For an account of eight such ways, see Roderick M. Chisholm and Thomas D. Feehan, "The Intent to Deceive," *Journal of Philosophy* 74 (March 1977):143–59.

23. Irving M. Copi, *Introduction to Logic* (New York: Macmillan, 1978), p. 114.

24. Martin Benjamin, "Moral Agency and Negative Acts in Medicine," in Wade L. Robison and Michael S. Pritchard, eds., *Medical Responsibility* (Clifton, N.J.: Humana Press, 1979), pp. 169–80.

25. Anthony Shaw, "Dilemmas of 'Informed Consent' in Children," *New England Journal of Medicine* 289 (25 October 1973):885.

26. Ibid., p. 886.

27. St. Augustine, *The Enchiridion*, quoted in Sissela Bok, *Lying: Moral Choice in Public and Private Life* (New York: Pantheon, 1978), p. 32.

28. Immanuel Kant, *Doctrine of Virtue*, quoted in Bok, *Lying*, p. 32.

29. Immanuel Kant, "On a Supposed Right to Lie from Altruistic Motives," excerpted in Bok, *Lying*, p. 269.

30. Alan Donagan, *The Theory of Morality* (Chicago: University of Chicago Press, 1977), p. 89.

31. Bok, *Lying*, p. 26f.

32. Ibid., p. 223.

33. Lewis Thomas, *The Lives of a Cell* (New York: Viking, 1974), pp. 81–86.

34. Bok, *Lying*, p. 63.
35. Howard Brody, *Placebos and the Philosophy of Medicine* (Chicago: University of Chicago Press, 1980), pp. 25–44, 96–114.
36. This case is a variation of one reported in Kathleen A. Mahon and Sally J. Everson, "Moral Outrage—Nurse's Right or Responsibility: Ethics Rounds for Nurses," *Journal of Continuing Education* 10 (no. 3, 1979):4.
37. James R. Allen, "Health Care Workers and the Risk of HIV Transmission," Special Supplement, *Hastings Center Report* 18 (April/May 1988):4.
38. Based on a case, "Keeping Test Results Confidential," *Nursing 88* 18 (August 1988):22.
39. See Leslie Brennan and the editors, "The Battle against AIDS: A Report from the Nursing Front," *Nursing 88* 18 (April 1988):60–64.
40. Case created for this text.
41. Brennan and the editors, "The Battle against AIDS," 60–64; "Nursing News, Nursing Attitudes," *Nursing 88* 18 (September 1988):10.
42. Florence Nightingale, *Notes on Nursing: What It Is and What It Is Not* (Philadelphia: J. B. Lippincott, facsimile of first edition, 1859), pp. 19–20.
43. American Nurses' Association, *Ethics in Nursing: Position Statements and Guidelines* (Kansas City, Mo.: American Nurses' Association, 1988), p. 6.
44. Ibid., pp. 6–7.
45. James R. Allen, "Health Care Workers and the Risk of HIV Transmission," pp. 2–5; Elizabeth C. Reisman, "Ethical Issues Confronting Nurses," *Nursing Clinics of North America* 23 (no. 4, December 1988):789–802.
46. Peter Vinten-Johansen, "A Comparative Historical Perspective on AIDS," unpublished paper available from the Department of History at Michigan State University.
47. Ibid., p. 10.
48. Wayne R. Dynes, *Homosexuality: A Research Guide* (New York: Garland, 1987); Jonathan Ned Katz, *Gay/Lesbian Almanac: A New Documentary* (New York: Harper and Row, 1983); see also Carla E. Randall, "Lesbian Phobia among BSN Educators: A Survey," *Journal of Nursing Education* 28 (September 1989):302–6.
49. Joseph Goldstein, Anna Freud, and Albert J. Solnit, *Before the Best Interests of the Child* (New York: The Free Press, 1979), p. 5.
50. Ibid., p. 21.

4

Recurring Ethical Issues
in Nurse-Physician Relationships

1. Conflicts between nurse and physician

Conflicts arise when either the nurse or the physician disagrees with the other's professional practice. In some situations the nurse believes that the physician's orders or actions may result in poor care or be unsafe; in other instances the physician believes that the nurse's activities are similarly wrong; in still other instances each disagrees with the other about questions of ethics or values. The following is an example of a conflict resulting from a nurse's independent assessment of a need for immediate medical care.

4.1 The doctor won't come

After working eight years as a nurse in an emergency room in a medium-sized city and in an inner-city hospital pediatric unit, Jackie Nardi presently is charge staff nurse two afternoons a week on a sixteen-bed pediatric unit in a community hospital.

Six-year-old Laurie Thoma was a new diabetic who, in Jackie's judgment, was close to respiratory arrest. Jackie first phoned the resident on call, who happened to be new to the hospital. When he arrived, he was not only younger than Jackie but seemed to be uncertain of himself. Jackie gave him some suggestions regarding immediate medical care for Laurie, but according to her, he "just threw it down the tubes because I'm the nurse and he's the doctor." Then he left, saying he'd return after dinner.

Meanwhile, Jackie still believed it was a life-threatening situation for the child and called the pediatrician, Dr. Bauerlein, who was working in the hospital emergency room. When he learned that the resident had been there moments earlier, he refused to come. Jackie was frustrated: "I could see Laurie's condition worsening. I could see a lot of things that needed to be done, but I couldn't do anything about it because I can't write orders." She thought Laurie needed more than her observations and decisions, so she started calling Dr. Bauerlein every five minutes. She also called her supervisor and convinced her that Dr. Bauerlein had to come immediately. Finally, the supervisor went to the emergency room and brought him over. He was angry at Jackie for her persistent calls, but he ordered, basically, the medical care Jackie had suggested earlier to the resident.

Although Jackie never regretted getting emergency help for Laurie, she dislikes the way Dr. Bauerlein now treats her. At times when a resident or another nurse, especially her supervisor, is within hearing distance, he asks Jackie medical questions relating to his various patients—questions he knows she cannot, without a medical educaion and pediatric background like his, answer correctly.

This case raises a number of questions: What should a nurse's responsibility be in making medical decisions (in the technical sense)? What should a nurse do when her well-grounded recommendations are ignored? What, if anything, should a nurse do when she disagrees with a physician's actions or lack of action? On the face of it, the easiest solution for Jackie, of course, would have been simply to wait for the doctor and follow his orders; but the result, if her assessment of Laurie's precarious situation was correct, might have been Laurie's death. Jackie's awareness of the medical situation placed her in an acute conflict between complying with Dr. Bauerlein's wishes to be left alone and meeting Laurie's need, as Jackie saw it, for emergency medical care.

Several factors contribute to tension in this and similar situations. Among them are the historical legacy of nurse-physician relationships, the expanding scope of nursing practice, the socioeconomic and educational distance between nursing and medical professionals, and the ideology of professionalism in nursing. Since these factors often impede or distort efforts to engage in ethical inquiry, it is important to have some understanding of them.

A. Historical legacy

During the earliest period of nursing history, nursing and medicine developed independently and had little contact until recognition of the medical value of bedside nursing brought them together in the late nineteenth century. With the development of the modern hospital came the introduction of the trained nurse, and patterns of relationships in hospitals developed that affect current nurse-physician relationships.[1] Physicians developed the medical staff, but as a part of that staff, they were not employed by, subordinate to, or responsible to the hospital administration. Physicians could and did, however, issue orders directly to nurses. The nursing staff's position was quite different from that of the medical staff. Nurses were employed by, subordinate to, and directly responsible to the administration. Thus, nursing developed under the dual command of physicians and hospital administrators. Even today, the two lines of authority severely limit and complicate the decision-making role of a hospital nurse.[2]

The Nightingale plan for nursing schools, which included instruction in both scientific principles and practical experience, appeared in the United States in 1873. Unfortunately for American nursing, the schools had no endowment or financial backing, and hospitals quickly seized the opportunity to gain inexpensive student nurse labor. Nursing educaion was essentially an apprenticeship, and as late as the 1930s student nurses received little formal instruction in some hospitals.[3]

Under the dominance of male doctors and administrators, schools of nursing grew, and they were not noted for encouraging nurses to think critically and for themselves. Students entered nursing schools already expecting that women would defer to men, and, therefore, that nurses would defer to doctors. Adding to the traditional subordination of nurses to physicians, nursing school faculties often culled out overly questioning and rebellious students.[4] The students' socialization and education taught them to be deferential. Many diploma schools included the study of textbooks such as L. J. Morison's *Steppingstones in Professional Growth*, published in a revised edition in 1965, which tells the student to cultivate loyalty, prudence, willingness, and cooperation since the physician has the right to expect such qualities. Further, the nurse must follow orders and uphold the physician's professional reputation.[5] Expected by society and trained by the nursing school to act as subordinates, most nurses behaved accordingly.

Yet tradition and nursing education alone cannot be blamed for the dominance of physicians and the deference of nurses. Beatrice and Philip Kalisch argue that a physician who sees himself as an independent, omnipotent man with mystical healing powers relates to co-workers as he does to patients and therefore insists that nurses and other health care providers serve him in his "so-called captain of the ship role."[6]

The relegation of nursing to the subordinate position in the nurse-physician relationship has limited collaboration between the two professions. Empirical studies show that physicians are at the center of the decision-making process and that nurses carry out those decisions.[7] In 1968, psychiatrist Leonard Stein described nurse-physician relationships in terms of a doctor-nurse game in which a nurse must appear to be passive. In this game any suggestion a nurse makes to a doctor must be masked in such a way as to seem as if it were his idea, and a doctor may not openly seek advice from a nurse.[8] The historical legacy of nurse-physician relationships, while affecting specific nurses and doctors in various ways, gives decision-making power to a doctor and requires passivity (or biting one's lip) of a nurse. If a nurse and a physician deviate from this pattern, the exchange of information and recommendations must occur in such a way that the doctor still appears to lead, the nurse to follow.

A study published in 1985 reports, among other things, that the "doctor-nurse game" described by Stein nearly twenty years earlier was still being played. A resident interviewed for the study commented:

I have seen nurses, who really knew a lot more than an intern, kind of gently guide him [the intern] into making the right decision. . . . They make some very good decisions and make some very helpful suggestions sometimes. . . . It is like trying to guide the ship without actually taking hold of the wheel. . . . There are nurses who are good at that.[9]

A nurse in the same study claimed:

You have to be careful whenever you talk to them [physicians] that you are not telling them what to do. You have to talk to them in such a way that you are asking their opinion and work in what you want to say without being overbearing or threatening . . . make them think that the idea is partially in their mind too.[10]

In 1990 Stein claimed most nurses have stopped playing the doctor-nurse game.[11] But until the relationship between doctors and nurses can be fully restructured so as to be egalitarian and collaborative, nurses may still have to choose, on occasion, between optimally serving their clients and playing the game.[12] In Case 4.1, Jackie was the obvious loser with both doctors, the resident and Dr. Bauerlein. The new resident rejected Jackie's recommendations because, as she said, he was the doctor and she the nurse—a statement that indicates that she was well aware of the usual rules of the doctor-nurse game. Jackie forgot or ignored important rules by aggressively and publicly seeking out Dr. Bauerlein. The doctor, however, from the evidence of his later attempts to belittle or embarrass her, clearly remembered the game and placed importance on the rule that he must, as the doctor, be treated as the leader who needed no obvious assistance from her. If they continue their relationship in this historically spawned, stereotypical manner, the game effectively limits their communication, and Jackie has little chance of involving Dr. Bauerlein in an investigation of their overlapping roles and responsibilities as colleagues. In addition, had the resident and Jackie not been involved in the doctor-nurse game, the situation probably would never have developed into a problem. If Jackie and the resident had been able to exchange information freely and examine each other's ideas about Laurie's treatment, the resident would have been quick to recognize the validity of Jackie's suggestions.

B. The expanding scope of nursing practice

In some clinical situations, as in Case 4.1, a nurse believes she can correctly diagnose and treat a particular problem in an emergency, but she is not allowed legally to act upon her knowledge. In another kind of situation, it is not the nurse but the physician who wants the nurse to perform activities that are legally prohibited, such as making rounds and prescribing postoperative medications. Thus, to carry out tasks that are outside the scope of professional nursing practice sometimes requires the nurse to break the law. However, the line between medicine and nursing is blurred and in some complex medical procedures and institutional organizations, it is difficult for a doctor and nurse to differentiate tasks that are strictly medical from those that are legitimately within the realm of nursing.[13]

The expansion of knowledge, together with the technological and social changes that have occurred rapidly in the last quarter century, have necessitated redefinitions of the scope of nursing practice and have contributed to tensions in nurse-physician relationships. Such changes include the use of life-maintenance machines, automatic clinical laboratory equipment, computers, complex medical interventions, artificial replacements of human parts, human organ transplants, and resulting specialization within both medicine and nursing.[14] Among the many social changes affecting the scope of nursing practice are increased social mobility; increased pluralism of religion, culture, race, and age among patient populations seeking care; and increased concern for good health among certain groups as evidenced by interest in physical fitness, health foods, alternative care plans for childbirth, alternative health care providers in addition to physicians, and new health care systems such as health maintenance organizations. Given these technological and social changes, certain nurses, through in-service education, college or university courses, independent study, or experience, may know more about some aspect of a particular treatment or apparatus or machine than do the physicians with whom they work. For example, an experienced and knowledgeable nurse working full time in an intensive care unit may know more about certain treatments in that unit than a physician working there only briefly during his educational program. In addition, nurses, who usually spend more time with patients than do physicians, often know considerably more about their patients' strengths, weaknesses, desires, and needs than do some physicians, who may see patients only during short visits. Furthermore, some nurses, in viewing nursing as a "caring" more than a "curing" profession, see health education needs as important and as requiring more professional time and effort than that allotted in some medical treatment programs that focus on specific disease processes. In response to pressures to clarify the expanding role of nursing, in recent years nearly all states have attempted to redefine the scope of nursing practice.

In 1955 the American Nurses' Association approved a model definition of nursing practice that prohibited nurses from performing any medical act. Yet nursing education had already been strengthened to the extent that nurses were making diagnostic and therapeutic decisions in providing nursing care; the disclaimers that they were not to do so were out of date at the time that various states incorporated the model definition into their practice acts. During the fifties and sixties, nursing functions continued to expand into the overlapping areas of medical and nursing practice. Pressure from both within and without the nursing profession mounted, and legal changes came rapidly in the seventies.

In 1981, the ANA included "diagnosis . . . in the promotion and maintenance of health" in its model definition of nursing practice for new state legislation. By 1984, twenty-three states used the words "diagnosis," or "nursing diagnosis" or some other term for diagnosis in their nursing practice acts.[15]

Nurses, depending upon their state of residence, may or may not practice under a nursing practice act that allows them to carry out nursing diagnosis and treatment and/or medical diagnosis and treatment. They may live in a state that requires special certification or agency protocols, rules, and procedures before they engage in diagnosis and treatment. In some states, diagnosis and treatment functions must be delegated to nurses. In others, nurses may be absolutely prohibited from diagnosing and prescribing treatments. Finally, in some states, regulations and broad definitions only vaguely differentiate nursing diagnosis and treatment from medical diagnosis and treatment.

Given this variety, and changes in legal definitions of the scope of nursing practice, it is understandable that physicians and nurses may disagree or be confused as to the legality of nurses' performing diagnostic and treatment procedures. As discussed in Chapter 1, before engaging in ethical inquiry the nurse needs to have the facts about a given situation clearly in mind, and the scope of nursing practice as defined in the state practice act is one such fact. Unless nurses keep themselves informed and educate other health care workers in their community concerning current revisions of their state practice acts, nurses and physicians are likely to view the nurses' functions from conflicting and perhaps erroneous points of view. Nevertheless, ethical inquiry into conflicts between nurse and physician may be impeded by disagreements about the nurse's rightful functions even though both the nurse and the physician may be aware of their state practice acts and related rules and regulations. This is especially true if the acts or rules are open to broad interpretation or if the physician and nurse disagree about the scope of nursing thus described.

To return again to Case 4.1, both Jackie's recognition of legal constraints on her practice as a nurse and her perception of the scope of nursing practice, which differed from that of Dr. Bauerlein, influenced their relationship. Although Jackie is currently a registered nurse with eight years' experience, she did not have the required additional education for certification as an advanced nurse practitioner. Legally, according to her state's nurse practice act, she could not medically treat Laurie. When both persons authorized by law to provide medical help for Laurie chose not to act, Jackie enlisted the help of her nurse supervisor, but she also kept calling persistently herself. Jackie clearly demonstrated that, since she recognized she could not treat Laurie herself, she had to get help from a doctor. Thus, the conflict between Jackie and Dr. Bauerlein was affected not only by the historical legacy of the health professions in the form of the doctor-nurse game and her failure in that game but also by the scope of her duties as determined by her state's current nursing practice act.

We are not suggesting that the public should have no legal protection from unqualified health care providers. Nurses, such as Jackie, must recognize the general value of practice acts and observe their constraints. Nonetheless, at times the nurse must override a practice act, as she might any law in the name of a more stringent moral obligation. Note that no matter what the practice act stated about a nurse's making a diagnosis, Jackie disregarded that issue when she observed Laurie and decided that the child was in a life-threatening situation. Dr. Bauerlein's later attempts to discredit Jackie's ability to think for herself indicate that he thinks nurses should not diagnose. Quite simply, Dr. Bauerlein and Jackie did not agree as to the scope of Jackie's nursing practice.

Jackie, believing that her responsibility to get immediate help for Laurie fell within the scope of her nursing practice, did not obey Dr. Bauerlein and stop calling him; rather, she persisted until he came to the unit. Certainly, the nursing practice act did not forbid her from aggressively seeking his services. The tradition that the nurse should obey the doctor automatically is in conflict with the conception of a nurse who thinks for herself when she has strong grounds for evaluating a particular diagnosis and course of treatment. Yet time-worn attitudes linger in both professions. They are seen in a physician who expects a nurse's unconditional obedience and in parallel form in a nurse who hesitates to disagree with a physician even when she has good reason to do so. The following case presents a nurse in conflict between obeying or acting upon her own diagnosis and treatment plans.

4.2 Orders not to teach

Fran Hilkenmeyer, fifty-one-year-old clinical supervisor for South Lake Community College student nurses, has observed a mastectomy patient who, in her assessment, needs instruction. However, as was true of several other mastectomy patients she has seen recently at Mercy Hospital, the team of physicians that did the surgery does not want the nurses to teach the

patient exercises for the affected arm. When Fran asked the head nurse why,
she did not receive a clear answer and learned only that the doctors do not
want special rehabilitation groups to come to the hospital to talk to their
patients. Fran knows that nurses in many hospitals offer classes to promote
the recovery of postmastectomy patients.

Fran says she "feels strongly about the woman." She sees that the patient
needs help, but she has not questioned the physicians about their orders that
there be no teaching because "I don't know the physicians well enough to
meet them head-on. I'm sure my hesitation goes back to my earlier ideas
about not questioning doctors, which I don't really believe in any more but
which just crop up every once in a while. I happen to think very highly of the
surgeons involved. If I were to have surgery, they would be the ones I would
go to. I hate to question them because I know they are good. When I get the
chance, I do a bit of relationship building with them, and I will probably
face them with the question before very long. My courage is mounting."

Fran, who was graduated almost three decades ago from a major university school of nursing, was inclined to act in conflicting ways because of the
historical legacy of the nursing profession, which inculcated a deferential
role, and because she recognized the expanded scope of contemporary
professional nursing. She saw the importance of being assertive and acting
upon her diagnosis; yet, she held back. She chose not to attempt to instruct
mastectomy patients until she herself talked with the surgeons, which would
probably not occur until after this particular woman had left the hospital.
She hopes, of course, to obtain their approval of her plans for teaching;
however, her hopes are probably unrealistic since these physicians have
allowed no other nurses to instruct their patients. In attempting to define the
problem, Fran asked only one question: Should I approach the physicians
with my questions? An underlying question, which she did not explicitly
identify, was, If the physicians say that they do not want me or any other
nurse or student nurse to teach their patients, should I proceed to teach
without their approval or against their wishes? By focusing attention on the
first question, Fran may ignore ethical inquiry into the underlying question
of whether nurses should be obedient to physicians.

Before continuing the discussion of obedience, two remaining major
factors need to be examined since a combination of factors simultaneously
contributes to tension in many nurse-physician conflicts.

C. Socioeconomic and educational distance
between nursing and medical professionals

Until recently, access to medical education was generally limited to white
males of upper-middle-class family backgrounds,[16] which meant that physi-

cians, as a group, had higher social-class backgrounds than nurses, as a group. In addition, the unequal incomes of the two professions have allowed physicians to remain in a much higher socioeconomic class than most nurses. With disparity of income come differences in values and lifestyles; thus nurses and physicians tend to live in different neighborhoods and socialize in different groups. Of course, people do not have to be best friends to work congenially and effectively together, but they must be able to share important information with one another. Empirical studies, however, show that nurses and physicians are not generally sharing colleagues; rather, they work side by side with severely limited communication and minimal interaction.[17]

In Case 4.2, Fran's problem in overcoming the communication gap between herself and the physicians, whom she viewed as highly competent, is no different from problems experienced by other nurses, some much younger, less experienced, and less well-educated than Fran. Nurses, generally, have less formal education than do physicians. Nursing education for registered nurses requires two, three, or four years of study in a nursing school; for some nurses, nursing education includes an additional one or two years in a master's level graduate program, and for a still smaller number of nurses the educational program includes several more years in a doctoral program. Medical education for doctors of medicine and osteopathy usually includes three to four years of college study, three to four years of medical school, a one-year internship, and, for most physicians, two to four years in a residency program. In simple numbers, educational programs for most nurses last two to four years while educational programs for most doctors extend from nine to thirteen years, although professionals in both groups engage in lifelong education. Needless to say, medicine remains a more prestigious and powerful profession than nursing.

D. The ideology of professionalism in nursing

In recent years nurses have intensified their efforts to gain a higher level of professionalism, but the process has been and continues to be stressful.[18] Although some nurses have felt threatened, other nurses have gained support and courage from positions nursing leaders have taken concerning various professional nursing issues, such as the goal that baccalaureate nursing education be the minimum preparation for the professional nurse as outlined by the American Nurses' Association in 1965. The ANA position linked professionalism to baccalaureate preparation at a time when more than 88 percent of the 582,000 employed registered nurses were diploma graduates.[19] Since that time, the shift of nursing education from diploma programs operated by hospitals to two-year associate degree programs in community colleges and four-year baccalaureate degree programs in colleges and universities has continued. Twenty years later, 68.1 percent of an estimated 1,887,697 employed registered nurses still had less than a baccalaureate education, and pressure within the nursing profession for individual nurses to return to college for baccalaureate and master's degrees in nursing remains strong.[20]

Reflecting this drive for more education, recognition, and higher professional status, many in nursing have tried to enrich nursing's conception of itself. But, according to Marlene Kramer's research, students who enter nursing schools continue to hold outdated conceptions about nursing, and they leave school still believing that "real" nursing is *only* bedside nursing.[21] Nevertheless, many nurses think that nursing must develop a more complex self-conception and move beyond the "downstairs maid" image symbolized by the nurse's uniform, which Dorothy Mereness once described as a house dress complete with dustcap. To Carol Garant,

> "real" nurses do not necessarily wear white uniforms and caps, carry lamps or long stemmed roses at graduation, give bedpans, bed baths, injections, and enemas or "push" pills. "Real" nurses also engage in research, deliver babies, teach health, do group and individual psychotherapy, work with drug addicts, administer anesthesia, own their own mental health centers, and "hang out shingles" in private practice. "Real" nurses also diagnose patients and clients—no longer do they *presume* patients to be dead or are their clients *thought* to be pregnant. "Real" nurses use their brains as well as their hands and feet.[22]

Garant's "real" nurse relates directly to the advanced practice or the nurse practitioner model of practice, which is now firmly established.

By 1986 more than twenty thousand nurses were qualified for advanced practice as master's prepared clinical nurse specialists.[23] The expanded role of nursing, in providing nurse practitioners with both a wider range of activities and an acknowledged role in decision-making, offers meaningful incentives to other nurses to acquire new skills and a means for upward mobility in clinical nursing practice. Thus, while the nurse practitioner model of practice may change the economic distance between medicine and nursing only slightly, it reduces some of the social and educational distance between the two professions, both through the nurse's clinical experiences and formal education and through her exhibition of clinical skills that demand recognition.

But while particular physicians may respect an individual nurse's expertise and judgment, the struggle for the control of nursing continues. It can be seen at the national level, for example, in the split between the ANA and the American Medical Association over the AMA's proposal to train registered care technologists, a move that the ANA regarded as being designed to "strengthen medicine's control over bedside care givers . . . and undermine nursing's efforts to standardize nursing education."[24]

Supporting an up-to-date conception of nursing, as described above, however, are social changes related to the women's movement. While most nurses isolated themselves from the women's movement during the 1970s, and while some feminists have, at times, rejected nursing because of its stereotypical handmaiden image, nursing has gained from the movement.[25] In analyzing the use of sexist language, feminists have helped underscore the increasing awareness of nurses that the professional image of a thoughtful, independent, well-educated, responsible nurse is incompatible with the image implied by references to staff nurses as "the girls" or "the kids" or by physicians' requests prefaced by "Hey, honey."

Conflicts between nurses and physicians arise, at times, when a nurse tries to gain and use increased skills and education or responds to interactions from a feminist point of view. To return to "Orders not to teach," Fran acknowledged her acceptance of the ideology of professionalism in nursing when she said she no longer believed that the doctors must not be questioned and by her obvious concern that the patient needed instruction which, she believed, she was prepared to give. Yet this did not automatically lead her out of the deferent role or convince her at once that teaching the patients was legitimately within the scope of her nursing practice; nor did it instantly convince her that she must bridge the communication gap between herself and the physicians.

In summary, nurse-physician conflicts are affected by the historical legacy of the health care professions, the expanding scope of nursing practice, the socioeconomic and educational distance between nurses and doctors, and the ideology of professionalism in nursing. Although these are not all the factors involved in such relationships (and they overlap in many respects), they are major sources of tensions. These tensions at times not only contribute to nurse-physician conflicts but block ethical inquiry into them.

2. Nurse autonomy

The question, Is a nurse free to act upon her own judgment? arose in both cases previously described in this chapter and is a central concern in the following cases. As suggested in Chapter 3, free action as well as rational deliberation and moral reflection are necessary if a person is to be ethically autonomous. Yet, for nurses in certain situations, free action remains problematic, as in the following case.

4.3 Disagreement with a feeding order

Cheryl Pulec worked during her last two years in school as a nursing assistant on a gynecology floor in a large university medical center and has had six months' experience in a neonatal intensive care unit as a registered nurse. When the unit is busy, she cares for two babies, but she has cared for only one baby, Matthew Brenner, since his admission a week ago.

Last night, one of the residents wrote orders to start feeding Matthew and then left the unit. When Cheryl read them, she thought they were "crazy orders" since they included "giving sterile water over twenty-four hours." She had never seen such a beginning feeding order, and she was concerned about possible fluid and electrolyte problems. She told another resident in the unit her grounds for objecting and that she felt uneasy about beginning Matthew's feeding according to that plan. Nevertheless, he told her to proceed according to the written orders.

Even though directed by two doctors to start the feedings, Cheryl thought that since she still disagreed with the feeding plan, she would not begin it. She liked her staff nurse position and tried to do a good job, which included, of course, carrying out medical orders and working well with the doctors: but she thought Matthew's well-being was more important than the possible repercussions she might suffer for her efforts to get the orders changed and her refusal to carry them out. Therefore, she considered whether she should approach a third resident and repeat her reasons for not wanting to carry out the feeding order.

Ms. Pulec's reasons for acting in this situation are based on her obligations to Matthew as a health care provider, to the hospital as an employee, and to the physicians as a co-worker. When she became a registered nurse, she assumed an obligation to provide safe, effective, and morally responsible care to her clients. Therefore, she has a duty to do her best for Matthew Brenner. She is well within her legal obligations, as defined by the state nursing practice act and her contract with the hospital, to question any medical order and to refrain from implementing it if, in her judgment, the order is unsafe. Nevertheless, since nurses have traditionally obeyed physicians, she recognizes that the physicians expect her to carry out the orders as a part of the traditional nursing role. Finally, Ms. Pulec believes she must act so as to maintain her self-respect as an autonomous, thoughtful, reliable person.

Ms. Pulec has time to make a thoughtful decision since the risk to Matthew is very slight if she delays the feedings briefly. The question is, Will Matthew be harmed by the feedings in any significant or lasting way? Given Ms. Pulec's limited experience—she has been employed in the neonatal intensive care unit for only six months—her opposition to the feedings perhaps should not be given the weight of the two resident physicians' decision in favor of the sterile water feedings since they have had more education and clinical experience than she. Her apparent lack of experience, however, is offset by her scientific education regarding fluids and electrolytes, her study of other babies during her employment, and her acute awareness of Matthew's needs since he has been the only baby in her care during the past week. It is possible that the first physician wrote the order while thinking not specifically of Matthew but of babies generally, and that the second physician, not seeing a gross error in the feeding order, elected to let the orders stand. Given the second physician's decision not to act, and given that Ms. Pulec based her decision on her brief nursing experience and on the negative evidence that the order was wrong because she had never seen any like it, she could conclude that the feeding order might be within the limits of acceptable medical practice, even if it were not ideal. Therefore, she might proceed without causing Matthew undue harm. But even though the feedings are probably not unsafe, Ms. Pulec is convinced that they are not best for Matthew since they may upset his fluid and electrolyte balance.

Ms. Pulec's obligations to Matthew and the physicians are in conflict. She cannot obey the orders and thus act as a loyal subordinate to the physicians in the traditional sense and simultaneously meet Matthew's needs as she has defined them. But a nurse's primary obligations, in the end, are to clients, not physicians. The reason a nurse works with a physician and his medical treatment plan is to help provide a client with the best possible health care.[26] Whatever the strength of the historical legacy and the dominating status of medicine, whenever a nurse faces a choice between obligation to a physician and obligation to a client, she must recognize that her obligation to a client is primary. In Ms. Pulec's case, her obligation to the physicians is clearly secondary to, and based upon, her obligation to the baby; the choice of overriding the obligation to the physicians carries only a relatively small risk. While Ms. Pulec may lose her reputation as a congenial worker, Matthew has much to gain if, in fact, a different feeding order would be better for him.

Ms. Pulec's situation, like other situations in which a nurse considers alternatives to what a physician has ordered, rests at some point on a wide "spectrum of urgency," that is, on a continuum of cases in which the available time to make decisions varies. The spectrum begins at one end with problems that may be solved at a leisurely pace, allowing time for reflection, collection of further data, debate, and discussion, and ends at the other end with urgent questions that demand quick solutions and immediate actions. The low-urgency end of the spectrum includes such situations as those in which a physician and nurse disagree about the correct answer to a question that a young pregnant woman asks in trying to decide if she should choose a home delivery attended by a midwife or a hospital delivery attended by a physician. In such a situation, the physician, nurse, and client have several months to study and to debate all aspects of the situation. The high-urgency end of the spectrum includes emergency situations in which a physician and a nurse disagree about an order for actions that must be carried out immediately. For example, a nurse and a physician may choose to allocate care differently for three accident victims admitted simultaneously to an emergency room.

The "spectrum of urgency" can be used as a guideline for nurses who question a physician's orders in situations involving practices that fall within the range of generally acceptable medical care. In situations in which urgency is low, when ample time is available for reasonable reflection and discussion, a rule-utilitarian argument (see Chapter 2, Section 2, Part A) that nurses obey doctors as the best course of action to insure the best overall outcome for clients is much less strong than in emergency situations. To return to Case 4.3, if Ms. Pulec agrees with the utilitarian goal of the greatest happiness for the largest number of patients, a goal supported by many hospitals in numerous policies, she might agree that she should be obedient and follow all physicians' orders that appear to fall within the broad range of acceptable practice, including the feeding order that a second physician supported. She could conclude that all nurses should follow all such physicians' orders because most of the time the orders would be correct; the greatest number of persons would thus be effectively served.

Two problems with this argument, however, immediately come to light. First, physicians' orders, like all human judgments, are sometimes wrong. If a nurse blindly followed all of them, harm to the patient could result, as the research study described in Chapter 1 illustrated. Thus, insofar as a nurse has an obligation to follow a doctor's orders, it is only a prima facie obligation and may be overridden in certain circumstances by other factors. A nurse must be careful not to confuse a well-grounded prima facie obligation with blind faith. Second, nurses who operate under such a regime may become automatons, unable to make the responsible decisions that are necessary for high-quality nursing care. Thus, while in the short run the result might seem to be the greatest happiness for the greatest number of patients, over the long run, the harm to some patients and the poor quality of care delivered by automatons would significantly compromise overall happiness. The idea that nurses should obey physicians, when examined in low-urgency cases, appears to have little to be said for it apart from appeals to tradition.

The nearer a case is to the other end of the spectrum, the greater the need for a nurse to follow a physician's orders without debate. In general, a physician's medical expertise should be greater than a nurse's medical expertise since a nursing education, by its very nature, focuses upon nursing rather than medicine. In most emergency situations the greatest number of satisfactory outcomes for clients will occur if a nurse refrains from blocking acceptable orders and cooperates in delivering quick, efficient help, although she might judge that a particular course is not the one that she believes would be best. The main goal in a crisis is to provide adequate help quickly, and this goal would obviously be blocked by lengthy debate and discussion. In a cool moment after the crisis has passed, the nurse should engage the physician in a discussion regarding the feasibility and worth of alternative actions which may have been more appropriate. A nurse, especially an experienced nurse, may be more knowledgeable than a physician about a specific client, situation, or procedure. Through calm, rational discussion the nurse and the physician might learn from each other and agree how best to manage similar crises in the future.

Although a nurse generally presumes that a physician is right in an emergency situation, there are nonetheless limits to what can reasonably be presumed. When the medical care a physician orders clearly constitutes unacceptable practice, a nurse is obligated to disobey orders. For example, an emergency room nurse and a resident physician disagreed about whether the use of a local anesthetic was acceptable practice in the case of a five-year-old girl who had suffered a huge vaginal laceration. After the doctor had ordered the nurse to pry the terrified and wildly struggling girl's legs apart while he repeatedly tried but failed to inject a local anesthetic, the nurse, believing that such treatment was unacceptable because of the child's fear and pain and the size of the laceration, refused to continue assisting the physician. She demanded that another resident physician be called, which resulted in the child being taken to surgery and given a general anesthetic.[27] Given the psychic trauma caused the girl by repeated attempts to repair the laceration, further efforts in the emergency room clearly fell outside the bounds of acceptable practice.

In summary, if an order for action is clearly outside acceptable medical practice, a nurse should not obey it even in an emergency and should seek safe care for the client from another source as did the emergency room nurse in the previous example. If a physician's order is within the wide range of acceptable practice and time is pressing, the nurse should obey that order, even if she would prefer another course of action, and she should discuss the matter with the physician later.[28] At the lower levels of the spectrum of urgency—and most medical care allows some time for consideration—the nurse should calmly and rationally discuss with the physician those orders that she questions, including orders that fall within the wide range of acceptable medical practice, in order to provide the best possible care for each client. Given these guidelines, the nurse in the feeding order case, Ms. Pulec, should discuss the situation with her nurse manager to see if she missed something a more experienced nurse would know. Then she should call the first resident to explain her reasons for not following the feeding order in the hope that he will cancel the order and write a new one. The first resident ought to learn his order is being questioned; in addition, Ms. Pulec's asking a third resident could confuse the situation.[29]

In the following case, a nurse who is striving to be ethically autonomous in her practice confronts the complexities of autonomy in nursing, including the question of free action.

4.4 Is it right?

Ann Fiske enjoyed the first seven months on a medical unit, her first nursing position. But since being assigned as primary nurse to Mr. James Bering, a seventy-one-year-old retired widower suffering from a rapidly growing, highly malignant sarcoma of the peritoneum, Ann is finding her responsibilities unsettling. Mr. Bering's days and nights are filled with intractable pain, and despite her care and that of others, he suffers much from insomnia and discomfort. Further, his various medications often cloud his mind. During the past two days, Mr. Bering has talked briefly with Ann of his approaching death.

Today, after Mr. Bering's attending physician, Dr. Rhodes, checked Mr. Bering and spoke at length with Mr. Bering's two children, he increased Mr. Bering's morphine dosage. As he handed the chart to Ann, he said, "I want you to begin this now." Ann understood that, although it would provide additional control for Mr. Bering's pain, the increased morphine dosage would further depress his already depressed respiration rate and, as a side effect, increase the likelihood that he would soon die. Although the likelihood of an earlier death for Mr. Bering was not in itself troubling to Ann, she doubted whether Mr. Bering had explicitly consented to this course of action.

Since Ann knew that Dr. Rhodes was a highly respected physician with years of experience, she hesitated a moment before asking him whether Mr. Bering had given his consent. When she did ask, Dr. Rhodes quietly explained that he had not discussed the issue with Mr. Bering because to do so would be needlessly cruel. Nor, he said, would he saddle the relatives with "the burden of making this decision." In fact, he added, "I never ask families to make decisions that would leave them feeling guilty." Then he said firmly, "I've made hundreds of these difficult decisions—sometimes it's a little less potassium, sometimes too much oxygen, sometimes morphine—and you, if you're a good nurse, should know better than to say anything. If you're not going to be a good nurse, I'd better call your supervisor."

Recognizing both that Dr. Rhodes expected all nurses to follow his orders unquestioningly and that he was one of the nursing supervisor's favorite physicians, Ann thought that if she balked at his orders she would face problems not only with him but with the nursing supervisor. Ann did not want to make trouble for herself, but she was concerned about Mr. Bering. She asked herself, Is it right for us to administer treatment that may hasten his death without his or his family's explicit permission?[30]

Ann and Dr. Rhodes disagree on questions of ethics and values. The conflict centers on the ethical choice between simply administering the additional morphine, which will not only reduce pain but perhaps hasten death, and trying to determine whether, when informed of the consequences, Mr. Bering (or, if he is not competent, his family) wants the increased morphine. Underlying the first alternative are the values of reducing pain, suffering, and guilt; underlying the second are the values of self-determination and informed consent.

Inasmuch as this issue turns on a conflict of values, when Ann questions Dr. Rhodes' decision, she does not challenge his specialized medical knowledge and expertise. Nothing in Dr. Rhodes' training certified him as an "expert" on ethical matters, if indeed there are any such experts. Furthermore, in asking for his reasons and even subjecting them to critical examination, Ann is not venturing into matters beyond her competence.

If Ann discusses the matter further with Dr. Rhodes, it will be to her advantage if her position is based on rational deliberation and moral reflection rather than on intuition or "gut feeling." Dr. Rhodes has already given reasons for preferring his course of action. If she is to maintain her position, Ann must be able to provide stronger reasons why the doctor should obtain informed consent before she proceeds with the morphine medication.

The main consideration to which Ann could appeal is the respect that is owed to Mr. Bering as a person. Mr. Bering has a right to accept or refuse various forms of medical treatment. This right is based on the right to self-determination, which is itself based on the respect that is owed persons as choosing beings. Mr. Bering, so far as we can tell, has not chosen to die sooner rather than later. He knows that death is imminent, but he has not consented that it be hastened. To administer the additional morphine is, of course, likely to hasten his death. Therefore, to provide medical treatment that will, as a side effect, be likely to hasten Mr. Bering's death without his explicit informed consent is to deny his freedom and dignity as a choosing being, as a person.

On the surface, this argument for Ann's position is at least as strong as Dr. Rhodes' argument for administering the morphine without further discussion with the patient or his family. If Ann is to be thorough in her deliberations, however, she must be able to anticipate and respond to the objections Dr. Rhodes might make against her reasoning. First, he might emphasize that although the principle of informed consent is fine in theory, it is often inapplicable in practice. Self-determination and informed consent presuppose that the patient (or, if not the patient, the patient's family) is capable of rational deliberation in such situations; but this, according to Dr. Rhodes, is not often the case—and is certainly not the case with Mr. Bering or his family. Mr. Bering, Dr. Rhodes might claim, is not mentally competent to make this decision himself, and his family would be plagued by guilt if it were to be thrust upon them.

The question of patient autonomy is a complex conceptual-empirical matter.[31] If Ann is to neutralize this objection, she must be able to show that

Mr. Bering or his family is capable of understanding and deciding this matter, or at least that Dr. Rhodes has not yet demonstrated their incapability. Since patient autonomy must be presumed, the burden is on him to show why they are incapable.

A second possible objection to Ann's line of reasoning is that increasing the morphine dosage will maximize happiness. Appealing to the principle of utility, Dr. Rhodes could point out that not only would Mr. Bering's suffering be diminished but his family would be spared the agonies of decision-making and of witnessing Mr. Bering's pain and distress. Furthermore, since obtaining informed consent takes valuable time, if Dr. Rhodes and Ann did not seek it, they would have more time to provide the high-quality medical and nursing care that they are able to give.

As is often the case, however, these utilitarian considerations may be neutralized by others. In the long run, for example, it is likely that if the practice of possibly hastening the deaths of suffering persons without their explicit consent were to become more widely practiced and more widely known, the result would be loss of trust throughout the health care system. Any suffering person with a terminal illness might wonder whether this or that treatment would hasten his or her death. Such loss of trust might create anxieties and a fear of medicine that would actually reduce the net balance of happiness.

Thus, as matters stand, Ann's doubts appear to be well grounded. The question remains, however, whether Ann can be ethically autonomous, which requires that she be free to act upon the results of her reasoning and moral reflection.

Let us suppose that Dr. Rhodes either refuses to discuss the matter with Ann any further, or that after discussing it he stands by his initial decision. Let us also assume that he has little evidence that Mr. Bering and his family are in no condition to decide the matter themselves and that Ann has good reason to believe that at least one of them is perfectly capable of doing so. If, then, Ann were to give the morphine injections at this point, she would be acting contrary not only to what she regards as Mr. Bering's rights but also to her own deeply held moral convictions. She would be compromising her integrity as a person. What, then, should she do?

An adage in ethics that "ought implies can" is pertinent to Ann's dilemma. It is usually taken to mean that if we say someone morally ought to do something, it must be true that he or she can do it. If a person cannot do something, it makes no sense or is morally unjust to say that he or she morally should do it. Thus, if a person cannot swim we cannot say that he or she ought to have gone into deep water to rescue a drowning swimmer. If a physician is prevented at gunpoint by a terrorist from treating a wounded hostage, we cannot say that he ought nevertheless to have treated the hostage. Thus, in determining what Ann ought to do in the case before us, we must try to clarify what she can actually do.

Deciding what she can do, however, is difficult because Ann's freedom of action is in doubt. On the one hand, perhaps Ann is being coerced into following Dr. Rhodes' orders. If, for example, she resists giving the injection, Dr. Rhodes may find a number of ways to make her job very unpleasant. He may also complain about her to her nursing supervisor, who may have considerable power over her. Because she is relatively new in this unit, and this is her first position, Ann may fear losing her job. If there were no other hospital in town, and Ann were the sole support of her ailing mother, the risk of losing her job would indeed be serious. Thus, in light of such de facto conditions, we might conclude that Ann is not entirely free to act in accord with her ethical views.

On the other hand, perhaps Ann finds herself in more favorable circumstances. Experienced and with a strong record, she believes that being harassed by Dr. Rhodes or being reprimanded or disciplined by her nursing supervisor is a small price to pay for protecting Mr. Bering's rights and for acting in accord with her deepest ethical convictions. Suppose, too, that she is not committed to living in the area where she is currently employed or that she could readily find another nursing position if her job became too unpleasant. If this were Ann's situation, we might conclude that she is not being coerced into following Dr. Rhodes' orders. As a result, she is free to act in accord with her considered moral views, and therefore she ought to do so.

The main question, then, is this: Is Ann free to act in accord with the results of her rational deliberation and moral reflection or is she coerced into giving the morphine injections? If we conclude that she is not free to act in accord with the results of her rational deliberation and moral reflection, then she is neither fully autonomous nor fully responsible for giving the injections. If, however, we conclude that, despite the circumstances, she is free to act in accord with her considered ethical judgments, then she is both autonomous and responsible for what she does.

We have no simple solution to the problem of free action in nursing. On the one hand, we admire nurses who risk punitive responses from physicians and others for the sake of patients' rights and their own moral integrity. We think such nurses should generally be commended and supported. On the other hand, we recognize that many nurses face situations in which it would be extremely difficult to withstand the threat of punitive responses. Moreover, we do not believe that nurses should have to be heroines or make harsh personal sacrifices to do what they have good reason to believe is morally right or to preserve their moral integrity. So the nurse in this case may simply have to make the best of a very bad situation. But such situations may be avoidable. In Section 3, we suggest some systematic changes in the nurse-physician relationship that can reduce both the incidence and the severity of such predicaments.

The next case provides an additional illustration of the complexities of free action. Here, a nurse's independent actions resulted in an unfortunate nurse-physician conflict.

4.5 Giving information to clients

Mrs. Tuma, a junior-college nursing instructor, requested that she be assigned to care for Mrs. W., a fifty-nine-year-old woman acutely ill with myelogenous leukemia, so that one of her nursing students could learn about chemotherapy. When the physician told Mrs. W. that she was dying and that the only hope for prolonging her life was chemotherapy, he described the painful and disfiguring side effects of the treatment as well as the possibility of doing nothing. Although Mrs. W. had some degree of mental impairment caused by her condition, the physician believed that she was rational when he obtained both her and her family's consent for chemotherapy.

As Mrs. Tuma prepared the first chemotherapy dose, her student reported that she had found Mrs. W. crying. When Mrs. Tuma tried to comfort Mrs. W., Mrs. W. explained that she had fought leukemia for twelve years with God's help, by faithfully practicing the Mormon religion, by eating natural foods, and by avoiding drugs and stimulants. At this point Mrs. Tuma responded by discussing natural remedies for cancer with Mrs. W. She also determined, however, that Mrs. W. still consented to the chemotherapy and consequently initiated the chemotherapy intravenously as ordered. But Mrs. W. pleaded with Mrs. Tuma to return in the evening to discuss various natural treatments with her son and daughter-in-law.

When the daughter-in-law learned of the scheduled evening meeting with Mrs. Tuma, she phoned the doctor, who told her to attend the meeting and get the nurse's name. Early in the evening, the doctor phoned an order to suspend the chemotherapy because of Mrs. W.'s changed attitude. After Mrs. Tuma's discussion with the family, which included chemotherapy and its side effects, alternatives provided by natural foods and herbs, the unavailability of Laetrile in the United States, and Mrs. W.'s problem of obtaining blood transfusions if she were to terminate chemotherapy, all agreed that Mrs. W.'s best course was to continue with chemotherapy.

Later in the evening the physician ordered the chemotherapy to be resumed. The next day he demanded that the college remove Mrs. Tuma from her position, which the college authorities consequently did. He also complained to the hospital, which notified the State Board of Nurses, which, in turn, initiated a petition for the suspension or revocation of Mrs. Tuma's license. The Hearing Officer for the Board of Nurse Examiners determined that Mrs. Tuma had interfered with the physician-patient relationship, an act that constituted unprofessional conduct, and the Board suspended her license for six months. Mrs. W. died two weeks after the chemotherapy was started.[32]

An examination of this case reveals arguments that both support and criticize Mrs. Tuma's actions. A nurse, *as a person*, has the right to function autonomously as does every other person. Every person—client, physician, or nurse—can demand that he or she be recognized as a person worthy of dignity and respect with the right to act autonomously and to make justifiable claims on others for these general rights. However, the physician did not lodge a complaint against her as a person. Rather, in her discussions with Mrs. W., Mrs. Tuma had acted *as a nurse*. As Sister A. Teresa Stanley pointed out in her discussion of this case, no ethical dilemma would have resulted had a neighbor discussed the same information with Mrs. W.[33]

Yet Mrs. W.'s questions about alternative treatments made a claim upon Mrs. Tuma for information; Mrs. Tuma agreed since she believed that she, as a nurse, should meet Mrs. W.'s needs. Both Mrs. Tuma and Mrs. W. perceived Mrs. Tuma's role as that of a well-informed care provider, someone who knew about and could explain alternative cancer treatments. Further, the professional nursing role, as Mrs. Tuma understood it, allowed her to insure that a client's consent to therapy was fully informed.[34] As Sally Gadow has persuasively argued, "Patients can be assisted in reaching decisions which express their complex totality as individuals only by nurses who themselves act out of the same explicit self-unity, allowing no dimension of themselves to be exempt from the professional relation."[35] Acceptance of this notion, with its requirements for recognition of a nurse *as a person*, necessitates that a nurse be allowed to be ethically autonomous in her nursing role, that is, that her actions be free from coercion or manipulation, be the result of rational choice, and be in accord with her own values and principles.

Clearly, however, Mrs. Tuma had placed herself in a risky situation. Even though she included in her definition of the nursing role that nurses function autonomously, she recognized from the outset that not all persons, including the physician, shared that viewpoint.[36] In her state, the nursing role did not confer upon nurses the privilege of autonomous action in a situation such as that involving Mrs. W. The Hearing Officer for the Board of Nurse Examiners disallowed as evidence the American Nurses' Association Code for Nurses because the Board had not adopted it, as well as any testimony or definitions by the ANA. He determined that Mrs. Tuma had interfered with the physician-patient relationship, which constituted unprofessional conduct. Thus, the Board judged that Mrs. Tuma did not have the privilege of functioning autonomously in her role as a nurse in this situation since her actions interfered with the physician-patient relationship.[37] To the Board, the nurse-client relationship apparently played a secondary role.[38]

A nurse in a situation similar to that of Mrs. Tuma could respond in a number of different ways. She could assume the traditional deferential role and do nothing autonomously. Or she could play an expert doctor-nurse game, pretend that she knew nothing when the client asked, and later, if possible, indirectly get the doctor to discuss alternative cancer treatments with the client. Or she could work as if she had a collaborative relationship with the physician and view his presentation of only two choices (chemotherapy with its terrible side effects or no treatment) as morally unacceptable while at the same time recognizing that such a presentation of choices fell well within the scope of acceptable medical practice. She could, for example, contact the physician and try to persuade him that the patient and her family had a right to a discussion of alternative treatments. If he did not want to participate in such a discussion, she could offer to do it herself. If he not only refused to participate himself but also told her that she was not to discuss this matter with the patient, she could, as an act of conscientious refusal, decide to meet with the patient and her family anyway (see Section 5). If the physician filed a complaint, a State Board of Nurses still might react as it did in Mrs. Tuma's case. But such a nurse would now be perceived as having acted collaboratively as a professional who notified colleagues of her intentions and shared her reasoning with them.

3. Collaboration

Collaboration implicitly assumes that nurses, in their nursing roles, like physicians, in their medical roles, are morally autonomous or self-determining. Collaboration is crucially important if nurses are to meet their social obligation to provide high-quality nursing care because, as nurses, they are often in the middle of indeterminate and complex health care situations.[39] The following case summarizes such a situation, one in which nurses and physicians disagree as to whether they should continue aggressive treatment.

4.6 Should treatment be stopped?

Susan Cory is a twenty-nine-year-old critical care staff nurse who enjoys the nursing challenges of a medical intensive care unit in a large medical center. Her reputation among the nursing and medical staffs is that of a caring and exceptionally competent nurse. At present, however, she is at odds with most persons working in the ICU over whether aggressive treatment should be continued for Marsha Hocking, a severely brain-damaged, young, single woman her own age, a victim of viral encephalitis. Marsha's parents are so overwhelmed by the situation that they are relying completely on the judgment of the care providers. Susan and the medical and nursing staffs agree as to the medical details of the case, that is, the extent of brain damage and the very poor prognosis.

After careful deliberation, Susan concluded that aggressive treatment in Marsha's case should be reduced sharply because no hope remained for her recovery. Susan based her decision on her belief that no one would want to be kept alive in Marsha's condition and therefore to continue treating her was morally wrong. Without aggressive treatment, which includes artificial ventilation, Marsha would die quickly.

Susan has asked the other nurses and the physicians to think about her recommendation. Some nurses agree with Susan. Others agree with most of the physicians, including the one in charge of Marsha's case, that now is not the time to give up. They point to a variety of reasons for continuing aggressive treatment—Marsha's age, the sudden onset of the disease, her previously excellent condition, and their personal beliefs about the value of life. Throughout the discussion, which has continued for two weeks, Susan has not requested of the ICU nurse manager that she be excused from the case, an infrequent request but one that has been honored in the ICU for other nurses.[40]

In complex cases like this, an authoritarian conception of the physician-nurse relationship is best replaced by a collaborative conception. In collaborating to meet the health-related needs of patients while respecting their rights, physicians and nurses, as well as patients and families, share knowledge, discuss differences, and work together with mutual respect.[41]

This is not to deny, however, that sometimes authoritarian structures are needed and morally justifiable. In our discussion of the spectrum of urgency, we indicated that emergency situations often require such structures. In addition, as John Ladd has suggested, specialized contexts such as the operating room are highly suited to the exercise and recognition of medical authority.

In an operating room, the authority of the surgeon might be likened to the authority of the conductor of an orchestra: the surgeon is the chief performer and the one who "orchestrates" the proceeding. Let us grant that the aim of the procedure is to save the patient's life, i.e., a morally worthy goal. But here, as with the orchestra, we are dealing with a precisely defined, limited enterprise involving goals that we may assume are shared by all the parties involved, or, to be more nearly accurate, we should say that they ought to be shared by all of them.[42]

As Ladd goes on to point out, goals in most other health care contexts are not this simply defined. And where the goals of patients, physicians, and nurses do not clearly converge, both the need and the justification for authoritarian structures are considerably weakened.

When authoritarian relationships between physicians and nurses cannot be justified by the situation, we agree with Ladd's suggestion that "we try to find more 'democratic' procedures, procedures involving mutual counseling, consultation, and collaboration. Mutual accommodation and persuasion should take the place of one person['s] issuing commands to others below."[43]

If more collaborative relationships can be established, several positive results can be expected: (1) an increased likelihood that the parties will reach a well-grounded and mutually satisfactory decision; (2) an appreciation of the ethical dilemmas nurses face in being "caught in the middle"; and (3) lower medical care costs because of reduced "burnout" among nurses.

Collaboration can result in increased willingness among all parties to reach a mutually satisfactory decision. Persons who deliberate in a spirit of mutual respect share not only their ethical positions but also bits of information about a situation that all parties may not have fully known or appreciated. No matter how carefully one analyzes an ethical dilemma, it is always possible to have overlooked an important argument or fact.

If they initially disagree, nurses and physicians (and patients and families) who carefully try to hear each other out and to see matters from one another's perspective often find themselves shifting from their original positions and meeting each other halfway. In many cases, for example, one not only comes to appreciate the strength of an opposing position but also comes to recognize that one's own motives include self-interest as well as ethical considerations. Thus, it is not unlikely that Susan Cory's concern for the patient's autonomy and for efficient use of resources is heightened by her frustration with the very difficult nursing problems the patient presents. Similarly, the desire of most of the physicians to continue treatment may result in part from their desire to practice and refine certain skills. As Samuel Gorovitz has pointed out, "Skills that have been acquired at substantial personal cost are skills that people like to use. . . . There is an intrinsic payoff in satisfaction. State-of-the-art medicine is very sophisticated, and people who can do it often find it a very beautiful thing to be doing."[44] If such possible motivations are identified and discussed, there may be less self-righteousness and more willingness to reach a mutually satisfactory accommodation.

Collaboration can lead to an appreciation among all parties of the ethical dilemmas nurses face because they are "caught in the middle." A nurse is in an especially difficult position in our health care delivery system. She is expected to be a trustworthy team member who works within a hierarchical system structured from the top down, a hierarchy in which a physician is usually in command. Yet a nurse is expected to work in that health care system as if it were structured from the base up so as to meet assessed needs of the client and the client's family.[45]

Suppose the facts in Case 4.6 are altered and Susan Cory is "caught in the middle between family and physician." Suppose, for example, that mutually respectful discussion among the physicians, Susan, and other nurses does not occur. Suppose, too, that Susan has built a close and trusting relationship with the patient's mother, a frail, nervous woman with a serious heart ailment who has asked Susan for information about her daughter's condition. Let us also suppose that the physician in charge of the medical treatment plan does not wish the mother to have this information, and that he expects and trusts Susan to put the mother's questions off, or failing this, to lie to her. Finally, imagine that Susan believes that the mother has a right to the information and has strong grounds for believing she will not be harmed by it.

One can easily understand Susan's sense of frustration in such a situation. If she truthfully answers the mother, she breaks the trust of the treatment team that expects a nurse to be a dependable team player. If, however, she puts the mother off with noncommittal comments or with lies, she jeopardizes the mother's trust and her own sense of personal integrity.

Patients, their families, and physicians all presume that nurses are personally honest, open, and loyal to them. But when a nurse cannot fulfill the conflicting expectations, when she is quite literally "caught in the middle," she cannot be entirely trustworthy to all parties. On the other hand, collaboration, in which nurses and physicians present their ethical arguments to one another, share information, and deliberate in a spirit of mutual respect, helps to solve the problem of being caught in the middle between a top-down hierarchical system and an inverse system based on patients' needs.

We are not saying that a physician must always agree with whatever a nurse thinks is ethically correct. Rather, we are suggesting that physicians and nurses must respect each other as autonomous moral agents. This requires, among other responses, addressing each other's ethical concerns, mutually deliberating and reflecting upon various courses of action, and in some cases agreeing with or adjusting to the ethical views of others. There is a sense in which we can respect someone as a moral agent even when we disagree with him or her and ultimately reject his or her decision—if we hear that person out, give reasons for our views, and make good-faith efforts to show why we believe our view is better.

Collaboration also can result in lower medical care costs by reducing burnout, a well-documented problem among hospital nurses in the United States. Problems of burnout among nurses underscore the dangers of continued conflict, stress, and loss of integrity. After a few years in practice, many conscientious, sensitive, and highly skilled nurses leave nursing because they feel burned out by the stresses of their work. Replacing them is costly, since nurses must be attracted to a hospital and oriented for a time. Consequently, hospital costs rise while continual personnel turnover causes the quality of care to decline. One identified cause of nursing burnout is the difficulty many nurses have maintaining personal integrity when their ideals conflict with the real world of health care.[46]

Suppose that, in Case 4.6, the nurses and physicians do not deliberate in a spirit of mutual respect; they do not discuss whether to continue aggressive treatment for the patient, Marsha Hocking. In addition, the nurse, Susan Cory, understands that if Marsha has a cardiac arrest, Susan will be expected to "call a code." Given her understanding of the case and her ethical views, Susan believes that calling a code would be morally wrong. Suppose, also, that Susan is caring for another patient with similar problems but who is under the care of a different physician who orders less aggressive treatment and leaves directions not to resuscitate. In caring for this second patient, Susan believes she can act morally in the event of cardiac arrest. But, if Susan is the thoughtful, competent person described in Case 4.6, continued employment in such a unit, given the strikingly conflicting orders and expectations in medically similar cases, will certainly strain her sense of wholeness as a person. She cannot continue to think of herself as a nurse with integrity if situations continue to arise in which she must painfully face and agonize about inconsistencies in treatment policies.

Through collaboration among members of the health care team, the stress that nurses experience can be reduced. Positive results depend upon thoughtful, mutually satisfactory decisions, decisions that often require compromise among the various parties involved.

4. Integrity-preserving compromise

Compromise, construed as a settlement of differences in which each side makes concessions, must be clearly differentiated from being compromised, that is, to be forced to give up one's interests, principles, or integrity. To compromise does not require that a person be compromised. Nurses and physicians who deliberate in a spirit of mutual respect may be able to reach an integrity-preserving compromise. A well-grounded, integrity-preserving compromise is not to be confused with a lopsided "compromise" that merely repeats the doctor-nurse game in which a physician calls the shots and a nurse silently bites her lip.

Basic to a compromise that maintains integrity is an appreciation of the factual uncertainty and moral complexity of modern health care. In Case 4.6, it is not clear whether those advocating continued aggressive treatment or those advocating much less aggressive treatment have the more defensible position. Given the complexity of many issues in biomedical ethics and our limited knowledge and understanding of them, ethical disagreements often are not the result of simple conflicts between what is obviously right and obviously wrong. As Arthur Kuflik has pointed out:

Individuals must often base their respective moral judgments on a picture of their situation that is relevantly, but irremediably, incomplete. Their differences of opinion may have less to do with deficiencies of moral sensibility than with uncertainties that are inherent in the situation itself. . . . [Moreover] even individuals who are adequately informed and acknowledge the same fundamental principles can find themselves in disagreement when an issue engages several morally relevant considerations at the same time. In such cases the sheer complexity of the matter enables reasonable persons to form somewhat different assessments.[47]

Both of these factors, uncertainty and complexity, seem to be at the root of the disagreement in Susan Cory's case.

Susan Cory believes that no one would want to be kept alive in Marsha Hocking's condition. How can she be sure of this? Perhaps Susan and many of her acquaintances would not want to be kept alive in this condition, but what about Marsha? Susan would be on much stronger ground if she knew that before becoming ill Marsha had shared this view, but she does not have such knowledge. Similarly, those who are opting for continued aggressive treatment appeal to factors that are relevant to possible recovery—the patient's age, the sudden onset of the disease, her previously excellent health—but they have little else to go on when estimating her chances of survival. Perhaps more important, they cannot predict her future level of consciousness and activity even if she does survive. If they knew she would survive and that her ensuing condition would be good, or at least tolerable, they might be on stronger ground. They do not have such knowledge, however.

Moreover, apart from empirical uncertainty, each side can appeal to morally relevant considerations to support its view. Susan can appeal (although without full assurance) to the patient's right to autonomy and, perhaps, to the inefficient use of medical resources. The latter appeal will be considerably strengthened if the ICU is full or if other patients in the ICU are likely to benefit from the increased attention the staff can devote to them because they will not be doing so much for Marsha. Those taking the opposing view can invoke the value of each human life and the importance of their roles as protectors and preservers of life. Each side, then, may invoke ethical considerations on its behalf. If, in this case and in others similarly clouded by empirical uncertainty and moral complexity, health care workers can recognize the nature of their situation, they may be able to reach a well-grounded, mutually respectful accommodation that preserves the integrity of both sides.

First, each party may be persuaded to relinquish her or his original view and to replace it with a mutually agreeable new position. If both parties deliberate rationally and conclude that a third position is superior to their respective initial positions, they can adopt it with no loss of integrity. Strictly speaking, this would not be a compromise. Neither side would be making a concession to the other. Each would be embracing what is now believed to be the best position consistent with her or his own values and principles.

Collaborative discussion can also result in agreement when only one party changes positions. To change positions and to agree with another's views on the basis of ethical discussion does not lead to a loss of integrity if the new position is accepted autonomously and based on a reconsideration or re-evaluation of the applicability of one's own moral principles. Such an accommodation might, however, lead to questions of "saving face," especially if both parties have publicly staked their reputations on their initial positions. In such situations, the person shifting positions could be supported if both disputants clearly explained to all involved that the agreed-upon position or action, although initially advocated by only one person, is, on reconsideration, consistent with the moral views of both parties.

A compromise occurs when neither party gives up her or his original position but both agree to a decision based not only upon what they individually judge ought to be done but upon what they think ought to be done in light of their conflict and other values that they both esteem. Retaining one's original position and yet acting in accord with a compromise that makes some concessions to an opposing position may appear to present a difficulty. Does not this amount to being compromised, that is, having to give up one's principles or integrity?

To see how a compromise may be integrity-preserving it is important, following a suggestion of Kuflik, to distinguish (1) what Susan Cory or the physician believes ought to be done in this case, leaving aside for the moment that they disagree, from (2) what each judges ought to be done all things considered, when the things to be considered include their disagreement:

When an issue is in dispute there is more to be considered than the issue itself—for example, the importance of peace, the presumption against settling matters by force, the intrinsic good of participating in a process in which each side must hear the other side out and try to see matters from the other's point of view, the extent to which the matter does admit reasonable differences of opinion and the significance of a settlement in which each party feels assured of the other's respect for its own seriousness and sincerity in the matter.[48]

These considerations reflect values and principles that many of us hold dear and that partially determine who we are and what we stand for. If we suppose that Susan Cory and the physician hold them too, then it is not so clear that agreeing to a compromise constitutes a threat to their integrity. On the contrary, taking into consideration all their values and principles together with the fact that they disagree, a compromise solution may be more integrity-preserving than any available alternative.

The main point is that one's identity is constituted in part by a complex constellation of occasionally conflicting values and principles. In difficult cases it will not always be possible to act in accord with all of them. After as much consideration as the situation will allow, we will often pursue that course of action that seems, on balance, to follow from the preponderance of our central and most highly cherished values and principles. "Where ultimate values are irreconcilable," Isaiah Berlin has written, "clear-cut solutions cannot, in principle, be found. To decide rationally in such situations is to decide in the light of general ideals, the over-all pattern of life pursued by a man or a group or a society."[49]

Given the factual uncertainty and moral complexity characterizing the disagreement between Susan Cory and the physician, it seems unlikely that either can regard her or his position on the patient's treatment as more central or well grounded than the network of values and principles having to do with mutual respect, the acknowledgment of reasonable differences, not settling matters by force or rank, and so on. Thus, if integrity requires that they act in accord with the preponderance of their most basic values and principles, they may in this case agree to a proposed compromise.

Thus, if in Case 4.6 Susan and those wanting to continue aggressive treatment could find a position that more or less splits the difference between them and is in accord with the preponderance of their other values, they might be able to take this position without compromising their integrity. That is, such mutual accommodation would allow them to work together and respect each other while not requiring them to relinquish their original views.

In this case, an acceptable compromise might take the form of an agreement to continue treatment for a specified period and then to review the patient's condition and prognosis and the effective use of resources. If, after this period, certain changes made continued aggressive treatment appear to be a significantly more favorable option than it is at present, such treatment should continue. If there were no such changes, treatment should become less aggressive. If Susan Cory were to agree to this compromise, she would do so while fully preserving her ethical autonomy and personal integrity.

This is not, however, to say that the matter is fully settled. Although Susan Cory and the physician may agree that compromise at this point makes the best of a bad situation, they may try to ensure that the same situation does not arise in the future. Thus, each may make subsequent efforts to practice in settings where his or her colleagues are more likely to share his or her particular views on the treatment of patients like Marsha Hocking, or, each may continue to try to convince the other of the correctness of his or her view. If all co-workers agreed with their respective positions or if the decisions were ones they alone were qualified to make, they would act otherwise: Susan Cory would immediately call a halt to aggressive treatment while the physician would require that it continue indefinitely. As long as they must work together, and as long as neither can persuade the other of the correctness of his or her views, they may still arrive at an integrity-preserving compromise if they consider the full range of their important values and principles.

Such a compromise actually occurred in the real-life Susan Cory case. The nurses and physicians agreed to continue treatment for a specified period and then to review the patient's condition and their resources. All agreed that, after this period, if no change had occurred, treatment would be less aggressive. Thus, all members, nurses as well as physicians, maintained their personal integrity.[50]

5. Conscientious refusal

Placing a situation somewhere along the spectrum of urgency suggests one way for a nurse to begin to reflect upon when to question a physician's order. Further, as our previous discussion of the spectrum of urgency indicates, a nurse has the duty to override a medical order that is clearly outside acceptable medical practice and that may jeopardize a client in some way. In the following case, the nurse based her decision on her medical knowledge, discounted the risk that her actions might jeopardize her position as a nurse, and followed her own judgment without hesitation.

4.7 Emergency room

When Valerie Workman was graduated in 1965 from a university school of nursing, which she described as "an older school," she believed what she had been taught—when a doctor gives an order, follow it. But she no longer follows orders unquestioningly; she now questions doctors much more thoroughly, even though she recognizes that they often "aren't exactly thrilled that I question their judgment." In describing herself and other nurses, she says that, "the older we get, the wiser we get—sometimes."

In 1975, when Valerie was working in a hospital emergency room, Mrs. Brown, a twenty-four-year-old woman who was six months pregnant and in shock, was admitted following a serious automobile accident. The physician on duty was an older man who, Valerie felt, was not always competent in emergencies. Valerie, certain that the patient's life was in danger, suggested starting an IV, but the doctor rejected her suggestion. Alarmed, Valerie decided she must act, started the IV, initiated other emergency measures, and called for additional medical help. The physician was furious at Valerie's independent action, and she was extremely angry with him. Later, she remembers, she "got complete backing from other doctors" and the matter was dropped.

How did Valerie know not to accept the doctor's orders? Perhaps she reasoned that if a nurse believes that she has a moral obligation to meet a client's needs, then she must take risks, both by refusing to defer to a physician whose actions impede the delivery of adequate help and by taking independent emergency action. To Valerie, the young woman's chance to live must have seemed worth the risk to her own career. Had she chosen to obey orders, and had Mrs. Brown died, Valerie might not have been able to live with her conscience.

The doctor's decision against the IV differed so radically from usual emergency treatment that the other physicians in the hospital agreed that Valerie, not the doctor, had acted more appropriately. Moreover, Valerie's action was justified by well-grounded medical and ethical considerations. A nurse may sometimes be in a situation, however, in which a physician's actions fall within acceptable medical practice but the nurse may believe that she cannot be party to the disputed procedure or treatment because to do so would violate her integrity. At times, even the most cooperative and thoughtful health care workers will be unable to agree upon a compromise position. In such situations a nurse can justify a refusal to carry out an order or to participate in a procedure only on the basis of conscience. The following case focuses on what may be called "conscientious refusal."[51]

4.8 Amniocentesis to determine sex

Sylvia Hutton, a nurse practitioner with graduate-level education in genetics and counseling, is employed at the University Clinical Center. Among her many duties, she explains to women seeking amniocentesis (a procedure to obtain cells for fetal chromosome studies) what they can expect during the procedure. After the results are known, she is the person who meets with the woman and her partner to discuss the meaning of the findings. At times she meets with them alone; at other times she invites health care team members who have knowledge about the particular genetic problem facing the family.

Generally, chromosome studies are done when parents, because of the mother's advanced age or a family history of a specific genetic condition, suspect that the fetus may be affected by the condition. Before joining the Clinical Center, Sylvia thought about the implications of such work, including the possibility that most women would choose abortion if tests indicated that a child might be mentally retarded. Until recently Sylvia opposed abortion, but she now believes that abortion is permissible for parents who recognize that they do not have the strength, support, or money to rear a handicapped child; she believes that abortion in such cases may also be in the best interests of society, which must bear the cost of a person who will require a lifetime of care.

Susan Baker has asked for amniocentesis to determine the sex of her fetus.[52] Susan and her husband have two healthy, normal sons and have decided that, given the cost of rearing children, they can afford only one more child. Specifically, they want a girl to balance their family, and they plan an immediate abortion if the fetus is male.

Dr. Milton Ely, who usually performs the amniocentesis procedures, believes that the Bakers are as entitled to choose abortion as any other family and that they have the same right as other families to ask for the technical information that can be obtained through amniocentesis. But Sylvia believes that the procedure is not justified: the family has the means to raise the third child, boy or girl, and the potential cost or gain to society is basically the same whatever the sex of the fetus. Sylvia believes that to do the amniocentesis and a possible abortion is frivolous; therefore, she has decided that she must refuse to participate in any way in determining the sex of the Baker fetus.

Sylvia's supervisor knows Sylvia's objections but has asked her to meet with the Bakers, offer support, and perform her duties as usual. Dr. Ely has told Sylvia that her refusal to participate will not influence the Bakers' decision in any way, so she may as well stop making a fuss. Sylvia is afraid that if she submits to pressure from her supervisor and Dr. Ely, she will have the death of a male fetus on her conscience and she will have to admit that she is just one more spineless, manipulable nurse who has no meaningful convictions.[53]

In order to explore the question of when a nurse should (or may) use an appeal to conscience to refuse to participate in a particular procedure, we need first to analyze the notion of an appeal to conscience. For if appeals to conscience are to carry special weight, it is important to be able to distinguish them from appeals to self-interest or convenience. In a discussion of appeals to conscience, James Childress cites three cases which illustrate that "conscience is a mode of consciousness and thought about one's own acts and their value or disvalue."

1. On June 21, 1956, Arthur Miller, the playwright, appeared before the House Committee on Un-American Activities (HUAC) which was examining the unauthorized use of passports, and he was asked who had been present at meetings with Communist writers in New York City. "Mr. Chairman, I understand the philosophy behind this question and I want you to understand mine. When I say this, I want you to understand that I am not protecting the Communists or the Communist Party. I am trying to, and I will, *protect my sense of myself.* I could not use the name of another person and bring trouble on him. . . . I ask you not to

ask me that question. . . . All I can say, sir, is that *my conscience* will not permit me to use the name of another person."

2. On December 29, 1970, Governor Winthrop Rockefeller of Arkansas commuted to life imprisonment the death sentences of the fifteen prisoners then on death row. He said, "I cannot and will not turn my back on life-long Christian teachings and beliefs, merely to let history run out its course on a fallible and failing theory of punitive justice." Understanding his decision as "purely personal and philosophical," he insisted that the records of the prisoners were irrelevant to it. He continued, "I am aware that there will be reaction to my decision. However, failing to take this action while it is within my power, *I could not live with myself.*"

3. In late December, 1972, Captain Michael Heck refused to carry out orders to fly more bombing missions in Vietnam. He wrote his parents: "I've taken a very drastic step. I've refused to take part in this war any longer. *I cannot in good conscience* be a part of it." He also said, "I can live with prison easier than I can with taking part in the war . . . I would refuse even a ground job supervising the loading of bombs or refueling aircraft. I cannot be a participant . . . *a man has to answer to himself first.*"[54]

In analyzing these cases, Childress suggests that an appeal to conscience is based on a desire to preserve one's integrity or wholeness as a person (see subsection in Chapter 1, Section 4, entitled "Developing a systematic framework"). These conscientious refusers are predicting that if they were to act in certain ways they would betray themselves as being certain kinds of people having certain personal ideals and standards of conduct. Insofar as their conceptions of themselves as particular people are determined by having and abiding by certain standards of conduct, what is at stake is, as Bernard Williams argues, nothing less than personal identity.[55]

In addition, Childress suggests that appeals to conscience are personal and subjective, based on standards that one does not necessarily apply to others; are founded on a prior judgment of rightness or wrongness, since conscience itself is not a criterion of rightness or wrongness; and are motivated by personal sanction rather than external authority.[56] Sylvia's behavior in Case 4.8 seems to meet all of the conditions for making her act one of conscientious refusal. First, Sylvia spoke only for herself in this case. She did not attempt to imagine what another nurse or physician might think or feel about using amniocentesis to determine sex. Nor would she oppose or try to prevent some other nurse from performing her duties. Second, she judged that her participation would be wrong because amniocentesis for what she regarded as a trivial reason could lead to the abortion of a healthy fetus. Sylvia used her conscience as a guide only to the extent that she debated with herself; that is, when she debated with her conscience about whether she should participate or not. Sylvia's belief that the abortion of a healthy fetus for "trivial" reasons is morally wrong was the basis for her appeal to conscience. A "conflict of conscience" arose because, although she believed in general that parents have the right to choose abortion, she rejected the grounds for the decision in this particular case. The conflict here is similar to one that might be experienced by someone who endorses a strong interpretation of the right to freedom of speech while also being opposed to its being exercised to further the cause of Nazism. Third, Sylvia, like Miller, Rockefeller, and Heck in the three passages Childress cites, felt first and foremost answerable to herself (Miller: "I am trying to, and I will, protect my sense of myself"; Rockefeller: "I could not live with myself"; and Heck: "A man has to answer to himself first"). Sylvia believed that if she participated in the amniocentesis in any way she would have to acknowledge that she was a spineless person without the courage of her deepest convictions. Not only would she have felt guilt about the possible death of a healthy fetus but she also would have felt ashamed of herself for not having had the strength to act in accord with her personal ideals of conduct—ideals that in part determine her identity.[57] That her participation in this procedure is perfectly legal and that the act is not punishable by any external authority have no bearing whatever on her deliberations.

We may now turn to the general question of under what circumstances and for what reasons a nurse may appeal to her conscience and refuse to participate in a particular procedure. As the discussion of Case 4.8 indicated, a nurse may make an appeal to conscience as a last resort when she has exhausted all other arguments for justifying her action. The appeal to conscience is personal or subjective, although the moral standards on which it is based may or may not apply to other persons; it must *follow* a judgment of rightness or wrongness; and it must be based upon personal sanction rather than upon external authority. The individual nurse must determine the extent to which the act in question constitutes a rupture of her integrity or wholeness as a person or a particular self. Then she must determine whether the shame or "bad conscience" that would follow from her performance of the act constitutes a greater threat to her well-being than the possible punishment that may be forthcoming from whatever authority (agency or physician) may be displeased by her refusal. (A discussion of a nursing supervisor's response to a subordinate's appeal to conscience is included in Chapter 5.)

The question that the next case presents is whether a nurse's use of conscientious refusal is appropriate in a situation in which a physician's orders and a patient's wishes are in conflict.

4.9 Disagreeing with a full code order

Ms. Doris Winn, a staff nurse with two years' experience in a cardiac care unit, strongly disagreed with Dr. Cunningham's full code order for Mr. Chester Saukin, an eighty-seven-year-old retired farmer with a history of three heart attacks and three years of cardiac failure. Ms. Winn believed

Mr. Saukin was ready to die, for he had told her that was all he wanted. When she told Dr. Cunningham this, he simply walked away from her. She knew he always ordered full codes on all his patients. Ms. Winn understood, also, that legally she had to do the full code, but she thought it would be very hard for her.

Could Ms. Winn make an appeal to conscience and not carry out the full code order? Before discussing this question, we need to return to two earlier discussions, one concerning the spectrum of urgency and the other concerning medical decisions. When Mr. Saukin was first admitted, Ms. Winn acted as if the implied disagreement between Mr. Saukin's wishes and Dr. Cunningham's order for a full code fell at the lower end of the urgency spectrum. She had time to tell Dr. Cunningham of Mr. Saukin's statement that he was ready to die, even though the physician did not initially allow her to discuss her disagreement with the full code order. Dr. Cunningham's behavior indicated his belief that as a physician his order for the full code was indisputable. The question remains, is the decision for a full code a technical medical decision? If the answer is yes, then the nurse has little recourse; the physician's superior medical training gives him presumptive authority in technical medical decisions. If the answer is no, that the decision for a full code is a decision in the medical context but not mainly a medical decision in the technical sense, then the nurse may have something to contribute— especially when she has some reason to believe that the decision does not reflect the values and life plan of a conscious, competent adult.[58]

It is possible, however, that Dr. Cunningham's initial refusal to talk with Ms. Winn has resulted from his adherence to the letter of state law rather than from his denial of her possible contribution. The state where he and Ms. Winn practice has no "living will" legislation that would grant legal standing to a person's previously stated and documented opposition to certain kinds of intervention, such as full codes when a patient is terminally ill.[59] Further, strictly speaking, there is no legal justification for a "no code," even though the practice is not uncommon and in some medical-legal communities is accepted as standard practice. However, according to a strict interpretation of current state law, "no codes" may be considered abandonment and possibly even murder.

Many people believe that the law in this context has not kept pace with advances in life-prolonging technology. Although a conscious, competent adult has the right to accept or refuse medical treatment, in many states this right disappears as soon as the person is no longer conscious and competent. Efforts to draft legislation in this area aim to ensure that thoughtful directives with regard to life-prolonging medical intervention, made when one is conscious and competent, will be honored when one is no longer conscious and competent.

Ms. Winn strongly believes that such changes in the law are badly needed if the rights of patients are to remain in force toward the end of their lives. As she explained:

I think patients should have the right to say if they want to live and if they want to die; I think that we, as nurses and doctors, should be able to respect that. We're all here to heal people, get them well, and send them home. And if we aren't able to do that, and the patient has suffered for a long time and wants to die, I think we have to deal with our own insecurities. Maybe I don't agree with that decision, maybe the doctor doesn't. But it's the patient's; it's his life. Who has more right?

Now the question is, what should Ms. Winn do in *this* case when, let us suppose, (1) the patient, Mr. Saukin, genuinely does not want to be resuscitated, and (2) Dr. Cunningham, after finally discussing the matter with her, agrees that the law should be changed to permit "no codes"—at least when requested by patients like Mr. Saukin—but that until such changes are made he sees no alternative to responding in all such cases with full codes? On the one hand, Ms. Winn believes that she is morally required to respect Mr. Saukin's wishes and that her moral views on the matter are well grounded and shared by many others, including the patient and Dr. Cunningham. On the other hand, what many regard as antiquated laws and Dr. Cunningham's concern for the letter of the law require her to override Mr. Saukin's wishes by carrying out a full code.

Ms. Winn knows that some nurses pretend to follow the law by carrying out "slow codes." That is, when a patient who is in a situation similar to that of Mr. Saukin goes into cardiopulmonary arrest, some nurses take the defibrillator into the room slowly and fumble getting the airway in place, though in the end, as they know they must, they do the full code. The patients survive sometimes, but "only to spend a few more days in agony before finally dying," according to Ms. Winn. However, Ms. Winn does not want to compromise herself and carry out a slow code under the guise of a full one.

In deciding whether to conscientiously refuse to comply with the orders for a full code, Ms. Winn needs to explore her reasoning with other people—other nurses, her nursing supervisors, Mr. Saukin and his family, and Dr. Cunningham if possible. Thoughtful discussion with others will help ensure that she has not overlooked certain important considerations; it may also change the views of others and possibly soften or eliminate Ms. Winn's dilemma. Above all, if she decides that she simply cannot participate in a full code, she must be sure that arrangements are made to ensure that her participation is not indispensable in the carrying out of a full code. Finally, she must realize that conscientious refusal carries risks, which range from simply antagonizing others to reprimands or possibly even the loss of employment. For, as the examples of Arthur Miller, Winthrop Rockefeller, and Michael Heck, cited above, indicate, the price of personal integrity in a complex world is often extremely high. (For a discussion of the extent to which nurses ought to be involved in furthering legislative change in this and other areas, see Chapter 6.)

6. Determining responsibility

Much of nursing care occurs as part of team action that involves nurses and physicians as well as numerous other persons. The composition of various teams differs, depending upon their functions, as, for example, an operating room team, a resuscitation team, a primary care team, a rehabilitation team, or a dialysis team. As Edmund Pellegrino has pointed out, the common feature of the health care team is its collective action with final accountability belonging in one sense to each team member, and in another sense to the entire team.[60]

One difficulty in a transitory team, which comes together to provide services for an individual patient and which disbands when that particular person leaves the institution, is in defining who is accountable for the care it provides.

4.10 Treatment of urinary tract infection

Mary Beth Mezinski had worked in various hospitals and nursing positions for nine years—as a nurse's aide, ward clerk, nurse extern when a student nurse, graduate nurse for a short time, and staff nurse. She had applied recently for the position of in-service instructor for the ICU, Burn Unit, and Emergency Room nursing staffs in the large private hospital where she was employed.

Gladys Cary, admitted to Mary Beth's unit with a myocardial infarction, had been complaining constantly of irritation and painful urination. Two urine specimens had been sent to the laboratory and, on the third day, Mary Beth sent another which she described as "the pussiest urine upon catheterization I have ever seen." At that time, she called the intern, Dr. Bob McClintock, and told him about Mrs. Cary's urine and that the specimen was the third to be sent to the lab in three days.

The next morning Mary Beth learned that Mrs. Cary had not been started on any antibiotics. Nothing had been done about her problem, and she was urinating blood and mucus. When Dr. McClintock came on the floor with Dr. Valois, the internist whom he was following, Mary Beth, aware that Mrs. Cary was lying in pain while nothing was being done, was ready. As a nurse, Mary Beth knew that she "couldn't give Mrs. Cary quality care while she was so uncomfortable" with the urinary problem. Mary Beth also knew that she was being considered for the hospital's instructor position and that Dr. Valois was an old friend of the Director of Nursing, who would soon decide the appointment. She did not want Dr. Valois to think she would be too critical and difficult to work with, and she knew her director valued nurses who could get along well with the medical staff. But she also knew of herself that "as I get older in the profession, I get bolder. I'm not as afraid to speak up to interns and residents and some physicians about the quality of care that I see being given."

Knowing what she had to do, Mary Beth said to the intern, "You're just the man I want to see. I told you about this urine specimen yesterday." She knew she was not being very tactful and had put him on the defensive, but she continued, "How come you haven't ordered anything?" He snapped, "Would you want to write the orders?" When Mary Beth said she probably could, she noticed that Dr. Valois walked away from them and wondered if he felt embarrassed by the argument. When Dr. McClintock said that the cultures were not back, Mary Beth retorted that they were and proceeded to enumerate the findings. To his excuse that he had not known, she countered that he could have telephoned the lab. At that, he grabbed the chart and said he would assess Mrs. Cary. Mary Beth followed the doctors into the room and back to the nurses' station, where they wrote a couple of orders. As they started to walk down the hall, she checked the orders and, to her frustration, found that nothing had been done about the urinary problem. She again asked them what they wanted to do about it. Dr. McClintock answered that he'd be back; Mary Beth, still angry, muttered, "I'll expect you." He did return in half an hour and wrote some antibiotics orders, which were started immediately, intravenously. But, as Mary Beth later said, "He was really hosed off at me, and I was really pissed off at him, and he knew it."

That afternoon Dr. McClintock came back and apologized for losing his temper. Mary Beth accepted his apology but told him that she "wasn't about to back down because I really felt that I was right in the situation." It struck her as unusual that three days later Dr. McClintock sat down with her and told her that she had really put Dr. Valois on the spot that day. For, not only had the intern failed to act immediately when called, but Dr. Valois had somehow missed the problem for three days. She admitted knowing that she might be criticizing Dr. Valois through her attack on an intern, but she had felt that something had to be done. Dr. McClintock agreed that she had been tenacious. Dr. Valois never said anything about the incident to her. A few weeks later she received her new appointment. According to Mary Beth, she and Dr. McClintock developed "a close working relationship."

This case raises questions relating to responsibility: What should a nurse do when she disagrees with a physician's actions? Or if she thinks that a physician is following an unsafe practice? Who is responsible for monitoring individual and team competence? To whom are lapses reported—the person making the error, the team, the institution?

A discussion of these questions must include both individual and team responsibilities. "Personal" physicians admit their patients to a hospital, and a patient quickly enters a relationship with the hospital (through a team composed of the personal physician, resident physicians, consulting physicians, nurses, therapists, and social workers) which is very much like the relationship a patient has with his or her own physician. A patient's right to effective medical treatment obligates his or her physician to provide that treatment. When a patient is admitted to a hospital, he or she makes a similar claim upon the hospital for safe, effective, morally responsible care, which the hospital fulfills through the employment of health care workers, including nurses. According to Pellegrino's view, one can interpret the responsibilities of a health care team in two ways. In one way, responsibility is allocated only to individuals. In the other, responsibility is allocated to the team and is not reducible to the individuals.

According to the interpretation of team ethics that allocates responsibility only to individuals, Pellegrino suggested that the problem of monitoring, correcting, and revealing a fellow team member's incompetence is an unavoidable complication. Unfortunately, when some member fails to perform competently, his or her failure blocks or compromises the actions of other team members.[61] In Case 4.10, the physician's failure to treat Mrs. Cary for her urinary tract infection seriously compromised Mary Beth's attempts to provide high-quality nursing care. Therefore, Mary Beth's duty to provide nursing care obligated her to act in a way which would make certain the competent functioning of other team members; thus, in order to meet her own professional obligations, Mary Beth had to convince the physicians to assess Mrs. Cary's need for treatment of the urinary infection.

Furthermore, according to the interpretation of the team ethic that allocates responsibility to the entire team, all team members are accountable for the patient's well-being. Therefore, in this situation, all were to blame when the team's total care (which included overlooking signs of infection) resulted in Mrs. Cary's discomfort. In situations in which lapses in competence recur or bring discomfort or danger to a patient or in which optimal care is not given, the entire team may be morally (and legally) culpable.[62]

Mary Beth had two reasons for convincing the physicians to assess Mrs. Cary more thoroughly: First, as an individual professional, she was directly obligated to give the best possible nursing care, but the physicians' lapse of competence compromised her efforts. Second, she was obligated as a team member for Mrs. Cary's total care, which was frustrated by the physicians' lapse of competence. Given these reasons, Mary Beth was obligated to obtain optimum medical care for Mrs. Cary, which answers the first two questions the case raised. The actions a nurse should take, when she disagrees with a physician's actions or when she thinks that a physician is following an unsafe practice, must be based upon her responsibilities to the client both in her capacities as an individual practitioner and as a team member. The nurse may develop several strategies to meet her responsibilities. Mary Beth chose not to play a doctor-nurse game; after alerting Dr. McClintock, taking independent steps to have the laboratory results available, and waiting for the physicians to act, she chose to confront Dr. McClintock directly about his inaction. Evidently, her intense commitment to Mrs. Cary's welfare and the seriousness of the situation mitigated any real or imagined errors in etiquette that she may have made, and she and Dr. McClintock were able later to work well together. Although Mary Beth cannot *justify* the intemperate way in which she conveyed her objections, her conduct under the circumstances is in our view *excusable*.[63]

The answer to the third question, Who is responsible for monitoring individual and team competence? is based on the same dual interpretation of responsibility. Since each professional is responsible for his or her own actions, and since as a team member each professional is also responsible for the team's total effectiveness, each member of the team is obligated to monitor both the activities that affect his or her services and the outcome of the team's efforts. Of course, all team members cannot be aware of all aspects of one another's activities. Each professional, however, will be able to assess to varying degrees the effectiveness of other team members since the whole team focuses its attention on the same client.

Difficulty arises in answering the last question, To whom are lapses reported? The dual interpretation of responsibility suggests that insofar as responsibility can be allocated to an individual, that individual is also responsible for correcting his or her error. But to correct a problem an individual needs to learn of it.

Given the power structure of the health care professions, some persons—perhaps especially physicians—often view themselves as more important than other members of the health care team. Open communication in such situations is sometimes difficult. Ideally, the nurse should talk directly to the person who she believes made an error, but telling another person about a suspected lapse of competence is a delicate matter. When the nurse cannot trace the problem to an individual, she should share the information with the whole team. Within the health care team structure, the most effective course of action is usually for the nurse to report any lapse of competence to the person or persons who are directly responsible and to involve other people in the nursing and medical hierarchy only after attempting to solve the problem at its source.

Notes

1. George Rosen, *From Medical Police to Social Medicine: Essays on the History of Health Care* (New York: Science History Publications, 1974), p. 296.

2. Catherine P. Murphy, "The Moral Situation in Nursing," in Elsie L. Bandman and Bertram Bandman, eds., *Bioethics and Human Rights* (Boston: Little, Brown, 1978), p. 315.

3. Joann Ashley, *Hospitals, Paternalism, and the Role of the Nurse* (New York: Columbia University, Teachers College Press, 1976), pp. 8–15.

4. Beatrice J. Kalisch and Philip A. Kalisch, "An Analysis of the Sources of Physician-Nurse Conflict," *Journal of Nursing Administration* 7 (January 1977): 52.

5. Marjorie J. Stenberg, "The Search for a Conceptual Framework as a Philosophic Basis for Nursing Ethics: An Examination of Code, Contract, Context, and Covenant," *Military Medicine* (January 1979):13.

6. Kalisch and Kalisch, "Sources of Physician-Nurse Conflict," pp. 51–52.

7. Murphy, "Moral Situation in Nursing," p. 315.

8. Leonard Stein, "The Doctor-Nurse Game," *American Journal of Nursing* 68 (January 1968):101–5.

9. Patricia A. Prescott and Sally A. Bowen, "Physician-Nurse Relationships," *Annals of Internal Medicine* 103 (July 1985):129.

10. Ibid.

11. Leonard I. Stein, David T. Watts, and Timothy Howell, "The Doctor-Nurse Game Revisited," *New England Journal of Medicine* 322 (22 February 1990):546–49.

12. Quoting a physician who does not share Stein's view, *Nursing 90* has expressed some reservations and has undertaken a survey of the "current status of nurse/doctor relationships from a *nursing* perspective. "The Nurse Doctor Game: Are the Rules Changing?" *Nursing 90* 20 (June 1990):54–55.

13. Ada Jacox, "Role Restructuring in Hospital Nursing," in Linda H. Aiken and Susan Gortner, eds., *Nursing in the 1980s: Crises, Opportunities, Challenges* (Philadelphia: J. B. Lippincott, 1982), p. 78; see also, H. Tristram Engelhardt, Jr., "Physicians, Patients, Health Care Institutions—and the People in Between: Nurses," in Anne H. Bishop and John R. Scudder, Jr., eds., *Caring, Curing, Coping: Nurse Physician Patient Relationships* (Tuscaloosa, Ala.: University of Alabama Press, 1985), pp. 63–67.

14. Lucie Young Kelly, *The Nursing Experience: Trends, Challenges, and Transitions* (New York: Macmillan, 1987), p. 74.

15. Bonnie Bullough, "The Law and the Expanding Nursing Role," *American Journal of Public Health* 66 (March 1976):249–54; Darlene M. Trandel-Korenchuck and Keith M. Trandel-Korenchuck, "How State Laws Recognize Advanced Nursing Practice," *Nursing Outlook* 26 (November 1978):713–19; Clare LaBar, *Statutory Definitions of Nursing Practice and Their Conformity to Certain ANA Principles* (Kansas City, Mo.: American Nurses' Association, 1984), pp. 1, 42, 51.

16. Barbara Ehrenreich, "The Health Care Industry: A Theory of Industrial Medicine," *Social Policy* 6 (November/December 1975):7; Arnold S. Relman, "The Changing Demography of the Medical Profession," *New England Journal of Medicine* 321 (30 November 1989):5040–42.

17. Kalisch and Kalisch, "Sources of Physician-Nurse Conflict," p. 53.

18. For a discussion of the ideologies of domesticity and professionalism in nursing, see Linda Hughes, "Professionalizing Domesticity: A Synthesis of Selected Nursing Historiography," *Advances in Nursing Science* 12 (July 1990): 25–31.

19. Lucie Young Kelly, *Dimensions of Professional Nursing*, 3rd ed. (New York: Macmillan, 1975), p. 169.

20. American Nurses' Association, *Facts about Nursing, 1986–87* (Kansas City, Mo.: American Nurses' Association, 1987), p. 24.

21. Marlene Kramer, *Reality Shock: Why Nurses Leave Nursing* (St. Louis: C. V. Mosby, 1974), p. 21.

22. Carol A. Garant, "The Process of Effecting Change in Nursing," *Nursing Forum* 17 (1978):158.

23. Patricia S. A. Sparacino and Diane M. Cooper, "The Role Components," in Patricia S. A. Sparacino, Diane M. Cooper, and Pamela A. Minarik, eds., *The Clinical Nurse Specialist: Implementation and Impact* (Norwalk, Conn.: Appleton and Lange, 1990), p. 14.

24. Edith P. Lewis, "ANA Convention '88," *Nursing Outlook* 36 (September/October 1988):239; after more than two years of opposition by the American Nurses' Association and state nursing associations, the American Medical Association dropped its plan to implement the registered care technician (RCT) pilot sites: "AMA Votes to Abandon Plan to Create RCT," *The American Nurse* (July/August 1990):25.

25. Bonnie Moore Randolph and Clydene Ross-Valliere, "Consciousness Raising Groups," *American Journal of Nursing* 79 (May 1979):922–24; Angel Barron McBride, "Editorial: Nursing and the Women's Movement," *Image: The Journal of Nursing Scholarship* 16 (Summer 1984):66; see also Sheila Bunting and Jacquelyn C. Campbell, "Feminism and Nursing: Historical Perspectives," *Advances in Nursing Science* 12 (July 1990):11–24; and Carole A. Shea, "Feminism: A Failure in Nursing?" in Joanne Comi McCloskey and Helen Kennedy Grace, eds., *Current Issues in Nursing*, 3rd ed. (St. Louis: C. V. Mosby, 1990), pp. 448–54.

26. See Dorothea F. Orem, *Nursing: Concepts of Practice* (New York: McGraw-Hill, 1971), pp. 47–50, 115.

27. From a case collected by Leah L. Curtin, Acting Director, National Center for Nursing Ethics, Cincinnati, Ohio. It is one of sixty documented cases collected by NCNE.

28. Not only what a nurse says but the way in which she says it is important. While not advocating continuation of the doctor-nurse game, the authors recognize the need for nurses to be highly skillful in talking with certain physicians, especially those who cling to outmoded or stereotypical views of nursing.

29. This recommendation is based in part on a suggestion to authors from Betty Meyer, RN, CCRN, 16 May 1989. In the actual situation, Ms. Pulec did choose to ask a third resident, who, after listening to her reasons, told her that she was correct and canceled the feeding order. Ms. Pulec did not say why she did not try to ask her nursing supervisor.

30. For one physician's defense of an outlook similar to that attributed here to Dr. Rhodes, see Richard C. Bates, "It's Our Right to Pull the Plug," *Medical Economics* 54 (16 May 1977):163–66.

31. For an illuminating account of the elements of patient autonomy, see Bruce L. Miller, "Autonomy and the Refusal of Lifesaving Treatment," *Hastings Center Report* 11 (August 1981):22–28. Most accounts of autonomy in biomedical ethics focus on patient autonomy. We have benefited from Miller's analysis and we have drawn on parts of it in developing our account of ethical autonomy as it applies to health care professionals. See also David L. Jackson and Stuart

Youngner, "Patient Autonomy and 'Death with Dignity,'" *New England Journal of Medicine* 301 (23 August 1979):404–8.

32. Based on a case described by Sister A. Teresa Stanley, "Is It Ethical to Give Hope to a Dying Person?" *Nursing Clinics of North America* 14 (March 1979):69–71.

33. Ibid., p. 75.

34. Jolene L. Tuma, "Professional Misconduct" (Letter), *Nursing Outlook* 25 (September 1977):546.

35. Sally Gadow, "Existential Advocacy: Philosophical Foundation of Nursing," in Stuart F. Spicker and Sally Gadow, eds., *Nursing: Images and Ideals, Opening Dialogue with the Humanities* (New York: Springer, 1980), pp. 90–91.

36. Stanley, "Is It Ethical to Give Hope to a Dying Person?" p. 78.

37. Ibid., pp. 75–76.

38. Three years after Mrs. Tuma's license was suspended, she won a reversal of the suspension ruling when the state's supreme court made a unanimous decision in her favor. Although licensed, she did not immediately resume practice because she felt it "unwise," given the climate of her local medical-nursing community. The junior college did not reinstate her. "Nurse Upheld in Idaho Court Case," *Concern for Dying* 5 (Fall 1979):7.

39. David Mechanic and Linda H. Aiken, "A Cooperative Agenda for Medicine and Nursing," *New England Journal of Medicine* 307 (16 September 1982):747–50; see also Linda Carrick Torosian and Marianne Dietrick-Gallagher, "Overcoming Sex-Role Stereotyping in Nursing," in Katherine W. Vestal, ed., *Management Concepts for the New Nurse* (New York: J. B. Lippincott, 1987), pp. 329–31.

40. This fictitious case, which is based on an actual situation, was prepared especially for this volume.

41. For an encouraging account of recent changes along these lines, see Mila Ann Aroskar, "Establishing Limits to Professional Autonomy: Whose Responsibility?" in Nora K. Bell, ed., *Who Decides? Conflicts of Rights in Health Care* (Clifton, N.J.: Humana Press, 1982), pp. 67–78.

42. John Ladd, "Some Reflections on Authority and the Nurse," in Stuart F. Spicker and Sally Gadow, eds., *Nursing: Images and Ideals* (New York: Springer, 1980), p. 171f.

43. Ibid., p. 172.

44. Samuel Gorovitz, "Can Physicians Mind Their Own Business and Still Practice Medicine?" in Nora K. Bell, ed., *Who Decides? Conflicts of Rights in Health Care* (Clifton, N.J.: Humana Press, 1982), p. 89f.

45. See Christine Mitchell, "Integrity in Interprofessional Relationships," in George J. Agich, ed., *Responsibility in Health Care* (Dordrecht: D. Reidel, 1981), pp. 163–84.

46. Frances J. Storlie, "Burnout: The Elaboration of a Concept," in Edwina A. McConnell, ed., *Burnout in the Nursing Profession: Coping Strategies, Causes, and Costs* (St. Louis, Mo.: C. V. Mosby, 1982), pp. 81–85; see also Judith M. Wilkinson, "Moral Distress in Nursing Practice: Experience and Effect," *Nursing Forum* 13 (no. 1, 1987–88):17–29.

47. Arthur Kuflik, "Morality and Compromise," in J. Roland Pennock and John W. Chapman, eds., *Compromise in Ethics, Law, and Politics: Nomos XXI* (New York: New York University Press, 1979), p. 49.

48. Ibid., p. 51.

49. Isaiah Berlin, *Four Essays on Liberty* (Oxford: Oxford University Press, 1969), p. 1.

50. For a more thorough analysis of these considerations, see Martin Benjamin, *Splitting the Difference: Compromise and Integrity in Ethics and Politics* (Lawrence, Kans.: University Press of Kansas, 1990).

51. John Rawls, *A Theory of Justice* (Cambridge, Mass.: Harvard University Press, 1971), pp. 368–71.

52. Amniocentesis carries a smaller risk of inducing abortion than a first-trimester chorionic villus sampling; see Malcolm A. Ferguson-Smith and Marie E. Ferguson-Smith, "Relationships between Patient, Clinician, and Scientist in Prenatal Diagnosis," in G. R. Dunstan and E. A. Shinebourne, eds., *Doctors' Decisions: Ethical Conflicts in Medical Practice* (New York: Oxford University Press, 1989), p. 21.

53. This fictitious case was prepared especially for this volume. For a discussion of the unprecedented issues it raises see the series of responses accompanying John Fletcher, "Ethics and Amniocentesis for Fetal Sex Identification," *Hastings Center Report* 10 (February 1980):15–20.

54. James F. Childress, "Appeals to Conscience," *Ethics* 89 (1978–79):316–17.

55. Bernard Williams, "A Critique of Utilitarianism," in J. J. C. Smart and Bernard Williams, *Utilitarianism For and Against* (Cambridge: Cambridge University Press, 1973), pp. 115–17.

56. Childress, "Appeals to Conscience," pp. 318–21.

57. Herbert Fingarette, *Self-Deception* (London: Routledge and Kegan Paul, 1969), passim, especially pp. 138–39.

58. Robert M. Veatch, *Death, Dying, and the Biological Revolution: Our Last Quest for Responsibility* (New Haven: Yale University Press, 1976), pp. 116–63; Jackson and Youngner, "Patient Autonomy and 'Death with Dignity,'" 404–8.

59. For an account of the nature, value, and limits of such legislation, see President's Commission for the Study of Ethical Problems in Medicine and Biomedical and Behavioral Research, *Deciding to Forego Life-Sustaining Treatment* (U.S. Government Printing Office, 1983), pp. 136–53.

60. Edmund D. Pellegrino, "The Ethics of Team Care: Some Notes on the Morality of Collective Decision Making" (presented to the American Cancer Society, Second National Conference on Cancer Nursing, St. Louis, Missouri, 9 May 1977), p. 6.

61. Ibid., pp. 7–8.

62. Ibid., p. 9.

63. The notion of an act that is excusable, though not justifiable, is important in a wide variety of contexts in ethics and the law. People who violate laws or moral principles under conditions of duress may be excused for what they do, even though their actions cannot, strictly speaking, be justified. A harried parent, for example, who loses his or her temper and yells at or even spanks a persistently cranky or annoying child, may be excused for what he or she does even though it cannot be justified. So too, if a nurse "loses her cool" after her reasonable attempts to correct a situation have been unsuccessful, her exasperated outburst, though perhaps not justified and even counterproductive, may under the circumstances be excused.

5

Ethical Dilemmas Among Nurses

1. Tensions between nurses

In their practice, nurses work closely with other nurses. Since a nurse's activities normally overlap with those of other nurses, her practice affects and is affected by the practices of others. In addition, most nurses either supervise or are supervised by nurses. Given such interdependence, ethical dilemmas involving relationships among nurses are inevitable and understandable. The following case illustrates one such dilemma.

5.1 Medication cover-up

Jane Robinson, a twenty-eight-year-old nurse with a BSN and several years' nursing experience, has been working part time for three weeks in a small rural community hospital. She is evening charge nurse on a twenty-bed medical and pediatric floor two evenings a week and on a surgical floor the third evening. When Jane accepted her position, she realized that she would be meeting a new set of challenges nearly every evening. One busy evening when a patient on the medical floor was supposed to get phenobarbital, gr ¼, Jane mistakenly went to the wrong cabinet, took out codeine, gr ¼, and gave it to the patient. At the end of the shift Jane checked the narcotics count with Shirley Tucker, a thirty-two-year-old LPN on the midnight shift known for her thoroughness and who is planning to return to school to become an RN. As Shirley counted aloud the remaining narcotics and barbiturates, Jane wrote the same total that had previously been noted for each rather than writing the actual count. She did not realize what she had done.

The next night Shirley brought the matter of the extra phenobarbital and the missing codeine to Jane's attention, told Jane that she had "goofed," and said that she had fixed Jane's error during the night. She had "jimmied" the books by throwing away a phenobarbital and by falsely writing in the codeine book that she had given codeine, gr ¼, to a patient who conveniently had an order for it. The patient to whom Jane had mistakenly given the codeine apparently had experienced no effects and had been discharged during the day.

Jane does not know if she should report her mistake. On the one hand, she thinks she can overlook her medication error since the patient was not harmed and, although Shirley knows of the mistake, it is doubtful that others will discover it. By not reporting her error to the nursing administration, Jane could keep her total number of incident reports low. She knows that many nurses in the hospital believe that other nurses interpret a low number of incident reports as "no error" nursing, which, they believe, is synonymous with "good" nursing. Therefore, some nurses tend not to report small errors. On the other hand, Jane could easily make an incident report. She knows that as an honest person she ought to report her error, and she believes that honesty is an important part of her professional identity. Further, she believes that she should follow hospital policy and rules. But in admitting her mistake, she would expose Shirley's cover-up activities, including the falsification of narcotics records.

Among the questions this case raises are, To what extent, if any, should a nurse jeopardize her own or another's professional position by admitting an error, and must a nurse report a cover-up in order to maintain her authority as an RN and effectiveness as a role model?

Some basic information about relationships among nurses is necessary for a discussion of this case. Various general factors, as discussed in the previous chapter with regard to conflicts between nurses and physicians, also affect relationships between nurses. These include remnants of the historical legacy of nursing; technological and social changes; the expanding scope of nursing practice; and the ideology of professionalism and the increased importance of education, especially with regard to baccalaureate and graduate degrees in nursing. We can see the effect of these factors on tensions in nursing relationships by examining personal variables among nurses and structural variables in nursing practice. Since both personal and structural variables tend to block and confuse efforts to engage in ethical inquiry, it is important to recognize them.

A. Personal variables among nurses

Nurses differ from one another in many ways. Nursing is traditionally a woman's profession, but not all nurses are women. Some men have been and are nurses, even though as early as 1880 women nurses outnumbered men eleven to one and at present outnumber them thirty-three to one.[1] Like male nurses, ethnic minority nurses are fewer in number than their comparative percentages in the general population. Desegregation of nursing schools did not begin until after World War II, and by 1951 only 3 percent of nursing students were black. At present, some schools actively recruit minority students.[2] Sex and racial differences affect nursing relationships as they do relationships in other professions and in society generally. As the following discussion indicates, personal variables that add to tension in nursing relationships include a nurse's educational background, experience, view of nursing, and career goals.

Until recently, all persons seeking to become a registered nurse (RN) took the same licensure examination even though they may have graduated from one of three different educational programs—two-year associate degree, three-year hospital-based diploma, or four-year college or university baccalaureate program. North Dakota now requires graduation from a four-year baccalaureate program with a Bachelor of Science in Nursing (BSN) degree for entry into professional nursing practice, and other states have proposed similar legislation.[3] Disagreement exists within the profession, however, as to the comparative merits of the three programs, and research studies fail to differentiate a clear superiority of four-year program graduates.[4] Persons seeking to become licensed practical or vocational nurses (LPN or LVN) study for approximately one year before taking a licensure examination for practical nurses.

Another personal variable is experience in nursing practice. We have seen that in certain circumstances an experienced and skillful nurse may have knowledge that an inexperienced physician lacks. So too, certain situations will arise in which an experienced nurse who has kept up with new developments and has changed her nursing practice accordingly may know more about a particular nursing problem than a recent graduate from a prestigious nursing program. The quality and usefulness of nursing experience, like other personal variables, differs among individual nurses.

Given the variety of their educational backgrounds and their varying nursing experiences, nurses understandably vary in their views of nursing. As previously discussed (see Chapter 4, Section 1), nurses do not provide only bedside nursing care; they also give physical examinations and teach health care. Common to nurses, however, is a shared legacy of belief as to what nursing is. Nurse writers of the past and nurse theorists of today stress that (1) nursing assists both well and sick persons; (2) "health" is a general nursing goal; and (3) to accomplish the goal, nursing encompasses a wide range of activities based upon a problem-solving process that includes assessment, diagnosis, intervention, and evaluation.[5] Nurses, although they share a general historical view of nursing, place differing degrees of importance on various theoretical models of nursing and on various activities involved in the nursing process.

A nurse's career goal is also an important variable that sometimes increases tension in nursing relationships. Some nurses pursue nursing as a lifetime career, while others prefer not to work full time, especially during their child-rearing years. As Vern and Bonnie Bullough have pointed out, nursing leaders have generally been those who are most able to devote time and energy to nursing; thus, it is no surprise that many nursing leaders have been unmarried.[6] A number of changes such as the women's movement, tax credits for child care, and higher salaries could result in an increased number of married nurses becoming more active in the profession. But a gulf exists between general-duty nurses and nursing leaders. It is symptomatic that only approximately 10 percent of all registered nurses belong to the American Nurses' Association; this suggests a low interest in professional organization among the rank and file.[7]

To return to Case 5.1, notice that the educational backgrounds and experiences of the two persons involved are quite dissimilar; one is an RN with a BSN and the other an LPN. They may or may not hold similar views of nursing or similar career goals. Note, however, that their responsibilities are the same regarding the end-of-shift narcotic and barbiturate count. In at least some respects they have been employed to carry out the same duties. The dilemma of the medication cover-up is made complex not only because of the personal variables involved but because of an equally important reason—the structure of nursing practice.

B. Structural variables in nursing practice

The structure of nursing practice varies according to the settings and staff assignment designs in which nurses practice. For most nurses, over 68 percent, the setting is a hospital. Settings here include, for example, intensive care units, neonatal nurseries, medical inpatient care units, surgical inpatient care units, pediatric units, oncology units, in-service education programs, ambulatory care units, and obstetrical units. For other nurses the setting is an extended care facility. Still others are in clinics or the community, including, for example, nursing centers, offices, schools, and clients' homes. For a few nurse practitioners the setting is an independent practice.[8]

In addition to the practice setting, a nurse's employer describes his or her job responsibilities and assignments. Institutions use the following basic designs for describing nursing staff assignments: functional, team, and primary care nursing or some variation or combination of these designs, such as modular nursing. According to the functional method, the head nurse assigns staff members specific tasks—as medication nurse, treatment nurse, bedside care nurse, and so on. In team nursing, developed in the

1950s, a registered nurse team leader assigns duties to each team member, plans and coordinates care, serves as a resource person, and sometimes provides direct patient care. In primary care nursing, developed in the 1970s, a primary nurse accepts responsibility for the total twenty-four-hour care of a client by interviewing the client on admission, making a nursing diagnosis, issuing orders, and coordinating client activities with the client's physicians and family and with other health workers. Another staff nurse, termed an associate, cares for the client when the primary nurse is off duty, although the associate may phone the primary nurse to seek a change in nursing orders. In modular nursing, a variation of primary nursing, several persons, such as two RNs, or an RN and an LPN, or two LPNs with the charge nurse as modular leader, are assigned to care for a small group of patients.[9]

Nursing staff assignments, especially in institutional settings, have tended to ignore personal variables among nurses. After 1983, as health care institutions provided care for growing numbers of outpatients and as skill requirements and intensity of nursing care increased, hospitals increasingly substituted RNs for LPNs and aides, meanwhile expanding the work of RNs to encompass that of other professionals, such as discharge planners, case managers, and quality-assurance experts. The relatively small difference between RN and LPN salaries "made professional nurses a bargain";[10] thus, a widespread, undifferentiated substitution of RNs for other workers contributed to the severe nursing shortage of the late 1980s. Higher salary scales for RNs have now made this expanded use of RNs less attractive from an economic point of view. Donley and Flaherty predict that as RN salaries become significantly higher than those of LPNs, RN/LPN staffing ratios will shift.[11]

It is noteworthy that as change is occurring in the role of RNs, it is also affecting the role of LPNs. As nursing homes have admitted increasing numbers of patients requiring acute nursing care, disputes and controversy have surrounded state board rulings related to expanded LPN practice.[12] Structural variables in nursing practice, combined with personal variables among nurses, tend to complicate and add significant tension to nurses' relationships. Therefore, in analyzing ethical dilemmas that are primarily disagreements between nurses, it is important to recognize the extent to which these variables underlie the issues.

To return to "Medication cover-up," we can see similarities in the structural variables in that the RN and the LPN share the same rural hospital setting and some of the same job responsibilities. In addition, since they do not work the same shift, it is reasonable to assume that Jane, the RN, does not supervise Shirley, the LPN, as often occurs in a traditional nursing service hierarchy, but that they relate to one another more or less on an equal basis. In terms of personal variables, however, differentiation appears.

The LPN's actions were based, at least in part, on the assumption that she and Jane, the RN, shared the same view of nursing errors—the need to minimize the number of small errors and to cover them up. Jane's concern about how she should respond indicates that she does not unequivocally share Shirley's viewpoint. But while it is reasonable to assume that personal variables influence Jane's and Shirley's perception of the situation and of one another, none of the variables changes the fact that their employer, clients, and other health care providers expect that both women will provide safe, effective, and responsible care. Further, nursing organizations have adopted codes of ethics to guide their conduct. For example, the Code of Ethics of the National Federation of Licensed Practical Nurses states that LPNs must "recognize and have a commitment to meet the ethical, moral, and legal obligations to the practice of practical/vocational nursing." As Carmen Ross points out in her discussion of this code, examples of unethical procedures would be deliberate misuse of narcotics and barbiturates and falsely charting procedures and observations.[13] The Code for Nurses adopted by the American Nurses' Association states that "the nurse acts to safeguard the client and the public when health care and safety are affected by incompetent, unethical, or illegal practice of any person." The ANA's Interpretive Statements of the Code underscore the nurse's primary commitment to the client, direct her to express concern to any person engaging in a questionable practice and to report to the responsible administrative person when a client's welfare is threatened. In terms of accountability, Jane and Shirley are responsible for their own acts.

In complicated cases, a number of different factors affect the situation. Therefore, in order to take a position on Case 5.1, we will make the following assumptions:

1. The client who received the wrong medication needs no treatment to counteract the effects of the error.
2. Jane, the RN, wants to behave in a forthright, honest fashion in all her dealings, private and professional.
3. The nursing administration of this hospital happens to be unusually weak, ineffective, and rigid; therefore, little chance exists that, if Jane reports her error, a change to a more nearly error-free system of medication preparation, administration, and recording will result.[14]
4. Shirley, the LPN, had reasons for covering up Jane's error that were grounded in good intentions—to give Jane, a new employee, the benefit of the doubt in terms of number of errors and to protect her from criticism for having too many errors. Yet her intentions, however good they may have been, have no bearing on our judgment that throwing away a barbiturate and falsifying records are wrong. Thus, while Shirley may not be a bad person, she acted wrongly in this situation.

5. While Shirley did not harm any clients, and the cost of the wasted phenobarbital was negligible, her waste of materials and falsification of records, if carried on over time and in other situations, could result in harm to clients.

6. Simply reporting Shirley's cover-up would probably result in a poor working relationship among Jane, Shirley, and other nurses who have worked with Shirley; and it may result in strong disciplinary action against Shirley, thus creating a situation that could block provision of good nursing care and could possibly cause removal of an otherwise effective LPN.

7. If Jane chooses to take no action concerning the cover-up, she is condoning Shirley's activities and thus making herself partly responsible for the cover-up and harmful consequences that may arise in the future.

8. Since Shirley enjoys a reputation as a thorough worker and aims to become a registered nurse, she probably is motivated to function in a manner acceptable to a nurse like Jane.

Given the first three assumptions, if Jane should decide to report her error, it would be not to prevent harm to the client but rather to maintain a conception of herself as an honest professional. Given Shirley's involvement and assumptions (4) and (5), Jane must decide whether Shirley's motivation to be helpful to Jane cancels out the wrong she actually did. Notice, however, that had Shirley's action resulted in harm, excusing her behavior would not be possible. Given the last three assumptions, Jane must take some action if she is to maintain an independent identity as a responsible person and a professional nurse even though her actions would carry risk for Shirley, herself, and, if nursing care is affected, their clients. Finally, although Jane is not Shirley's supervisor, Shirley would probably try to act in accord with her suggestions.

We think that Shirley's reasons for her wrongful acts, the fact that the acts were not harmful even though wrong, and the possible deterioration of good nursing care and/or removal of the LPN, override Jane's prima facie obligation to report Shirley's conduct. Thus, Jane should talk with Shirley and explain that while she recognizes Shirley's friendly motive for the cover-up, she also recognizes that such acts are wrong. She should explain that although in this situation no harm resulted, the probability that harm could result requires Shirley to refrain absolutely from such acts. Further, she should tell Shirley that, although she expects no more false reporting, if it occurs, she will report it to their supervisor.

The questions in this case raised initially were, to what extent, if any, should a nurse jeopardize her own or another's professional position by admitting an error, and must a nurse report a cover-up in order to maintain her authority as an RN and her effectiveness as a role model? Our analysis, while not directly answering these questions, illustrates that there may be situations in which, all things considered, the best course of action lies somewhere between two extremes when neither is fully satisfactory and each has something to recommend it. In this case, simply reporting the error shows too little concern for the LPN's good intentions, and simply ignoring the situation sets a dangerous precedent.[15]

2. Respect for persons

Underlying the previous discussion, with its emphasis upon the nurse's decision about what she ought to do, is a presumption that the nurse is a self-determining person. A person cannot be held responsible for the consequences of her actions unless she is allowed to judge and choose for herself. Respect for persons, a principle discussed in Chapter 3, Section 2, and which we will explore in the following case, involves acknowledging people's rights as persons to do as they see fit within certain limits.[16]

5.2 Judgmental comments

Last week, public health nurse Mary Ann Rhoads went to a hospital to visit one of her clients, Debra Sharpe, who had just had her second baby. According to Mary Ann, "Debra is a seventeen-year-old, uneducated, black person from the South so it's very difficult for me to understand her thick dialect. I went to the nursery to see the baby, and one of the nurses looked disgustedly at me and asked, 'How old is that mother, anyway?' I said, 'Seventeen,' and she sneered, 'I thought so.' I felt that she was placing a very negative judgment on Debra and her baby."

Mary Ann did not say anything to the nurse, but now she is bothered. "I realize I have some health values. I know that Debra's baby is going to be a high-risk child; in fact, the older sibling had lead poisoning. But the decision to have this second baby was Debra's decision; my own values about her child's future health are irrelevant. All people make decisions about their lives for one reason or another. If we don't know what those decisions and reasons are, and even if we do, we can't pass judgment on another person."

Mary Ann does not know what to do. She thinks she has two problems. First, she does not know if she should return to the nursery and attempt to talk to the nurse. Is it appropriate for her, a nurse from one agency, to advise a nurse who is employed in another agency? Second, she does not know whether she should try to force her own values on another person, specifically, the nurse who made the judgmental comment.

Before examining Mary Ann's concern about her relationship with the nursery nurse, we need to discuss the two nurses' views of the young mother,

Debra. Mary Ann thinks her own values about Debra's decision to have a second baby are irrelevant at this point and that she cannot pass judgment on others. The nursery nurse implied that Debra was wrong to have the baby.

Mary Ann's statements indicate that she accepts a principle of respect for persons which holds that, generally and with certain qualifications, each person is in the best position to determine what will satisfy her or his interest, that is, each person is in the best position to determine her or his conception of the good and what means are most suitable to realizing it. According to this theory, a "person" is a being who is aware of herself or himself, not just as a process, happening, or thing, but as an agent, making decisions that make a difference to the way the world goes, and able to determine and attempt to realize some conception of the good.[17] *Respect for persons* involves acknowledging a person's right to pursue her or his conception of the good so long as doing so does not interfere with the right of other persons to do likewise. In terms of the principle of respect for persons, Mary Ann acknowledged Debra's right to decide to have another baby, which, of course, would not interfere with the rights of others to have babies. Mary Ann treated Debra as a person since she did not interfere with Debra's choice to have a baby; that is, she responded in a fashion that respected Debra's decision by continuing to offer nursing care to her and her children and by refraining from passing judgment on her.

Although basically sound, Mary Ann's understanding of the principle of respect of persons is mistaken in one crucial respect. Mary Ann's recognition of Debra's personhood, which includes recognition of her self-determination, freedom, and dignity, does not mean that Mary Ann could not or should not engage Debra in discussions involving health risks to her children and other health-related topics. Rather, the opposite is true. Mary Ann's respect for Debra as a person is a reason to engage in health teaching and rational discussions about what Debra ought to do. Mary Ann, in holding to the principle of respect for persons, must, of course, take into account Debra's point of view; she must acknowledge Debra's prima facie claim to noninterference; and she must not use her special status as a nurse to impose her values on Debra.[18] Mary Ann is mistaken, however, in thinking that her health values are irrelevant. When Mary Ann engages Debra in health teaching, Debra may decide to adopt some of Mary Ann's health values and information in making her own decisions about the health of her children or herself. Further, since Debra's right to noninterference is a prima facie claim and not an absolute right, Mary Ann may override a particular decision of Debra's if she recognizes that it interferes with certain of the baby's rights. For example, a nurse might choose to override a mother's feeding plan if that plan would obviously lead to her infant's becoming dangerously overweight. In short, although Mary Ann's respect for Debra as a person requires that she not resort to manipulation or coercion, it does allow and perhaps requires that she engage her in dialogue and, where she thinks Debra is misinformed, attempt to educate her or alter her views with rational persuasion. Mary Ann's mistake here is in part attributable to a failure to realize that Debra's right as a person to decide for herself what she will do with her life does not imply that all decisions made in this fashion are the right or best ones. (See Chapter 3, Section 3, for an account of the distinctions beween rational persuasion, manipulation, and coercion.)

The nursery nurse's behavior and remarks to Mary Ann, on the other hand, probably indicate that she does not regard clients in the same way as does Mary Ann. She may, like Mary Ann, believe in the importance of rights but believe that more important rights than Debra's are involved in the situation. For example, she may think that her right as a taxpayer to have lower taxes or to receive public services, which Debra's possible collection of public assistance would reduce to some extent, should override Debra's right to have a second baby. Or she may take a purely utilitarian view and believe that society's interest as a whole will be maximized if poor, uneducated, minority women like Debra are prevented from having a second child. Or she may simply be prejudiced and not have analyzed her feelings about Debra and her children.

Mary Ann's problems as she presented them in the case are, first, whether she should try to talk with the nursery nurse, an employee of another agency, and second, whether she should try to force her own values on another person. Both nurses should have as their primary concern the welfare of clients and, more specifically, Debra's and the baby's care. Mary Ann's worry about whether to discuss her concerns with the nursery nurse indicates that she views personal and/or structural variables as separating them as colleagues. Even though they may not be "peers," may not have equal standing in rank or class because of differences in educational background and other personal variables, and even though they differ in employment settings and nursing assignment responsibilities, both are equal as persons. As equal persons working to provide good nursing care to clients, each should be free to talk with the other about their practice of nursing; thus, Mary Ann should feel free to tell the hospital nurse about her concerns that focus on the primary issue in nursing—client care.

The second question, whether Mary Ann should try to force her values on another person, must be answered with a no. This does not imply that she cannot try to engage the other in dialogue and use rational persuasion to convince her of the soundness of her values. On the contrary, dialogue with the nursery nurse, as opposed to manipulating, coercing, or simply ignoring her, is the way for Mary Ann to show respect for her as a person. If Mary Ann is to be consistent in her dealings with others, she has to respect the other nurse's right to formulate and express views, opinions, and actions just as she respects her client's right to do so. Therefore, she must deal with the nurse as a rational being. But the nurse, like Debra and all persons, has only a prima facie right to noninterference. Mary Ann could question the nurse's actions (prejudicial comments about a client) because she believes she can show that those actions could infringe upon a vulnerable client's basic rights of self-determination, freedom, and dignity. In this case, however, the nursery nurse's disgusted look and her sneered "I thought so," are heavily nonverbal and would be difficult to discuss meaningfully a week or more later.

In summary, Mary Ann is free to talk as a person and colleague with the nursery nurse. In accordance with the principle of respect for persons, she could engage the nurse in a rational discussion about poor, young, minority mothers and their rights as persons. In discussing respect for persons, she could point out that judgmental negative comments may undermine a client's dignity. The effect of such a discussion would depend upon the nursery nurse's ability and willingness to accept and use the information. Because so much time has elapsed since the incident, Mary Ann might well decide at this point not to revive the issue with the nurse. After thinking through this situation, however, she should now be prepared to deal with similar judgmental comments by nursing personnel as they occur.

3. Professional obligations

As we discussed in Chapter 4, Section 6, each nurse is responsible in one sense for her own professional practice and in another sense for the practice of the health care team of which she is a member. The following two cases present questions relating to a nurse's responsibility as a member, not of a health care team, but of the nursing profession.

5.3 Working extra hours

Diane MacIntyre has two and one-half years' experience as staff nurse on a general medical unit that serves many diabetic and stroke patients. As a team leader she both gives direct patient care and plans basic care for other nursing personnel to carry out. In the past, when she worked extra hours at home or in the hospital library writing procedures, the other nurses (especially another team leader, Arlene Estes, who is a single parent with three children) have said that Diane (who is single and without children) was foolish to work without pay. During the last few months Diane's attendance at weekly meetings of a multidisciplinary team, composed of professionals from physical therapy, occupational therapy, and social services who are active in rehabilitation efforts on her floor, has strained her relationships with nursing co-workers. According to Diane, "The other nurses think I'm crazy to come in on my own time. I go to practically every weekly meeting, which are mainly on my days off. I get a lot of positive reinforcement from being with that group of people, and I think they have a little better impression of nursing due to my participation."

Diane's decision to participate with the multidisciplinary team stems from her desire to get more out of her job than just a paycheck and her conclusion that "nursing is one of those jobs that you really have to put a lot of effort into in order to get any satisfaction at all." She wants to show that "nursing is an important profession and nurses have something to contribute besides passing 'meds' and giving baths." Despite her justification for working extra hours, Diane nevertheless feels hurt by the other nurses' reactions, especially those of her friend Arlene, whose skills and integrity she has always admired.

This case raises the following questions: What are the obligations of being a member of the nursing profession? Do these obligations include attending meetings on one's own time and expense? Working overtime?

The American Nurses' Association Code for Nurses addresses the question of responsibility to the profession. Item 8 of the Code, which states that "the nurse participates in the profession's efforts to implement and improve standards of nursing," includes an Interpretive Statement that "the nurse has the responsibility to monitor these standards [ANA standards for nursing practice, service, and education] in daily practice and to participate actively in the profession's ongoing efforts to foster optimal standards of practice at the local, regional, state, and national levels of the health care system." Item 11, which states that "the nurse collaborates with members of the health professions and other citizens in promoting community and national efforts to meet the health needs of the public," includes an Interpretive Statement that "Nurses should actively promote the collaborative planning required to ensure the availability and accessibility of high-quality health services to all persons whose health needs are unmet." The Code clearly expresses the view that nurses have obligations not only to themselves and to clients but to the nursing profession as well. While not stating that participation in activities to improve nursing as a discipline may require extra working hours, the Code implies as much.

Very few nurses have established independent nursing practices; rather, agencies—hospitals, nursing homes, community health departments, schools, industries, physicians, health maintenance organizations, etc.—employ the vast majority of nurses. A nurse makes a contract with an agency in order to carry out her primary obligation to the client—the provision of safe, effective, responsible nursing, be it, in the words of ANA Code, "the promotion of health, the prevention of illness," or "the alleviation of suffering." An employment contract, either written or oral, specifies a nurse's obligations in terms of working hours and specific responsibilities, as well as an agency's obligations in terms of pay, benefits, vacations, and so forth. In addition, nurses often feel obligated to do more than the contract specifies because they fall into the "compassion trap" by accepting the expectations of many agency employers, health care workers, and clients that nurses—members of a "helping profession"—will subordinate their own needs or desires to those of others.[19]

To return to the nurses in Case 5.3, both Diane and Arlene share high ideals about professionalism, and as dedicated nurses both are also affected by the "compassion trap," with its assumption that the nurse will sacrifice for others. Therefore, Diane is somewhat discouraged by Arlene's recent comments about working only for pay. Peggy Sayre, another nurse from a different unit in the hospital and a friend of both women, suggested that Diane, Arlene, and she talk during a break about problems relating to Diane's working extra. After listening to the other two nurses describe the situation, Peggy asked each of them why they felt as they did about working extra.

Diane had no difficulty in pointing out that her involvement with the interdisciplinary team and working on hospital procedures would lead to better care for a larger number of clients. She also emphasized that her professional goals of high-quality nursing care and the hospital's current inclusion of her in the multidisciplinary team were in perfect agreement.

Arlene acknowledged that Diane's contributions to client welfare were admirable but quickly shifted to her own feelings concerning Diane's extra work. Arlene believed that because Diane functioned as a "super nurse" the head nurse looked upon Arlene and several other nurses, who could not devote extra time to hospital matters, as less than adequate professional nurses. Further, they themselves were beginning to feel inadequate. One way for them to restore their private as well as professional self-esteem would be for them to match Diane's work load by working extra hours. Arlene predicted that client welfare would be negatively affected, however, since she and most of the other nurses would be worn out by the combination of home duties, regular job, and extra unpaid work.

Arlene also said that, perhaps more important, she believes the way a nurse feels about herself as a professional affects the way in which she approaches nursing care. Although Arlene did not think that her negative feelings about her current level of participation in nursing matters at the hospital had affected her practice, she thought that if her morale continued to deteriorate, her nursing might suffer. She also predicted that if the nurses continued to see themselves as inadequate, even though they did their best during every working hour, some of them would quit. The resulting nursing personnel turnover would cause confusion, and a reduction of the high-quality nursing care now being provided. Further, Arlene believed that if a high turnover rate persisted, the good that Diane's work did would be undermined.

Peggy thought that both Diane and Arlene had missed the major issue. As for Arlene, Peggy did not believe that the decline in unit morale and the increase in nursing staff turnover would be as great as Arlene predicted, but she agreed that these were important concerns. More important, she believed that Arlene, who recognized that she must meet her basic duties as a nurse and honor her contract with the hospital, had not completely accepted the view that idealized commitments to professional nursing might be overridden by other more stringent and immediate commitments, such as those to her children. To Peggy, Arlene, like all nurses, had personal as well as professional obligations, and Arlene, as a single parent, need not apologize for not working more than a forty-hour week. Peggy illustrated her point by describing a public health nurse, whom they all knew, who had been extremely active in collective-bargaining activities in the county health department. When her mother had become seriously ill and needed her every evening, the nurse could no longer attend special nightly meetings. Her obligations to her sick parent, while not excusing her from her contractual obligations to the health department, did excuse her from the additional commitments she had previously taken on. Arlene's personal obligations, like those of the public health nurse, were more basic and thus took precedence over her less stringent professional obligations.

Neither was Peggy convinced by Diane's argument that her professional nursing goals were being met, and that the end result would be an overall improvement in client welfare. Although she agreed with Diane that the initiation of a new program or change often required an initial period of voluntary effort, she argued that as soon as the program's value was recognized, it was necessary to press for its institutionalization. In Diane's case, Peggy believed, Diane had amply demonstrated the value of what she was doing. Therefore, she should now take steps to make hers a paying, institutionalized position. Peggy pointed out that since Diane's work depended entirely upon one nurse's willingness to work extra, when she left her current position for one with more responsibility—which all three nurses agreed that a young, effective nurse like Diane would do within a short time—there would probably be no one to carry on her good work. Nor, since the hospital had gotten Diane's work free, would their employer believe that another nurse would not also step forward to give free time and effort to the hospital.

Peggy predicted that at Diane's departure there would be no nursing contribution to the multidisciplinary team or to similar activities since no institutional changes to provide for participation by nurses would be made so long as Diane functioned as she did. Therefore, in the long run, clients would not be well served by nursing. Thus, Diane was not meeting her professional goals when the future was considered. Peggy summarized her position by saying that Diane's extra work was a problem because the nurses on the unit could not determine if Diane's special activities were merely an extension of her efforts to be professional by providing the highest-quality nursing care possible or if she had slipped into the hospital's institutionalized system of devaluing nursing, although the system was obviously more subtle than that which nineteenth-century hospitals had used to exploit nurses.[20] To Peggy, the major issue was that if Diane continued to attend special meetings without compensation, she would actually support the notion that her activities were not truly part of a nurse's employee role and that the hospital had no obligation to support nurses who work long hours to write procedures and attend multidisciplinary team meetings.

To return to the questions raised by this case, a nurse has certain obligations to the nursing profession, as discussed in the ANA Code for Nurses. At times those obligations may include working overtime and attending meetings on one's own time and expense. But as this case illustrates, when a nurse critically examines her obligations, she may see that basic personal commitments sometimes override less stringent professional commitments that might be met by "working extra." She may also see that "working extra," while appearing to fulfill professional obligations and the ideal of compassionate service, may only superficially meet obligations to clients and may actually lead to a less desirable state of affairs not only for nursing colleagues and the nursing profession but ultimately for clients.

In the following case, a nurse faces an ethical dilemma somewhat different from that involved in the problem of working extra hours. The questions the case raises involve conflict between a nurse's obligations as a care provider and her desire to be helpful to her friend and colleague.

5.4 A question of friendship

Cindy McNeal and Jerry White, RNs in an intensive care unit on the second shift, have been friends since they attended nursing school together five years ago. For the past few months, Cindy has been concerned about Jerry, who has admitted to her that he has been having severe headaches and occasional fainting episodes. Jerry attributes the symptoms to stress because he has been working two jobs while trying to establish himself and his young family financially. Although Cindy understands Jerry's position, she has been encouraging him to see a physician because she fears that the symptoms may indicate something more serious than simple stress. She also worries that Jerry's physical symptoms may affect his ability to make rational decisions concerning patients in his care. Jerry is not convinced that his symptoms are serious and says, "Besides, I don't have time to be sitting

*in the hospital for a week while a dozen tests are being run. I can live on
aspirin for a while until this thing blows over and I get used to the pace."*

*Over the past few weeks, Jerry has been making a few mistakes on duty.
While the mistakes have not been costly, Cindy is afraid that Jerry will make
an error that will harm a patient seriously. Cindy wonders if she should
discuss her knowledge of Jerry's problem with their supervisor before Jerry
harms himself or his patients. At the same time, she feels guilty about
betraying a friend who trusts her enough to share his problems with her.*[21]

Engaging in ethical analysis can help a nurse like Cindy think more clearly
about a troublesome problem because ethical analysis enables one to examine
not only personal feelings but all aspects of a situation. By analyzing this
situation in terms of ethical arguments, Cindy could step beyond personalities
and feelings and thus develop a more critical and objective perspective.

Cindy does face an ethical dilemma: Should she tell the supervisor about
her concerns and thus break the confidentiality implicit in her relationship
with Jerry? Or should she maintain confidentiality and risk the harm that
may result either to ICU clients or to Jerry himself? Either of these choices
can be supported by ethical principles. On the one hand, telling the supervisor can be supported by duty-based arguments, such as that a nurse's duty is
to safeguard a client when health care is affected by incompetent practice (as
stated in the ANA Code for Nurses), as well as by utilitarian arguments,
such as that provision of safe care in an ICU results ultimately in the
greatest happiness for all. On the other hand, not telling the supervisor, and
thus maintaining confidentiality, can be supported by appeal to friendship,
privacy, and trust.

The importance of trust between friends provides a strong basis for an
argument to support Cindy's not discussing her concerns about Jerry with
the supervisor. In breaking confidentiality Cindy would not only be betraying Jerry in this one instance but she could damage Jerry's trust in their
relationship. Cindy, too, would have to face her own feelings of inadequacy
and guilt stemming from her view that good people, herself included, ought
to keep their friends' confidences.

We value the keeping of confidences between friends. Our relationships
with one another depend upon being able to trust that certain personal
secrets will not be exposed; restricted information might lead to loss of self-
esteem if made public. We all have shortcomings that we would rather not
have widely known. We need the benefit of confidentiality when we seek
advice and aid, and when we share intimate concerns. Sissela Bok points to
four important considerations that support confidentiality: (1) respect for a
person's autonomy and his right to his secrets; (2) respect for the relationship between two persons; (3) the implicit promise of keeping a confidence;
and (4) the benefit that the security of confidentiality offers to us.[22]

Each of these considerations supports the argument that Cindy should guard Jerry's confidence. Keeping his problems to herself can be seen as confirming her respect both for him as a person and for their relationship. Cindy's worry that she will feel guilty about betraying Jerry suggests her belief that hearing a friend's troubles in confidence requires her not to reveal them. To reveal to others what Jerry has told her would cause her, therefore, to break an implied promise. Finally, Jerry and Cindy, like all of us, believe that they can explore ideas and questions with certain people in certain situations and not fear that such discussions will be used to hurt them. Cindy's silence would safeguard this important benefit of confidentiality.

A concern that may override the force of these reasons supporting confidentiality in this case is that Jerry's patients as well as Jerry himself face real dangers if he continues to make mistakes. Maintaining confidentiality because it preserves respect and trust, has been implicitly promised, or provides a general benefit are not convincing reasons if a consideration such as a potential danger to vulnerable patients is ignored. Given the danger of mistakes, Cindy could make three strong arguments for breaking confidence and discussing her concerns with the supervisor.

Briefly, the first argument centers on the welfare of clients who receive Jerry's care. Nurses, as nurses, have a duty to ensure that patients receive safe nursing care. An ICU is no place for even small mistakes. Given the serious condition of the patients and the fast pace of an ICU, mistakes can quickly lead to permanent damage. The clinical situation in an ICU is quite different from, say, a health care teaching situation in which a nurse can return the next day and correct erroneous information that she has given. Thus, Cindy ought to safeguard patients by reporting Jerry's problem to the supervisor.

A second argument that supports Cindy's breaking confidentiality is derived from concern for the greatest welfare for all. Mistakes that cause problems for a patient, even those that do not result in permanent damage, decrease an ICU's efficiency. Thus, nurses and physicians are less able to give needed attention to other patients in the ICU, which limits the well-being of those persons. In addition, loss in nursing time or supplies leads to increased health care costs, which, when passed on as increased costs to insurance companies or taxpayers, results in less well-being for those who must pay the bill.

The third argument that supports Cindy's discussing her concerns with the supervisor is that to do so would prevent Jerry from hurting himself. He risks losing his reputation as a dependable nurse if he continues making mistakes. Worse, if he makes a major error, he could face legal and professional problems. Since Jerry seems unable or unwilling to admit the seriousness of his situation, Cindy could protect him by discussing her concerns with the supervisor who, she assumes, will act to protect Jerry, even if it means removing him from the ICU. In other words, Cindy could treat Jerry parentalistically and act on his behalf, although not at his behest.

These three arguments in support of Cindy's discussing her concerns with the supervisor have some difficulties. First, Cindy does not know if Jerry's problem will increase or even continue. No one has been hurt yet. Jerry seems to be coping well enough so as not to make serious or costly errors. He seems to be able to concentrate on his work well enough to maintain a minimum level of competence.

Second, Cindy's acting parentalistically in this case may not be justifiable. As was discussed in Chapter 3, a parentalistic act can be justified if, and only if, it meets three conditions: the autonomy, harm, and ratification conditions. In terms of the first condition, Jerry seems to know he is making errors, and he is also apparently rational. Stress can cause errors, a fact he recognizes. According to his assessment, his situation should improve soon. In terms of the second condition, Jerry faces some danger. He has not, however, made a major error that could damage his career. Furthermore, all ICU nurses take risks every day because any one of them could make a mistake that could result in serious legal problems. In terms of the third condition, Jerry might ratify Cindy's discussing his problems with the supervisor if that discussion led to his recognition of a problem that could be treated or resolved soon. More likely, given the information in the case study, her discussion with the supervisor would lead to difficulties and even to a break in Cindy's and Jerry's friendship. In short, (weak) parentalism is not straightforwardly justified in this situation, at least according to these criteria.

This analysis of the case, while not clearly pointing out what Cindy should do, underscores both the high value we place on confidentiality and the probable dangers of Jerry's continuing to make mistakes. Thus, given the strengths and weaknesses of the various arguments, Cindy could propose to Jerry a plan that would address both the importance of maintaining confidentiality and of protecting ICU patients. Such a plan would require that Cindy first share her ethical analysis of the situation with Jerry. In other words, she could share with him her reasons for and against telling the supervisor about her concerns. She could also ask him to see the matter from her point of view and ask what he would do if he were in her shoes and why. If Jerry were not persuaded to make changes, Cindy could tell him that, in view of the real danger of harm to patients, she will, after waiting a week for him to seek health care, be obligated to override his wishes to procrastinate and will discuss her concerns with their supervisor. By giving him a week to act, Cindy would confirm the high value she places on maintaining confidentiality, but by setting a definite time limit, she would minimize the period in which patients might be harmed by Jerry's mistakes (a period in which, incidentally, Jerry would probably be very careful).

Once Cindy had told Jerry of her intentions and given him ample time to act, she could clearly justify discussing her concerns with their supervisor if Jerry failed to correct the situation. She probably could not persuasively argue that she should break Jerry's confidence for his own good, since the question remains whether he would ever ratify such a parentalistic act on her part. But she has two strong ethical arguments that support her telling the supervisor about Jerry's situation if he refuses to do anything about it: First, she has a duty as a nurse to protect patients; second, a safe, efficient ICU increases the well-being of all.[23]

4. Administrative dilemmas

Nursing administrators, whether directors, supervisors, unit managers, or head nurses, must decide how best to deal with nurses who are impaired, dishonest, or incompetent. The following is one such situation.

5.5 A nurse with a drug problem

Ms. Maria Romero, Associate Director of Nursing, is responsible for the daily nursing division operations of a three-hundred-bed hospital. During the past year she has met several times with Pam Altmann, a staff nurse with three years' experience in another city. According to Ms. Romero, "Last fall, Ms. Altmann lived with a pusher and overdosed. She was very honest about her drug problem, and I wanted her to make it. I knew she needed a lot of support and trust." Impressed by Ms. Altmann's honesty, Ms. Romero thought that Ms. Altmann should have a second chance.

Ms. Romero had to face the questions, Ought a nursing administrator allow a nurse with a history of drug abuse to continue to work, and how ought a nurse resolve a conflict between her professional obligations and her personal desire to befriend a fellow nurse? As the Associate Director of Nursing, Ms. Romero has as her primary obligation the provision of safe, effective nursing care to all clients served by the hospital. Clients must be guaranteed that nurses will always be clearheaded and not under the influence of alcohol or mind-altering drugs. On the other hand, as a sensitive and compassionate person, Ms. Romero also recognized her desire to help Ms. Altmann overcome her drug problem. Thus, there was a conflict between Ms. Romero's professional obligation to maintain standards and her desire to be a friend and helper to Ms. Altmann.

Ms. Romero knew that Ms. Altmann would have daily access to drugs and that consequently she would face extraordinary temptations to steal drugs for her own use. She also recognized that the length of Ms. Altmann's previous nursing experience and the fact that she had not been found stealing drugs decreased the probability that drug-related problems would interfere with her effectiveness as an RN. Given these reasons, Ms. Romero thought it would be wrong simply to refuse to rehire Ms. Altmann. Therefore, Ms. Romero encouraged her to attend weekly counseling sessions and waited until Ms. Altmann's therapist submitted a written statement that she was able to work safely in a clinical setting before employing her again. Rather than sacrificing either her professional obligations or her personal desire, Ms. Romero apparently found a solution that satisfied both. The case developed as follows:

In order to help as much as possible, Ms. Romero assigned Ms. Altmann to work with a competent and supportive head nurse, where she did well for four months. Then, last week, the head nurse learned that 500 milligrams of Demerol had been signed out but not given to a patient. The head nurse talked with the patient, who was coherent enough to verify that he had not received the drug, and with Ms. Altmann, who admitted she had taken it.

When Ms. Romero met with her, Ms. Altmann said that something had happened that she could not handle. Ms. Romero was disappointed, for she had expected Ms. Altmann to overcome her drug problem "not only for herself as a person but because she was a nurse." Ms. Romero has "higher expectations for people in certain roles." She believed that Ms. Altmann was a good RN who was embarrassed by the difficulty she had caused.

Ms. Romero knows she is obliged to report Ms. Altmann to the State Board of Nurses and that they will discipline her by rescinding her license to practice. Ms. Romero does not want Ms. Altmann to go elsewhere to work, where she may steal narcotics and falsify records again, but, because of her personal involvement, it is difficult for her to fire Ms. Altmann and to make the report.

Ms. Romero now faces the question, Ought a nursing administrator allow a nurse who has stolen drugs to continue to work? The law says that nurses as well as other people may not steal drugs. Although it is understandable that Ms. Romero feels a personal loss, since she sincerely wished for Ms. Altmann's success and gave her practical support, the law and hospital policy require that Ms. Romero must discharge and report Ms. Altmann because she has not fulfilled her legal obligations as a nurse. If Ms. Romero believes that Ms. Altmann was unable to control her desire for drugs, she must acknowledge that Ms. Altmann cannot fulfill the demanding responsibilities of a registered nurse. Thus, Ms. Romero must let her go and report her in order to protect clients from possible unsafe care. If, on the other hand, Ms. Romero believes that Ms. Altmann was able to control her desire for drugs but nonetheless *chose* to steal the narcotics, Ms. Romero should still take the same action. Not to punish Ms. Altmann would be to fail to respond to her as a person with the ability to make choices and to assume responsibility for the consequences of her own choices.[24] Finally, Ms. Romero could simply ignore the situation or forgive her for stealing the Demerol. But either of these courses would have a number of undesirable effects: (1) Ms. Romero would be violating the law and thus involving herself in possible legal difficulties; (2) she would be disregarding professional nursing standards; (3) she would be ignoring a strong sign that Ms. Altmann's future clients might be deprived of needed pain-relieving drugs; and (4) she would be contributing to Ms. Altmann's continuing dependence on drugs. These possible consequences make it unacceptable for Ms. Romero—even given her desire to be a helpful friend—either to ignore the drug theft or to forgive it. Therefore, as argued previously, Ms. Romero should let Ms. Altmann go and report her to the State Board of Nursing.

This case suggests two quite different approaches to the basic question of how a nurse ought to resolve a conflict between professional obligations and personal desire to befriend a fellow nurse. When Ms. Altmann's situation appeared merely to be that of a person with a history of drug abuse and who posed no clear threat to provision of safe, effective care, Ms. Romero was able to identify a course of action that appeared to satisfy conflicting claims. At this point the case underscored a suggestion made earlier in this chapter, that it is sometimes possible to select a course of action that allows one to reconcile what may appear to be competing alternatives. At the point when the situation shifted from an episode of drug abuse to a matter of drug theft, professional obligations and legal demands clearly overrode personal desires.

Does the fact that this case turned out badly imply that Ms. Romero's initial response was wrong? No, we think it does not. Sometimes it happens that the right decision in a particular case turns out badly. For example, a few decades ago doctors and nurses appeared to have good grounds for believing that premature infants in respiratory distress needed oxygen-enriched air in order to thrive. What no one knew until later, however, was that excessive amounts of oxygen caused the tiny babies to be permanently blinded. Although, given the limits of medical knowledge at the time, the doctors and nurses had conscientiously made the right decision, the results were unfortunate. With new knowledge and more refined methods of monitoring oxygen levels, this is no longer a problem.

Another dilemma that nursing administrators face is deciding the best response to nurses who believe they cannot follow certain orders or rules because of conscience. The next case presents such a dilemma.

5.6 Working in a bureaucracy: special favors

The only hospital in town, small Fairview Memorial, has a pediatric unit of eight beds, which is an extension of the general medical-surgical floor. Jason

Campbell, eleven-year-old son of Eric Campbell, a member of the hospital's Board of Directors, was admitted in the morning after a bicycle accident. He had minor surgery, was doing well, and was due to be released the next day. When Hilary Jones, evening charge nurse, learned that someone had ordered a special steak dinner for Jason, she protested. "Everyone should have the same care," she told Beth Otterson, the nursing supervisor. "Making sure that a certain child has everything—ordering a special meal, or giving special care, or providing the best nurse—goes against my grain. I think, being the nurse in charge, I should have control over what goes on on the floor." The nursing supervisor told her the decision that Jason was to have a steak dinner had come from the "higher-ups" and so would not be changed. Anyway, she added, the cost of the dinner was small, no one else had to know, and Mr. Campbell would appreciate the nurses' special concern for Jason.

Hilary was not convinced that giving Jason the special dinner was right, and she said that she would lose her self-respect if she gave in and allowed some patients to receive "VIP treatment." Therefore, she explained, she would not serve the meal to the boy even if it were prepared and sent to the unit.

Hilary's position concerning the special steak dinner presents a problem to Beth, since she must decide how to respond to Hilary's insubordination. The basic question she faces is, How should a nursing administrator deal with a nurse's conscientious refusal?

In order to discuss this case, we must assume that in this hospital the authority to make decisions concerning the many small details involved in nursing care—including meal selection—rests primarily with the unit charge nurse but that ultimately she is under the authority of her supervisor and the nursing administrative hierarchy. Given this assumption, the nurse must follow her supervisor's directives or risk disciplinary action. We must also assume that the unit level nursing staff will support the charge nurse's nursing decision (that is, in this case they will not serve the meal) unless a nursing supervisor intervenes. Beth can choose to respond to the immediate problem of Hilary's refusal by serving the dinner herself, by ordering another person to serve it, or by taking no action to get the meal served. But whether Jason gets the steak or not, Beth has to decide whether to report Hilary for insubordination.

Beth believes that all persons who are insubordinate should be reported and disciplined, so her first impulse is to report Hilary to the Director of Nursing. Beth also believes that she would cease to be a fair administrator if she did not deal with the nursing staff consistently, and she can cite reasons to support her position. If she did not insist that nurses at each level follow through on decisions and commitments made by persons at higher levels in the nursing and administrative hierarchy, discipline would break down. Further, if at a later date she reported another nurse for insubordination, that nurse could charge her with unfair labor practices.

However, a course of action very different from Beth's first impulse results if she recognizes her responsibility to a subordinate who disobeys because of conscience.[25] Therefore, Beth needs first to decide if Hilary's refusal to serve the meal is an act of conscientious refusal. To be recognized as an appeal to conscience (as discussed in Chapter 4, Section 5) the appeal must (1) be personal or subjective, although the moral standards on which it is based may or may not apply to others; (2) follow a judgment of rightness or wrongness; and (3) be motivated by personal sanction rather than external authority. Hilary's refusal passes all these tests: she spoke only for herself; she based her decision not to serve the meal upon her previous judgment that "VIP treatment" was wrong; and she acknowledged her personal sanction—that she would lose self-respect if she served the meal. Once Beth recognizes that Hilary's refusal is based on such an appeal to conscience, she ought to rethink her initial impulse to report her. Having established that Hilary's apparent insubordination is motivated by conscience, Beth must consider a number of additional factors.

Mechanically responding to people who violate certain rules or directives without considering their reasons can lead to injustice, a fact which the legal system recognizes. For example, very often a judge or jury may select from a range of penalties when determining how severely to punish persons who, for different motives and under different circumstances, have committed similar crimes. In the present case, Hilary's conscientious refusal to serve the special dinner is quite different from a refusal based on her dislike of the child. Thus, for a supervisor to be fair in a case of insubordination involving conscientious refusal, the supervisor should take the nurse's reasons into account.

Another important consideration is that a nurse who conscientiously chooses to refuse an order is often representative of the more effective and thoughtful nurses in an institution. A nursing administrator needs to keep these valuable nurses employed in order to provide the best nursing care possible. Further, a hospital nursing organization will not collapse if it allows some room for the exercise of conscience. Hilary's refusal was not intended to undermine the authority of the nursing system. Rather, she was attempting to strengthen nursing service by ensuring that it was fair to all patients. The nursing administration, given this view, has an obligation to support Hilary's independent nursing judgments based on conscientious refusal as long as the resulting actions fall within acceptable, safe practice. Beth should be relieved that Hilary is not going further by publicizing the hospital's preferential treatment.

Most important, since the nursing administration permits and even encourages nurses to make independent nursing decisions in questionable cases, it has the responsibility to try to reduce the risks that nurses must take in making such decisions. In the steak dinner case, a question remains as to what is the right course of action concerning the provision of a special dinner to a child of an influential person. Both Hilary's and Beth's positions have something to recommend them. Hilary's position is that Jason's preferential treatment is unfair to other children on the unit who would enjoy or who might even be helped by a dinner they especially liked instead of having only "regular" hospital food. As the charge nurse, Hilary believes that she is in the best position to assess nursing care needs and that the nursing administration is attempting to override her skills and judgment in such a way that her other patients will not be treated fairly. Hilary's right-based appeal to equality and fairness does not, however, diminish the force of Beth's utilitarian appeal to the possible consequences of preferential treatment in this case. Since Mr. Campbell is in a position to influence the hospital's resources, it is likely that the hospital and especially nursing service will stand to benefit. Thus, there are good reasons on both sides, and the best course in the steak dinner situation is uncertain. Since the nursing administration encourages its nurses to think for themselves, it ought to be reluctant to discipline nurses who make well-grounded conscientious decisions. A possible negative consequence of disciplinary action in this case is that it will have a chilling effect on independent thought and judgment among the nursing staff.

In conclusion, if Jason is given the steak, his father will probably learn of the meal. If he is not given the steak, his father will probably not ever know that it was ordered, but some people in the nursing and/or hospital administration will be displeased, including Beth. Since Beth believes that giving Jason the special dinner is in the hospital's best interest, she may decide to serve the steak herself or ask another person to serve it.

Yet, she still must answer the basic question the case raised: How should a nursing administrator deal with a nurse's conscientious refusal? As the discussion has shown, the administrator must first recognize whether the nurse's position qualifies as conscientious refusal. Once she has determined that it does qualify, as it does in Hilary's case, she must not decide too hastily for disciplinary action. In determining how she ought to respond, she must consider the reasons in favor of the refusal, the value of thoughtful, conscientious nurses, the capacity of the institution and the profession to allow some latitude for conscience, and the extent to which an indiscriminately harsh response will repress independent judgment. On balance, we believe that the reasons for not reporting Hilary in the case outweigh those in favor of reporting her.

An administrative dilemma associated with increased numbers of AIDS patients being admitted to general medical-surgical hospital units is deciding the best response to nurses who refuse to accept assignments to provide nursing care to these patients. In Case 3.11, "Refusal to care for an AIDS patient," Mary Duncan-Keilman threatened Crystal Mahorn, the unit nurse manager, that she would leave her position if she had to care for Glenn Admunson, a patient with AIDS.

Crystal believes that nurses who refuse to accept assignments should be dismissed. Yet she also believes in respecting a nurse's appeal to conscience or personal integrity. Thus, like the nursing supervisor in Case 5.6, she believes she must first decide if Mary's refusal to care for Glenn is an act of conscientious refusal, and if it is, she will try to make accommodations to support Mary.

Mary's refusal, however, fails to meet the three tests of an appeal to conscience: Mary's claim that the assignment violated her rights might be based upon a personal or subjective moral standard; she did not, however, mention what that standard might be, although she did say that her life was worth more than her job. The appeal did not follow a judgment of rightness or wrongness; that is, Mary did not say that providing nursing care to AIDS patients was morally wrong. She did not claim that she was motivated by personal sanction; that is, she did not say, for example, that she would lose her self-respect if she gave care to Glenn.

Before dismissing Mary for refusing to accept an assignment, Crystal needs to make certain that she, as unit nursing manager, has met her obligations as unit leader; that is, that she has provided Mary as well as the rest of her nursing staff with adequate education and support for caring for AIDS patients. Assuming that Mary is a reliable and caring nurse to all other patients, Crystal needs to determine if Mary's refusal is related to inadequate information about AIDS and/or lack of institutional support for job stress related to care of AIDS patients. A nurse manager can combat staff nurses' fears of contracting AIDS by providing the nursing staff (or having others provide) instruction on epidemiology and procedures for self-protection and by organizing small-group discussions focused on nurses' feelings about homosexuality and drug abuse as well as on legal and ethical issues. A nurse manager can also insist that all nurses in the hospital have adequate employee health services as further tangible support for them.[26]

Assuming that an ongoing and adequate education and support program for nurses and an adequate employee health service are and have been available to all nurses on the unit, Crystal needs, also, to determine if she is being unfair to Mary in assigning her to Glenn rather than to another patient. Glenn presents a challenge since he is very weak, nearly blind, and forgetful, but nearly all patients on the unit present significant nursing challenges. Having to care for Glenn is not more difficult or risky in terms of contracting AIDS than having to care for several other patients on the unit. Therefore, Mary's being assigned to care for Glenn is not unfair.

In summary, Crystal has no choice but to let Mary go for her refusal to care for Glenn. First, Mary's refusal fails to meet the three tests of an appeal to conscience. Second, adequate educational, support, and employee health programs are and have been available to Mary. And, finally, the assignment to Glenn is fair, that is, it is no more difficult or risky than that of other patients on the unit. Of course, Mary, if she carries through her threat to walk off the job, will herself sever her employment immediately.

But what if Glenn had presented a different clinical picture? What if he were angry and aggressive; what if he unpredictably tried to scratch, bite, or spit at any nurse or physician caring for him? What if he were uncooperative when receiving injections? What if he purposefully or irrationally attempted to infect health care workers with HIV? In assigning nurses to care for such patients, a nursing manager would need to make certain that assignments were fair; that is, the nurses assigned must be prepared both for caring for patients with infectious diseases and for uncooperative, unpredictable, and aggressive patients.

Asking for nurses to volunteer to care for an uncooperative and aggressive patient with AIDS may, of course, be an adequate option for a short period of time. It may even be a necessity until a nursing staff can be well educated and supported in their care of such patients. A problem, however, could develop if assignments continued to rest upon volunteerism; in such a situation a nurse manager could be reinforcing the perception that caring for an uncooperative AIDS patient is somehow different than caring for other uncooperative and aggressive patients. Thus, the manager could unwittingly be emphasizing fear of AIDS among the nursing staff. The number of nurses prepared to provide care to AIDS patients in such a situation could remain dependent upon volunteers rather than upon a well-developed education, support, and health services program that would prepare all nurses in an institution to care for AIDS patients. Given the widespread HIV infection rate in certain populations, all nurses, not just a few volunteers, must be prepared to provide nursing care to persons with AIDS.[27]

Notes

1. Robert E. Riegel, *American Women: A Story of Social Change* (Rutherford, N.J.: Fairleigh Dickinson University Press, 1970), p. 182; American Nurses' Association, *Facts about Nursing 1986–87* (Kansas City, Mo.: American Nurses' Association, 1987), p. 10.
2. Vern V. Bullough and Bonnie Bullough, *The Care of the Sick: The Emergence of Modern Nursing* (New York: Prodist, 1978), p. 192; Joy Curtis, "Final Progress Report: Minority Project in Nursing, 1972–1977, A Study Related to the Admission, Counseling, Program Planning and Instruction of Minority Students Who Have Indicated an Interest in Nursing," supported by NU 00003-05 ORD 17603, Division of Nursing, United States Public Health Service, Department of

Health, Education, and Welfare, Michigan State University, 1977); see also M. Elizabeth Carnegie, *The Path We Tread: Blacks in Nursing, 1854-1984* (Philadelphia: J. B. Lippincott, 1986).

3. Barbara Velsor-Friedrich and Diana P. Hackbarth, "A House Divided," *Nursing Outlook* 38 (May/June 1990):129.

4. Mary Ann Rose, "ADN v. BSN: The Search for Differentiation," *Nursing Outlook* 36 (November 1988):275-79; see also Helen E. Hansen, "Entry into Practice: Nursing's Deferred Destiny," in Mary Stull and SueEllen Pinkerton, eds., *Current Strategies for Nurse Administrators* (Rockville, Md.: Aspen, 1988), p. 288; for a report on a North Dakota statewide project to differentiate levels of practice, see Judy Blauwet and Patty Bolger, "Differentiated Practice in an Acute Care Setting," in Gloria Gilbert Mayer, Mary Jane Madden, and Eunice Lawrenz, eds., *Patient Care Delivery Models* (Rockville, Md.: Aspen, 1990), pp. 261-74.

5. Florence Nightingale, *Notes on Nursing: What It Is and What It Is Not* (Philadelphia: J. B. Lippincott, facsimile of first edition, 1859), p. 6; Virginia Henderson and Gladys Nite, *Principles and Practice of Nursing* (New York: Macmillan, 1978), pp. 15-36; Ann Marriner-Tomey, ed., *Nursing Theorists and Their Work*, 2nd ed. (St. Louis: C. V. Mosby, 1989), pp. 7-13 and passim.

6. Vern L. Bullough and Bonnie Bullough, *History, Trends, and Politics of Nursing* (Norwalk, Conn.: Appleton-Century-Crofts, 1984), pp. 43-45.

7. Personal communication, American Nurses' Association, Kansas City, Missouri, 27 June 1990.

8. American Nurses' Association, *Facts about Nursing 1986-87* (Kansas City, Mo.: American Nurses' Association, 1987), pp. 98-101.

9. Dee Ann Gillies, *Nursing Management: A Systems Approach*, 2nd ed. (Philadelphia: W. B. Saunders, 1989), pp. 232-35; Marian Keels Bennett and Janice Parks Hylton, "Modular Nursing: Partners in Professional Practice," *Nursing Management* 21 (March 1990):20-24; see also Mayer, Madden, and Lawrenz, *Patient Care Delivery Models*.

10. Rosemary Donley and Mary Jean Flaherty, "Analysis of the Market Driven Nursing Shortage," *Nursing and Health Care* 10 (April 1989):185.

11. Ibid.; for information on RN and LPN salary increases, see "Salaries Seen Swinging Higher Again This Year," *American Journal of Nursing* 90 (May 1990):140-41; for an example of planned change in staffing ratios, see "Humana Revamps Its Staffing and Opens Three LPN Schools," *American Journal of Nursing* 90 (February 1990):106, 117-18; see also Peter T. Kilborn, "Nurses Get V.I.P. Treatment, Easing Shortage," *New York Times*, 6 May 1990.

12. "LPNs Widen Their Role; Disagreement Grows," *American Journal of Nursing* 90 (February 1990):16-17; "Florida Struggles to Define What LPNs Can Do with IVs," *American Journal of Nursing* 90 (May 1990):136-37.

13. Carmen R. Ross, *Personal and Vocational Relationships in Practical Nursing*, 4th ed. (Philadelphia: J. B. Lippincott, 1975), p. 158.

14. For an example of a systematic plan designed to help managers and staff nurses, see Martha Davis Cobb, "Dealing Fairly with Medication Errors," *Nursing 90* 20 (March 1990):42-43.

15. In hospitals in which nursing staffs enjoy the support and guidance of well-qualified nurse managers, administrators face dilemmas associated with medication errors similar to the dilemma faced by Jane Robinson, the BSN staff nurse in this case; see also Winifred J. Pinch, "Nursing Ethics: Is 'Covering-Up' Ever 'Harmless'?" *Nursing Management* 21 (September 1990):60-62.

16. Respect for persons can be a principle in each of the four types of ethical theories outlined in Chapter 2, Section 2: goal-based, duty-based, right-based, or intuitionist. The main difference is whether, as a principle within a certain systematic framework, its status is basic, derivative, or subordinate.

17. S. I. Benn, "Abortion, Infanticide and Respect for Persons," in Joel Feinberg, ed., *The Problem of Abortion*, 2nd ed. (Belmont, Calif.: Wadsworth, 1984), p. 141.

18. R. S. Peters, "Respect for Persons," in James Rachels, ed., *Understanding Moral Philosophy* (Encino, Calif.: Dickenson, 1976), pp. 205–9.

19. Margaret Adams, "The Compassion Trap," in Vivian Gornick and Barbara K. Moran, eds., *Women in Sexist Society: Studies in Power and Powerlessness* (New York: New American Library, 1971), pp. 555–75.

20. Joann Ashley, *Hospitals, Paternalism, and the Role of the Nurse* (New York: Columbia University, Teachers College Press, 1976), pp. 16–18.

21. This case was prepared by Linda Rowell, RN, BSN, while she was a student at Michigan State University.

22. Sissela Bok, *Secrets: On the Ethics of Concealment and Revelation* (New York: Pantheon Books, 1982), pp. 119–24.

23. In the actual case, Jerry's co-worker did not discuss his behavior with the supervisor, and Jerry's problems continued for nearly a year before their cause—a deepening addiction to a tranquilizer—resulted in his being dismissed from the hospital.

24. Herbert Morris, "Persons and Punishment," in James Rachels, ed., *Understanding Moral Philosophy* (Encino, Calif.: Dickenson, 1976), pp. 210–27.

25. See Ronald Dworkin, *Taking Rights Seriously* (Cambridge, Mass.: Harvard University Press, 1977), pp. 206–22.

26. Gillies, *Nursing Management: A Systems Approach*, pp. 389–90; see also Jacquelyn Haak Flaskerud, ed., *AIDS/HIV Infection: A Reference Guide for Nursing Professionals*. Philadelphia: W. B. Saunders, 1988.

27. See also John Sumser, Barbara Gerbert, Bryan T. Maguire, and Maria Tadd, "Are Nurse Practitioners Prepared for the AIDS Epidemic?" *Nurse Practitioner* 15 (April 1990):48, 50, 53–54, 56.

6

Personal Responsibility for Institutional and Public Policy

1. The scope of individual responsibility

Up to this point we have been discussing ethical issues that involve identifiable individuals; ethical inquiry, however, may lead us beyond specific individuals to social structures. For what reasons, if any, do ethical considerations require us to identify faults in social structures and then attempt to remedy them?

6.1 Short-staffed in ICU

Last weekend, staff nurse Andrea Moore, who works in ICU, felt she was not able to give patients the kind of care, including frequent enough observations, that she should provide because the unit was short-staffed. After she told the charge nurse that she had too much to do, the charge nurse called the supervisor, whose answer was to "make do." Andrea knew then that she had to handle the situation as best she could and leave low-priority work undone. One of her patients was on a respirator and required numerous treatments, including IVs. Another man had an aortic aneurysm and two women had had major surgery. When the physician ordered a variety of treatments and observations, including some scheduled for every fifteen minutes, the charge nurse again called the supervisor for more help and again was told to make do with the staff on duty. Andrea found herself thinking, "I should be doing this and checking that but I don't have the time." When one of the physicians told Andrea that he needed help with another treatment, she exploded angrily, "We just can't do it! We are really short-staffed today." She was sorry immediately for her outburst, but she remembers thinking, "I don't want to hear him yelling at me because I should be doing something and I am doing the most I can."

At the end of the shift Andrea went home upset, knowing that she should have done more, and could have, if there had been better staffing. The longer she thought about the day, the more she came to believe that no one understood the situation. The physicians wanted done what they judged needed to be done, the nursing supervisor believed the nurses could make do, and Andrea was left to juggle details. Andrea thought that the doctors and the supervisors seemed to be doing their best, but still everything was a mess.

Andrea's exasperation and distress arise not only from the way she is limited by the hospital's allocation of resources to providing substandard nursing care but also probably from an apprehension that the situation may be beyond her—or perhaps anyone's—control. What may underlie her feeling of hopelessness is the sense that her difficulties are the result not so much of the deliberate intentions and choices of identifiable individuals but rather of the impersonal and complex interplay of social forces and structures—"the system."

This situation, of course, is not unique to nursing. Yet it does raise the question, To what extent and for what reasons should Andrea try, first, to determine why the ICU is chronically understaffed and, second, to do something about it?

According to the rules and principles defining the institution of nursing, nurses have social as well as individual obligations. The Code of the International Council of Nurses states that "the nurse shares with other citizens the responsibility for initiating and supporting action to meet the health and social needs of the public" (Appendix A), and Point 9 of the Code of the American Nurses' Association maintains that "the Nurse participates in the profession's efforts to establish and maintain conditions of employment conducive to high quality nursing care" (Appendix B). Although the codes do not argue for these claims, we believe that their concern with questions of social as well as individual ethics is well grounded.

Generally, an obligation to provide a certain level of care to individuals entails as a corollary an obligation to take steps to ensure that conditions exist for providing that level of care. As John Ladd has pointed out,

A parent's responsibility for the health or welfare of his child implies, for example, that if he does not have the power (e.g., the money) or the competence (e.g., the knowledge) to take care of his child, he should forthwith try to get them. There is no reason to think that the same logic does not apply to participants in a social process: if they do not have the power or competence to fulfill their responsibilities they should take all the necessary steps to obtain them.[1]

In the nursing context, this line of reasoning implies that in Case 6.1 Andrea's obligation to provide standard nursing care to the patients to whom she is assigned entails a further obligation to make an effort to identify the source of the staffing problem and to correct it. Since the grounds of this obligation are not limited to nursing, however, it is important to note that the responsibility in question does not fall solely on Andrea's shoulders. Nursing supervisors, physicians, hospital administrators, and possibly others are also obligated in various, and in some cases greater, degrees to attend to the problem. But if they do not appear to be fulfilling their responsibilities, Andrea's responsibility, though perhaps not increased, is not thereby diminished. She still owes it to her patients to make reasonable efforts to determine why the ICU is chronically understaffed and then to try to do something about it.

If we agree that Andrea has a prima facie obligation to try to remedy the situation and that the situation may involve a complex network of social structures, how does she discharge her obligation? Before addressing this question directly, we must explain what we mean by "social structures."

Social structures include organizations (like hospitals), institutions (like medicine and nursing), and practices (like fee-for-service or third-party-payment modes of financing health care). A particular combination of social structures dealing with a more or less restricted set of goods may be called a "system," as, for example, the health care system.

Following Etzioni, we take *organizations* to be "social units (or human groupings) deliberately constructed and reconstructed to seek specific goals."[2] Standard examples are corporations, armies, schools, churches, prisons, and hospitals. Organizations differ from the other kinds of social structures in having more explicit goal-directedness and greater control over their nature and destiny. The prominent characteristics of organizations are (1) explicit divisions of labor and power; (2) one or more power centers that control members' efforts and direct them toward the organization's goals; and (3) substitution of personnel.

Institutions, as we understand them, are social structures that differ from organizations principally in having less control over their nature and destiny. Examples of institutions are property, marriage, the family, nursing, and medicine. Social institutions fulfill certain functions in society and they are characterized by certain rules that fix roles and determine relationships in particular contexts. Nursing and medicine, for example, circumscribe different roles for patients and providers and presume different though complementary roles for nurses and doctors. Finally, although institutions as such do not exert direct control over their own nature and destiny, organizations may be created and maintained that are aimed at shaping and strengthening particular institutions. Thus, the American Nurses' Association and the American Medical Association, both organizations, have as their goal the shaping and strengthening of the institutions of nursing and medicine, respectively.

Practices are made up of rules that coordinate and regulate behavior in determinable ways. Common examples are the "-isms," like racism, sexism, capitalism, and socialism. Controversies over the merits of capitalism and socialism are mirrored in health care controversies over the merits of fee-for-service versus a nationalized health service. Practices often involve and relate different institutions and can be supported or opposed by various organizations. For our purposes, what is important about practices is that, like organizations and institutions, they explain various patterns of human behavior.

If we are to understand, for example, why the ICU in Case 6.1 was repeatedly short-staffed, we must try to identify, first, the organizational causes of this state of affairs and, if necessary, the extent to which the conduct of the organization in question—the hospital—is itself restricted by social institutions and practices. If it turns out that the actions of the organization are restricted by certain institutions and that the institutions are, in turn, limited by certain practices, then the organization can be fully understood only in terms of its role within the practices. In this event, by placing the action of the organization (e.g., hospital) within the context of a practice (e.g., fee-for-service or third-party payment for health care) we obtain a deeper understanding of its conduct and are, as a result, in a position to intervene more effectively (perhaps by joining or forming an organization to do so).

Returning to Case 6.1 and Andrea's obligation to make some effort to identify the source of the problem and to correct it, we suggest the following. Since our concern is not simply that nurses be able to explain situations such as Andrea's but that they be able to help change them, a helpful rule of thumb is to examine the *most alterable* possibilities first. In Andrea's case this means restricting her initial inquiry to the hospital and to its suborganizations, such as the nursing service. In discussions with the nursing administration, Andrea could explore alternatives based upon nursing management programs as well as methods to increase employee satisfaction in health care.[3] If that fails, she could then enlist the support and expertise of another organization, such as her state nursing association. The next step, if the problem is rooted in the practices governing the distribution and financing of health care, might be to become politically active at the local, state, or federal level.[4]

Apart from these schematic rules of thumb, Andrea should also be sensitive to the detailed history of the situation and the personalities of those involved. She should recognize that although her efforts may be necessary for a satisfactory resolution of the problem, they are unlikely to be sufficient. Any change in the situation may require the action and resources of nursing supervisors, physicians, hospital administrators, or patients. Thus Andrea must be careful not to alienate them by being overly self-righteous or condemnatory. Problems attributable to the unintended or unanticipated workings of complex social structures often require social solutions, and individuals who may be credited with initiating changes are unlikely to achieve their ends without the support and cooperation of others.

2. Institutional policies and strikes

Suppose that Andrea is able to identify the source of the staffing problem but that efforts by nurses to persuade those empowered to correct it are unsuccessful. Would they then be justified in shifting from rational persuasion to a more coercive mode of achieving their ends, such as a work stoppage or a strike? Before examining the ethical implications and possible justifications of such measures, we should briefly review the history and legal status of strikes and other forms of work stoppage by nurses.

Collective bargaining by nurses to change organizational policies has a short history, and the use of strikes and other work stoppages an even shorter one. A movement for collective bargaining began in California during World War II, and in 1946 the American Nurses' Association created an economic security program that endorsed state nurses' associations as bargaining agents.[5] But the 1947 Taft-Hartley Labor Management Relations Act, which specifically exempted nonprofit organizations from recognizing bargaining rights of employees, and the no-strike pledge made by the ANA in 1950, made collective bargaining difficult. Basically, nurses had to depend upon public relations campaigns and moral suasion when negotiating with health care organizations.

The 1960s brought changes. When collective bargaining became a right for federal employees in 1962, civilian nurses employed by the government gained the right to choose a bargaining agent. In 1966, when nurses in the San Francisco Bay area threatened to submit mass resignations after long, unproductive negotiations with area hospitals, the California Nurses' Association revoked the ANA no-strike policy and the nurses negotiated successfully. Nurses also struck successfully in Youngstown, Ohio, during that year, and the threat of resignations or strikes led to successes elsewhere. The ANA repealed the no-strike pledge in 1968, as did the National Association of Practical Nurses in 1969.

In 1974 the federal Labor Relations Act was extended to employees of nonprofit health care institutions so that at long last these hospitals were obligated to bargain with nurses. The law specifies dispute-settling and strike procedures by requiring time limits for notification of intent to modify contracts and, if no settlement is reached, notification of the Federal Mediation and Conciliation Service. Further, the law provides time limits for no-strike, no-lockout periods and requires a ten-day strike or picketing notice. Even though legal dispute-settling and strike procedures exist, not all nurses, as the following case illustrates, agree that strikes, mass resignations, or other work stoppages are appropriate.

6.2 Suggestion for a strike

For the past nine months Alice Byrum has worked part time as evening charge nurse on a twenty-bed surgical floor in Batavia Community Hospital. To help with nursing care she occasionally has three, but usually two, aides and on rare occasions only one. She finds two aides an inadequate number and one impossible. A recent State Department of Health inspection team indicated that the hospital is understaffed. Alice believes that the nursing supervisor and hospital administrators should avoid overloading the floor and hallways with patients and systematically understaffing nursing personnel. Administrators could tell physicians to stop sending patients when there is no more room in the hospital, and they could hire more aides and nurses.

Alice is frustrated because, as she says, "You are behind before you start. You can't give adequate care and you can't expect your aides to give good care. It's frustrating knowing the patients aren't getting the care they are supposed to get. I must spend so much time giving 'meds,' making time-consuming rounds with one particular surgeon who insists that I accompany him (the other doctors are more flexible), checking IVs and doing the paperwork that I can't do anything else. The aides do almost all the direct patient care."

Most of the aides rarely get two days off each week because the administration routinely calls them to cover a shortage when they are off duty. Needing to keep a steady job, they comply. Alice, too, has been called to work extra days, but she has repeatedly reminded the caller of her problems in making last-minute baby-sitting arrangements. She has also reminded the nursing administration that she stated clearly when she was hired that she wanted to work only two days each week, and she has asked administrators not to call her because refusing makes her feel guilty (which she assumes they want her to feel).

When Alice complained to her supervisor about the overworked nursing staff, the supervisor told her the day shift had 51 percent of the work load, the evening shift 34 percent, and the midnight shift 15 percent; therefore, the supervisor said, staffing was based on the percentages. Alice, knowing how much work she had to do, replied that the statistics meant nothing. She was offended at being told she had an exact percentage of the work load when she knew she was overworked and had only two aides for help. Alice suspects that her supervisor, a sympathetic listener, never reports her complaints to higher authorities.

Monthly "group gripe" sessions with the hospital nursing staff and nursing administration have brought no results—the same complaints have elicited the same answers. Alice has come to believe that the only solution to the problem is for the nurses to organize and, acting together, stage a walkout strike the next time staffing is hopelessly bad. She has suggested a strike to the hospital evening personnel, who all have the same problems, but no one has supported her. Alice believes that the nurses may "not be the type to do anything, but in any other situation you can bet people would not put up with that kind of staffing. So a strike is not going to happen here. But I am hoping that somehow and in some way . . ."

Alice believes that both nurses and patients would benefit from a strike. Her two main arguments for a nurses' strike appear to be that it would benefit clients by producing changes that would improve the quality of nursing, and benefit nurses by reducing job stress and requests that they work overtime. In an ideal situation, the nursing care that a hospital demands of its staff does not conflict with the nursing care that nurses believe they should provide. But Alice and the other nurses repeatedly find themselves in situations where they can only provide what they regard as substandard care because of the low ratio of nurses to patients. In Alice's view, the hospital's substandard health care is related to its exploitation of the nursing staff. The question now is whether a strike aimed at correcting the situation is ethically justified.

Deciding to initiate or participate in any form of work stoppage—sit-downs, mass resignations, strikes, and so on—is difficult for nurses because of their education and experience as women in a service profession and their inexperience in collective bargaining.[6] Strikes are especially problematic because they amount not only to withdrawing services but also to using the resulting distress as a lever to coerce the hospital or agency into meeting the strikers' demands. Even if efforts are made to provide warning and to staff certain units, such as intensive care, emergency rooms, and a minimal number of general nursing units, the strike will still force some people to wait for care, at the very least inconveniencing them and possibly even harming them. Since nursing strikes by their very nature require nurses to threaten patient services, such strikes bear a heavy burden of justification.

The presumption against nursing strikes, like the presumptions against parentalism, deception, and coercion discussed in Chapter 3, is very strong. Not only may strikes inconvenience and possibly harm clients, they are also likely to backfire. As with strikes by other groups providing vital social services, like police and fire departments, the public is likely to respond negatively when striking nurses seem to be using the sick and infirm as hostages to better their position. Such public perceptions may be detrimental not only to the strikers but also to the entire profession of nursing. Moreover, even if a nursing strike is successful, lingering acrimony between the strikers on the one hand and hospital administrators, physicians, and the public on the other may seriously compromise whatever gains the strike achieved.

Although the presumption against nursing strikes is very strong, we do not think that it is impossible to justify a nursing strike. Like the presumptions against parentalism and deception, it can, at least in principle, be overridden by appeal to certain ethical considerations. We turn now to a brief survey of arguments that attempt to justify such strikes.

A. Goal-based arguments

A goal-based argument in favor of a strike aimed at improving chronically substandard care is that while the strike will to some extent inconvenience and possibly harm *presently* hospitalized clients, it will in the long run contribute to significant improvement in the care of *future* clients. This assumes that the aggregate needs of future clients significantly outweigh those of presently hospitalized clients. A nurse choosing to honor obligations to presently hospitalized clients in such a situation would be making a decision based on short-term interests rather than on the long-term effects of perpetuating poor nursing care.[7]

To increase the net balance of good over bad consequences of a nursing strike, those making a goal-based argument could suggest that strikers not withdraw all services to presently hospitalized clients. Obligations to those who would be directly and severely harmed by the strike could be met. Advance warning of an impending strike would allow prospective clients to choose between seeking other sources of care or tolerating delay.

A less direct utilitarian defense of a nursing strike might focus on the long-term benefits to clients of a highly qualified nursing staff with a fairly low rate of turnover. Continued employment of a well-trained staff depends largely on the level of its salaries and working conditions. If these fall well below those offered by other health care organizations or even other occupations, the hospital or agency will be unable to attract and retain good nurses. Thus, nurses may argue that collective bargaining, strikes, and the threat of strikes aimed at improving their working conditions will indirectly, but significantly, benefit clients.

Whether such arguments can justify nursing strikes depends on two factors: the extent to which one accepts the conclusions of a goal-based or utilitarian argument as decisive on such matters, and the extent to which the utilitarian calculations of overall benefits and harms favor a strike. The first issue requires a review of the strengths and weaknesses of such arguments and whether one can accept the implications of adopting utilitarianism in contexts other than this one. The second requires taking into account all of the probable consequences of a proposed strike and not simply those that support one's predispositions. Thus, the long-term gains of a strike must be balanced not only against short-term losses but also against possible long-term losses, such as negative public perceptions and lingering acrimony between nurses and other health professionals.

One final utilitarian argument against a strike merits special consideration. It is often maintained that nursing strikes weaken the profession itself when staff nurses become adversaries of nurses in administrative positions. This objection, however, may ignore the possibility of the profession's being equally weakened by the submission of the rank and file to prevailing practices. Further, it assumes that an adversary relationship, with its conflict and stress, results only in harmful consequences. Such a relationship may, however, also offer certain benefits, such as mutual goal setting and the incorporation of diverse ideas and points of view resulting in improved nursing services.

Therefore, we conclude that utilitarian considerations may, in certain circumstances, support a nursing strike. Whether in any given situation a strike is justified must be determined by careful efforts to predict, weigh, and balance all of its likely consequences. In most cases, however, utilitarian calculations alone are unlikely to override the presumption against a nursing strike because the short-term negative consequences will always be more certain than the possible long-term benefits. Moreover, we have some misgivings about relying solely on utilitarian considerations in this as well as in other settings. Some duties or rights whose justification is independent of appeals to the overall social good may also have a bearing on the question of nursing strikes.

B. Duty-based arguments

At first glance it appears that we can construct a clear and unconditional duty-based argument against nursing strikes. A nurse's primary duty is to provide for the care and safety of her clients. Assuming that the clients in question are present rather than future clients, nurses would have to assure all clients of safe and adequate nursing care during a strike. But this, of course, would undermine the very point of a strike, which is to coerce management into altering its policies by withdrawing nursing services. Therefore, if a nurse's primary duty is to provide for the care and safety of her clients, and the clients in question are present clients, participation in a nursing strike will always be wrong because it requires the nurse to violate her fundamental duty.

This argument presents a plausible alternative to goal-based or utilitarian approaches to the question of nursing strikes. Its strength, however, depends in part on two important assumptions, which may not always be true. First, the argument assumes that the nursing care that would be withdrawn during a strike is safe and adequate. There may, however, be situations when nursing care in a particular hospital or nursing home is so substandard that patients would be better off if, during a strike aimed at changing these conditions, they returned home or were transferred to another institution. If, for example, a patient in Case 6.2 were hospitalized for elective surgery and the understaffing problem significantly compromised the safety and adequacy of his or her nursing care, nurses would not appear to be violating their duties to this patient by withdrawing their services. On the contrary, the patient would probably benefit from either postponing the operation or having it performed at another hospital. Moreover, it could be argued that, *under these circumstances*, providing seriously substandard nursing services constitutes a greater violation of the duty to provide safe and adequate care than not providing them.

The second assumption underlying the duty-based argument against nursing strikes is that the clients who would presently be harmed by the strike and the clients who would, in the future, benefit from it are entirely different groups of people. In a number of cases, however, especially when the clients in question are suffering from chronic illnesses requiring periodic hospitalization or nursing home care, those harmed or inconvenienced by the strike and those benefited may be one and the same. In such circumstances, when the benefits appear to significantly outweigh the harm or inconvenience, it could be argued that the nurse's duty to adequately serve the future interests of these clients justifies her taking limited risks with their present interests by engaging in some form of withdrawal of services. There would be no group of innocent victims whose interests would be sacrificed for the benefit of others.

Thus, although duty-based considerations provide a strong presumption against nursing strikes and other forms of withdrawal of services, we have tried to show that there are circumstances under which such actions might be justified within a duty-based framework.

C. Right-based arguments

Nurses, it may be argued, have the same rights as other people, and when employers violate these rights, nurses are entitled to defend themselves. When, for example, nurses are continually required to work overtime because of pesonnel shortages, are paid considerably less than people performing comparable tasks for other hospitals or agencies, or are denied a voice as professionals in determining the conditions under which they work, they have a right to do what is necessary to improve their situation. If less drastic means fail and nothing short of a strike appears likely to induce the organization to acknowledge their rights, then they have a right to strike.

A difficulty with this argument, however, is that the nurse's right to strike appears to conflict with the client's right to nursing care, and the latter, on the face of it, seems more important than the former. Most clients receiving nonelective treatment would be likely to prefer substandard nursing care to no nursing care at all. So it is unlikely that even clients who sympathize with the nurse's concerns would be inclined to waive their rights to care.

In response we must distinguish *special* from *general* rights.[8] Special rights are conditional, limited in scope, and grounded in special relationships. The rights to the repayment of a debt or the keeping of a promise are special rights. Such rights are conditional in two ways. They are held not against everyone but only against the person who borrowed the money or made the promise, and they depend on the nature of the special relationship between lender and debtor, promisee and promiser. General rights, on the other hand, are unconditional, unrestricted in scope, and grounded simply in one's being a person. The right to life and the right to liberty are general rights. The sense in which they are unconditional is the obverse of the sense in which special rights are conditional. Thus, they are held against everyone and depend on no special relationship between right-holder and those who have the corresponding obligation to respect the right. Although only people who have borrowed money or made promises are obligated to repay debts or keep promises to an individual, everyone is obligated not to kill others or restrict their liberty.

The question now is whether the "right to health care" is a special right, a general right, or both. To say, for example, that the right to nursing care is a special right is to say that it is grounded in the special relationship between particular nurses and particular clients. Once a nurse assumes care for a client she acquires an obligation to the client and the client acquires a right against her, just as the making of a promise creates special rights and obligations between promisee and promiser. But in both cases, once the respective obligations are fulfilled, the special relationship is ended and further rights and obligations are contingent upon reentering into the special relationship. If the right to nursing care is of this kind, then a nursing strike that results in the abandonment of clients who have already come into the health care system is likely to violate their rights to continued care. If, however, the strike is announced well in advance and makes provision for honoring prior commitments to those already in the system and to those requiring emergency care that can be provided by no other hospital or agency, the extent to which it violates the special rights of clients may be considerably reduced.

If in addition to such special rights there is a general right to health care that has the same status as the rights of life and liberty, health professionals probably could never justify withdrawing their services. Whether there is such a general right, however, is a matter of great controversy. A right to health care, unlike the rights to life and liberty, is a positive rather than a negative right. Whereas the latter requires only that one not be interfered with, the right to health care requires that the right-holder be provided with certain services. And it may be difficult to satisfy this as well as other positive general rights without coercing others to provide their time or money and thus infringe their negative general rights to liberty and property. For this reason, whether there is a general as well as a special right to health care is a matter of much debate. Therefore, an appeal to a general right to health care does not provide a strong basis for opposing nursing strikes, especially when the strikers scrupulously honor the terms of existing relationships with clients and continue to staff facilities providing emergency care that cannot be provided elsewhere.

To return to Case 6.2, we believe that Alice's suggestion for a walkout strike is at least premature and perhaps could never be justified on a right-based theory. First, since the monthly meetings between the nursing staff and administrators are unproductive, a reasonable next step would be for the nursing staff to ask for help from a bargaining agent, such as the state nurses' association, and to negotiate a contract that would address the staffing problems. The 1974 Labor Relations Act obligates the nursing and hospital administration to negotiate with such an agent in good faith. If these collective bargaining negotiations failed, the nurses could then decide whether to strike in support of their demands. Until then, however, a strike is untenable. Without further attempts at rational persuasion, a strike cannot be supported by goal-based, duty-based, or right-based ethical considerations.

If further efforts are unsuccessful, it is possible, though not likely, that utilitarian goal-based reasoning could justify a walkout strike. So too might duty-based reasoning if the strikers could show that current conditions require the violation of basic duties to present clients and that the situation can only be remedied by a walkout strike. On a right-based view, however, the special rights of presently hospitalized clients to even inadequate nursing care are stronger than the nurses' rights or the questionable general rights of the population at large to more adequate care. Indeed, insofar as such strikes require nurses to violate the special rights of those for whom they have already assumed care, it may be impossible to justify any *walkout* strike according to a right-based theory.

3. Institutional ethics committees

An awareness of the interplay between institutional policies and standards of nursing care focuses attention not only upon institutional faults that impede nursing practice but also upon the need to create new institutional structures to address new problems. Many ethical dilemmas confronting nurses cannot be resolved by nurses alone. They involve questions that may require the deliberation of patients, physicians, lawyers, social workers, administrators, allied health professionals, and others, as well as nurses. The next case points to a need for a hospital to establish ways for relevant parties to explore ethical dilemmas more systematically.

6.3 Withdrawing food and fluids

Abby Wilson, staff nurse, can barely contain her frustration. The issue is whether a feeding tube should be removed from a comatose patient. Melvin Thompson, twenty years old, was in an automobile accident four weeks ago and has never regained consciousness. At the time of his accident he suffered severe, irreversible brain damage. He is breathing on his own and is being fed through a nasogastric tube.

Abby is frustrated because she sees no way to address the dispute over whether Melvin's tube feedings should be continued. Melvin's parents have requested that the feeding tube be removed. They understand fully that Melvin will die without tube feedings, but they have told Melvin's physician that they want medical treatment stopped because he will never recover. They believe that Melvin "is just a vegetable" and that his existence "is a living nightmare." "If he were dead," they say, "we could bury him. Instead, it goes on and on. He is not here." They recently read in the local newspaper about another young man who is in a persistent vegetative state. The graphic description indicated that his weight had dropped from 160 to 90 pounds in six months and that his arms were rigidly flexed upon his chest. Melvin's parents believe that Melvin will also be reduced to the same unfortunate state in six months.

Melvin's physician, however, has told his parents that their request is "unthinkable" since neither the patient himself, nor his family, nor his physician could base the discontinuation of food or fluids on the right to refuse medical treatment. Food and water, the physician believes, are not medical treatments; they are basic necessities of life. He also emphasized to the parents that once care is started, it cannot be stopped. He told them that, in California, a pair of physicians who hastened a patient's death by stopping food and fluids were charged with murder.[9] As far as the physician is concerned, this lawsuit ended all dispute; there is nothing more to be said.

Abby, however, remembers reading about a recent Supreme Court decision in which tube-administered hydration and nutrition were classified as medical treatment.[10] But Abby has had little opportunity to discuss her views with others. Abby is not certain that she has thought about all aspects of Melvin's situation; neither is she certain that she is right and the attending physician wrong. She is frustrated because she does not see a way for all parties to work through this difficult situation.[11]

Abby needs access to a structure within the hospital that will help her address the dilemma about removing the feeding tube. As a nurse working with a physician who thinks the parents' request is "unthinkable," she feels caught between the physician and the family. The physician will no longer discuss the matter. The parents want the feedings ended.

An institutional ethics committee, or IEC, can be quite useful in helping families, nurses, physicians, and others address critical ethical dilemmas in health care. The first step an institution can take in deciding whether to form an IEC is to set up a study group of interested persons who agree to discuss ethical issues methodically over a considerable period, say, six to eighteen months. Such a group might profitably begin by discussing issues contained in two books published as part of the report of the President's Commission for the Study of Ethical Problems in Medicine and Biomedical Research: *Making Health Care Decisions* and *Deciding to Forego Life-Sustaining Treatment.*[12] The books summarize the current medical, legal, and philosophical literature and make thoughtful, well-reasoned suggestions on a number of difficult and important issues.

A study group gives members time to exchange ideas and viewpoints and to develop trust. After a period of studying and discussing issues among themselves, members of the group and the hospital administration can decide whether the hospital could benefit from an IEC. If they decide to go ahead with such a committee, they can then begin to determine its structure, composition, and functions.[13]

IECs are structured in various ways, but whatever form a particular committee takes, it will be maximally acceptable and effective if it is rooted in the needs and system of its home institution. The structure of an IEC in a small community hospital is likely to be different from that in a large university hospital. Whereas the former may have a single comprehensive committee, the latter may have instead a number of more specialized committees in particular units (for example, neonatal intensive care, dialysis, medical intensive care).

Multidisciplinary committees composed of nurses, physicians, clergy, social workers, administrators, and possibly others ensure that all relevant perspectives are brought into the discussion. This both increases the likelihood that nothing important is overlooked and assures members of various groups that their concerns have been adequately considered. Such a committee has the potential of promoting thoughtful decision-making and of devising sound policy with respect to "no code" decisions and so on, especially if its members can help one another identify and examine all relevant considerations. A nurse, for example, because of her long-standing and close contact with a patient or family, may be especially well prepared to illuminate certain aspects of a situation for the group.[14]

The major goal of most IECs is educational. After educating themselves about ethical issues in health care and the nature of ethical analysis and reasoning, members can develop and present various types of educational programs for the entire staff. This may include presentations by noted specialists, the showing of pertinent films followed by discussion led by a member of the IEC, roundtable discussions, and ethics case conferences in which a familiar type of case is discussed first by a representative panel and then by members of the audience. In addition to providing education, an IEC may make itself available for consultation.

In Case 6.3, for example, an IEC could be especially helpful to Abby, to Melvin's family, and to Melvin's physician. The committee might help the physician explore the ethics of terminating treatment. He is, of course, not alone in believing that, once a patient is started on a life-sustaining treatment, it cannot be stopped. Conventional wisdom maintains that it is one thing not to start such a treatment, and quite another to withdraw it after having started it. The first is sometimes permitted but the second always forbidden.

The President's Commission carefully analyzed the various arguments surrounding this issue and concluded that there is no significant difference, from an ethical point of view, between withholding and withdrawing a particular form of treatment: "Whatever considerations justify not starting should justify stopping as well. . . . Neither law nor public policy should mark a difference in moral seriousness between stopping and not starting treatment."[15] Although this is not to say that what the President's Commission has concluded is right, an IEC can make the physician aware of the Commission's arguments and the relevant literature if he was not already aware of them. This may make a significant contribution to a well-grounded, mutually satisfactory outcome.

Perhaps, after talking with Melvin's family, Abby, and the IEC, the physician comes to agree that stopping *medical treatment* would be permissible, but he still does not think that tube feedings count as medical treatment. Earlier he had told Abby that fluids and foods are basic necessities of life and are outside the scope of the right to refuse medical treatment. An IEC could also be helpful in this situation. Committee members should, as part of their responsibilities, be up-to-date on the most recent literature and court cases having to do with this issue,[16] and should therefore be able to help resolve this controversy between family and physician. Not everyone can keep up with all of the ethics literature and related court cases, but, in fulfilling its responsibilities, an IEC could. In other instances, an IEC might be able to show physicians and families that their uncertain ethical intuitions about some matters were supported by good arguments in the relevant literature. The IEC could also either point out additional viewpoints or arguments, or assure the parties that they had not overlooked something of importance.

Perhaps, after continued discussion, the physician in Case 6.3 agrees that fluids and food can be stopped in certain cases, but in this case he argues that treatment should not be stopped because it has only been five weeks since the accident. An IEC could be helpful in this situation by asking questions about the "timing" of the decision not to treat rather than questions relating to the patient's prognosis. The family and physician may be seeing the patient from totally different perspectives: Melvin's family might think that Melvin is going to be on tube feedings for ten years. The physician may think that the patient may not necessarily remain in the vegetative state permanently. The IEC, composed of persons from various disciplines, could help each side see the other's position.

In such cases, dialogue is the most important factor. The IEC could suggest that the family and physician make a contract stipulating that they will wait two weeks, or some other specific time, before deciding whether to terminate treatment. The specific period would allow the physician to make a more certain prognosis regarding Melvin's remaining in a persistent vegetative state. The two-week time limit would give the family reassurance that the situation will not go on indefinitely. In other words, the IEC could, in this case, guide the parties toward compromise (see Chapter 4, Section 4).

In conclusion, nurses and others who face difficult ethical dilemmas may find it useful to form IECs. IECs can provide educational forums and sources where concerned nurses, other health care workers, and families can obtain advice and support. They can also provide mechanisms for sustaining systematic decision-making processes. Finally, IECs can be more sensitive to individual cases than can courts of law, and they can provide support and information not available elsewhere in many hospitals.

4. Blowing the whistle

What should a nurse do if correcting a dangerous or unethical practice seems to require that she go outside of routine institutional channels? The term "whistle-blower" has recently been coined to refer to members of organizations who sound an alarm externally to call attention to internal negligence, abuses, or dangers that threaten the public. A civil servant, for example, whose attempts to correct corrupt or unsafe practices in his agency by proceeding through established channels are repeatedly frustrated, may feel there is no alternative but to "go public." This may take the form of writing a letter to an elected official or making a public revelation and accusation through the press. Nurses, too, may be tempted to blow the whistle on what they regard as slovenly, dangerous, unethical, or illegal care in hospitals. Although a nurse is expected to have a certain amount of loyalty to colleagues and co-workers, codes of nursing ethics stress responsibilities to clients and the general public. And in cases of conflict, it is the latter that are supposed to prevail. The following case, taken nearly word for word from a newspaper article, implies that a student nurse blew the whistle on a rather egregious instance of unethical and illegal conduct by a physician.

6.4 "MD suspended from operating room"

A . . . urologist who had his fourteen-year-old son assist him in an operation on a fifty-year-old woman has been prohibited from working in an operating room for two weeks.

The Michigan Board of Medicine reluctantly imposed the sanction Wednesday after [the physician] admitted that the incident occurred and that he had violated state law.

"He didn't err very much," argued . . . a board member from Detroit, who opposed any limitation of the doctor's license. "In the operating room, it's not a solemn wake. It's more like M*A*S*H. People walk in and out. Jokes are made. I can understand how this doctor could get carried away, not only as a teacher but as a father."

But [the] vice chairman of the board argued for the sanction. "We are here to protect the public. If this had been my mother, and he had allowed his fourteen-year-old son to assist with a major operation, I would be extremely upset. If we let this go by the board, I think we are telling the public that we are not here to protect them, we are here to protect the physician."

The incident occurred in March 1983 . . . while [the physician] was performing a bladder operation. He had his son scrub and come into the operating room because [he] said his son was interested in medicine and had asked repeatedly if he could watch an operation.

During the operation [the physician] instructed his son to insert his gloved hand inside the woman's abdomen and feel a catheter balloon in her bladder. As [the physician] was sewing together a layer of tissue over the muscles, he had his son put in two stitches, despite the objections of the anesthesiologist.

The woman, who recovered uneventfully, was not told that [the physician's] son participated in the operation. [The physician], former chief of staff at [the hospital], said he realized his mistake immediately after the operation and apologized to the anesthesiologist and the chief nurse.

A nursing student reported the incident to the Board of Medicine. State law requires that the board take disciplinary action in such cases.[17]

This case raises a number of interesting and important issues. Most important for present purposes is that it appears that the incident never would have come to light, and the physician never would have been suspended, had it not been for the student nurse. Neither the anesthesiologist nor the non-student nurses who must have assisted in the operation took any action. Of course, at least one person objected at the time and that person and others may have tried to pursue the matter through the hospital's internal channels. But, in addition to compromising his co-workers and being unethical with his patient, the physician also violated state law. Although there was no legal obligation to report this transgression, there was an ethical obligation to do so. No one except the student nurse appears to have had the courage to bring the incident to light.

We would, of course, like to know more about this central figure who receives only one brief line in the newspaper article. Did the nursing student observe or participate in the operation? Or did she simply hear of the incident through the hospital's grapevine? In either case, she appears to have shown more concern for protecting the public than did the other nurses, the chief nurse, and the anesthesiologist who participated in the surgery. Although state law requires the Board of Medicine to take disciplinary action when such incidents are reported, no one is legally obligated to make such reports (though there is an ethical obligation to do so).

Blowing the whistle is often a risky business. As an insider, one is presumed to have a certain loyalty to one's colleagues and organization. The whistle-blower, as Sissela Bok has pointed out,

> though he is neither referee nor coach, blows the whistle on his own team. His insider's position carries with it certain obligations to colleagues and clients. . . . When he steps out of routine channels to level accusations, he is going against these obligations. Loyalty to colleagues and clients comes to be pitted against concern for the public interest and for those who may be injured unless someone speaks out. Because the whistleblower criticizes from within, his act differs from muckraking and other forms of exposure by outsiders. Their acts may arouse anger, but not the sense of betrayal that whistleblowers so often encounter.[18]

In the present case the student nurse was accusing the urologist and, by her act of disclosure, was also implicitly criticizing the other doctors and nurses who knew of his action but refrained from reporting it to the Board of Medicine. We cannot help but wonder how they responded to her action. Did they regard her as a heroine or a snitch? Did the other nurses celebrate or condemn what she had done? Honor her or shun her? And how was she later regarded by doctors in the hospital? If no reprisals were taken directly against her, were new restrictions placed on subsequent groups of nursing students? As the newspaper account reveals, at least one member of the board was reluctant to sanction the urologist, even though he admitted that the urologist had violated state law and he was charged with enforcing it. Surely this sympathetic attitude was shared by other physicians who could subsequently exert both direct and indirect pressure on the student nurse.

Although there is a sense in which the whistle-blower's being a student made it more difficult for her to do what she did (because of her inexperience and academic vulnerability), there is also the possibility that this made it easier. As a student she was probably not close to the practicing nurses and physicians. She was probably not dependent on their continued friendship and goodwill. She may not have had time to develop close relationships with the others and, assuming her assignment was only temporary, she would not have to endure for very long the prospect of subtle—or perhaps not so subtle—harassment and reprisals from the urologist's friends and colleagues. It is the whistle-blower's inside position, his or her personal loyalty to the members of the group, together with a deeply rooted, widely shared antipathy to tattletales, that render blowing the whistle so psychologically difficult.

Despite its hazards, the practice of whistle-blowing has received guarded general endorsement. Bok has pointed out that

evidence of the hardships imposed on those who chose to act in the public interest has combined with a heightened awareness of professional malfeasance and corruption to produce a shift toward greater public support of whistleblowers. Public-service law firms and consumer groups have taken up their cause; institutional reforms and legislation have been enacted to combat illegitimate reprisals. Some would encourage even greater numbers of employees to ferret out and publicize improprieties in the agencies and organizations where they work.[19]

However, the oppositions involved are not simply between personal risk and public good. Not all acts of whistle-blowing are justified. Like parentalism, whistle-blowing is a descriptive notion. Having identified an action as whistle-blowing, we must then determine whether we can justify it.

All organizations require a certain amount of trust. "There comes a level of internal prying and mutual suspicion," Bok points out, "at which no institution can function."[20] Groups and societies riddled with members eager to curry favor with an external authority by informing on other members are in grave danger of disintegration. It is especially destructive of intimacy and trust when totalitarian regimes encourage family members, particularly children, to report various forms of private behavior to the authorities. Moreover, the motivation of a whistle-blower may often be impure. Accusations made by those holding grudges or who are paranoid, malicious, resentful, jealous, and so on, may be aimed more at settling scores or hurting certain people than at protecting the public. Some who blow the whistle may also be more concerned with getting public recognition and acclaim than with correcting a serious wrong. The use of internal channels is often more effective than going public. Thus the motivations of one who blows the whistle too soon—who regards whistle-blowing as a first rather than a last resort—are suspect.

There are important lessons to be drawn from this for whistle-blowing on the part of nurses. First, nurses should do all that they can to establish routine, internal channels for reporting and reducing the incidence of impaired, dishonest, and incompetent practice and for resolving various ethical disagreements. Whistle-blowing should be used sparingly and reluctantly, and then only to deal with a serious problem. Sound, everyday procedures will often minimize the need for it. Second, guidelines or criteria, as precise as the subject matter allows, should be developed for determining the conditions under which whistle-blowing is justifiable. Third, changes should be initiated to protect from reprisal those who justifiably blow the whistle. The remainder of this section expands on each of these.

In 1983 the Department of Health and Human Services (DHHS) issued a revised set of "Baby Doe" regulations that required hospitals receiving federal funding to place a notice in "each nurses' station" prohibiting the failure to feed and care for handicapped infants. The notice (which was required to be at least eight and one-half by eleven inches in size) was to include a toll-free, twenty-four-hour-a-day "hot line" number. Individuals with knowledge that any handicapped infant was being denied food or customary medical care were encouraged to use this number to prompt an outside investigation.

Apart from one's personal position on the question of when, if ever, aggressive treatment may be withheld from seriously ill newborns, this particular proposal for institutionalized whistle-blowing was premature and bound to breed alienation and mistrust. As George Annas suggested at the time, it was likely to drive a wedge between doctors and parents on the one hand and nurses on the other:

> The nursing station requirement . . . makes sense only in the light of [D]HHS Secretary Margaret Heckler's comments at her confirmation hearing. Without citing any evidence, she testified that the Baby Doe regulation was needed because nurses were afraid to report cases of child neglect to the appropriate authorities. Her department seems to believe that nurses have been unwilling but passive participants in child abuse. Nothing short of supplying them with a hotline number that they can use anonymously and with immunity will induce them to take their role of child abuse reporters seriously. This view of modern nurses is extremely demeaning, and at odds with their role as team members in most specialized pediatric units.[21]

The hot line, like the policies of totalitarian governments that encourage family members to turn each other in to the authorities, would have, if allowed to continue, promoted unnecessary, excessive fear and distrust, especially in view of the complexities of the issues and the failure at the time to explore less draconian, internal means of addressing them.[22] The policy was, under the circumstances, unwarranted. It put nurses at odds with the cares, concerns, and deliberations of the parents of seriously ill newborns and their physicians.[23]

Certainly there are circumstances in which nurses are justified in blowing the whistle. What general considerations should a nurse take into account in deciding whether a particular instance of whistle-blowing is justifiable? It is important, first, to determine if there is sufficient evidence of negligence, abuse, or danger to the public to warrant action. Hearsay or intuition is usually not enough. If one is about to make a serious accusation, fairness to the accused and maintaining one's own credibility require that it be well grounded. After getting the facts straight, a prospective whistle-blower should be very certain that relevant internal channels and procedures have been adequately explored. As Bok has pointed out:

It *is* disloyal to colleagues and employers, as well as a waste of time for the public, to sound the loudest alarm first. Whistleblowing has to remain a last alternative because of its destructive side effects. It must be chosen only when other alternatives have been considered and rejected. They may be rejected if they simply do not apply to the problem at hand, or when there is not time to go through routine channels, or when the institution is so corrupt or coercive that steps will be taken to silence the whistleblower should he try the regular channels first.[24]

A prospective whistle-blower should also analyze his or her own motives and make sure that personal bias, settling a score, jealousy, and so on are not the driving force behind the action and that protecting the public is the paramount concern. Finally, even after all of the foregoing conditions have been met, a prospective whistle-blower must carefully consider the likelihood of success, the negative effects on what we will suppose is an otherwise worthy organization, and various personal repercussions. With regard to the last, there are, we believe, times when retaliation by the accused is so certain and so powerful that a person cannot be blamed for refraining from blowing the whistle, even if his or her action is otherwise justified.[25]

This brings us to our final topic, structural protections for those who blow the whistle. Whistle-blowing is a risky undertaking. A number of individuals whose acts of blowing the whistle have been met with public acclaim also have lost their jobs, have lost large amounts of money and had their families disintegrate, or have been reassigned to meaningless, dead-end positions in their organizations. Others, however, though undergoing some hardship, have fared better.[26]

Apart from structural changes to reduce the need for whistle-blowing, then, we should also give some consideration to structural changes that protect those who find it necessary to blow the whistle. A number of laws have recently been enacted to protect certain federal, state, and corporate employees who blow the whistle. For example, Michigan's "Whistleblowers Protection Act" allows courts to award back pay, reinstatement to their jobs, and the costs of litigation to whistle-blowing corporate employees who can demonstrate improper treatment.[27] This law went into effect in 1981. Two difficulties, identified by Bok, with laws of this type are the availability of more subtle modes of retaliation against whistle-blowing employees that fall beneath the threshold of such laws and the difficulties encountered by courts in distinguishing legitimate from spurious complaints.[28] Although we know of no such laws protecting nurses, we believe that nurses ought to be trying to devise effective institutional protections for justifiable acts of whistle-blowing. In so doing, however, they must be aware of various limitations and pitfalls. A set of protections may, for example, turn out to be too strong, encouraging a degree of whistle-blowing that reduces openness, trust, and cooperation to a point where a basically good institution can no longer effectively function.

There is no simple solution to the problems of whistle-blowing; there is no simple list of dos and don'ts that will tell us what we should do in every case.[29] There are, of course, easy cases at either end of the spectrum—cases in which we can say with confidence that the whistle should or should not be blown. In between is a vast range of cases that require detailed knowledge of the particular circumstances and a sensitive, probing application of the sorts of considerations outlined above.

5. Public policy: advance directives

In addition to a concern for what goes on in the particular organizations within which they work, nurses' obligations to their clients may also require them to participate in shaping public policy. When, for example, an analysis of barriers to adequate nursing care reveals an outdated legal restriction, nurses, as well as other health professionals, have a responsibility to help remove it.

6.5 Hospital and public policy versus patient's wishes

Joan O'Brien is the evening charge nurse on a small, busy cardiac care unit. Mr. Joseph Mesick, aged eighty-one, has been hospitalized for four days following a severe episode of angina. Mr. Mesick is a retired lawyer who is much respected in the community. He plans to return to his daughter's home in the morning.

Although Mr. Mesick passively accepted treatment (including nasal oxygen and IV therapy during the first twenty-four hours), he later told Joan that he did not want to be treated again with "tubes and machines" and that he "had made his peace and was ready to die."

Upon responding immediately to his roommate's urgent cry for help, Joan found Mr. Mesick slumped in his bed. She could not detect a pulse, and he did not respond when she called his name. She believed that if she did not start cardiopulmonary resuscitation immediately, death was imminent. Joan also knew that the usual hospital policy in such cases was to initiate resuscitation and call immediately for help. But she believed, too, that she should honor Mr. Mesick's wishes not to be treated with "tubes and machines." Mr. Mesick's physician had made no comment or notation about whether to withhold aggressive treatment in an emergency. And since Mr. Mesick was pain-free after the first day and planned to return home very soon, Joan had not discussed the question of withholding resuscitation with other persons involved in his care or in detail with Mr. Mesick himself.[30]

Joan's dilemma is quite clear. If she is to respect Mr. Mesick's autonomy and respond to what she believes are his overriding wishes, she should not start cardiopulmonary resuscitation. If she is to act in accord with hospital policy, then she must start it. Given the facts of the case, there is no clear resolution. The situation is a bad one, and Joan must quickly determine which alternative is, all things considered, best.

Although we agree that patients in Mr. Mesick's position have a right to refuse treatment with "tubes and machines," we believe it is important that health care providers and others make certain that such refusals are genuinely autonomous.[31] Perhaps Mr. Mesick's decision was genuinely autonomous, but Joan has not adequately determined that it was. Even if she had, the hospital's policy to initiate immediate resuscitative measures and the questionable legal status of decisions not to resuscitate in cases like this one are troublesome. For, although a conscious, competent adult may legally refuse lifesaving medical treatment, the legal standing of a previously expressed refusal is unclear in a situation in which, due to illness or injury, the patient is no longer able to express his desires. Moreover, Joan's not having specifically discussed *this* type of situation with Mr. Mesick, his daughter, his physician, and others involved in his care further complicates an already complicated problem.

Thus, even though it is possible that Mr. Mesick does (or would) not want to be resuscitated, on balance it seems that Joan must proceed with cardiopulmonary resuscitation and immediately call for help. Resuscitation is, under the circumstances, the best thing to do. When the stakes are so high, it is better to err on the side of continued life if the competence and resolve of a patient are as problematic as here.

Given that this is the best that Joan O'Brien can do in these circumstances, she can nonetheless try to assure that similar situations do not recur. Making the best of a bad situation often requires that we subsequently take steps to make such situations better. For example, the first time Mr. Mesick told Joan that he did not want to be treated again with "tubes and machines" and that he "had made his peace and was ready to die," she could have discussed this matter with him further. She could have tried to determine exactly what he meant and, together with his physician and daughter, tried to determine whether his request was autonomous, that is, freely made, in accord with his long-standing character traits and values, and based on a clearheaded understanding of his prognosis and the probable consequences of further treatment. Had Joan made such an assessment, had all parties agreed both that Mr. Mesick's decision was autonomous and that cardiopulmonary resuscitation in the circumstances described in Case 6.5 came under the heading of what Mr. Mesick meant by "tubes and machines," then a decision not to resuscitate would have been more defensible.

Nevertheless, the questions of hospital policy and the law would remain. Even if Mr. Mesick, his daughter, Joan O'Brien, and the physician had agreed that resuscitation in such circumstances should not be undertaken, hospital policy and state law may have required it. If so, we believe that both Joan and the physician would have an obligation to make reasonable efforts to alter both hospital policy and the law. As was pointed out earlier in this chapter, obligations that we have to others generally entail as a corollary a requirement that we take steps to ensure that conditions exist for fulfilling these obligations. In the present case, this means that Joan's obligation to respect the rights and wishes of patients like Mr. Mesick entails a further obligation to do what she can to alter institutional and public policies that may interfere.

In dealing with legal restrictions, Joan and her colleagues should work for the adoption of legislation that assures that a patient's desire, expressed while he or she is conscious and competent, not to be resuscitated under certain circumstances would retain its legal standing even when, due to illness or injury, the patient is no longer able to express it. Laws allowing such "advance directives," either in the form of a "living will" or the durable power of attorney, have recently been passed in a number of states and been given qualified endorsement in prestigious medical journals and by the President's Commission on Ethical Problems in Medicine and Biomedical and Behavioral Research.[32] In Michigan, where such legislation has recently been passed after fifteen years of debate, individual nurses and professional nursing associations made important contributions to the deliberations of a Legislative Task Force on Death and Dying that worked on the problem.

6. Putting it all together

We mentioned at the beginning of Chapter 3 that, although we would be examining various sorts of questions, issues, and concepts separately, individual cases often raise more than one of them. In everyday life, considerations of parentalism, deception, confidentiality, and so on frequently overlap.

The same holds true of many of the topics covered in different chapters of this book. Although separate chapters are devoted to the relationships between nurses and clients, nurses and physicians, and nurses and other nurses, and to questions of personal responsibility for institutional and public policy, these topics too are often interrelated. The following nationally publicized case provides a rich and interesting illustration of this important point.

6.6 What would you do?

Shortly after coming on duty on a mid-September evening in 1983, Thomas P. Engel, RN, walked into the room of Joseph Dohr, a patient at St. Michael Hospital in Milwaukee. Eighteen days earlier the seventy-eight-year-old man had collapsed at his home, the victim of a stroke. Mr. Engel had cared for him since then.

The patient's brainstem was severely damaged, and despite extensive high-technology care, his condition was worsening each day. Earlier that morning Dr. Allan Kagen had told Mr. Dohr's wife and daughters that Mr. Dohr had suffered irreversible brain damage and would soon die. The family then asked the doctor to disconnect Mr. Dohr's life-support system, but he refused. Although hospital policy would have permitted this and Dr. Kagen later acknowledged that he could have acceded to the family's wishes, he decided not to because he believed that, even with life support, death was imminent.

Entering the patient's room, Mr. Engel found himself alone with Mr. Dohr. Mr. Engel proceeded to turn off the alarm systems on the patient's heart monitor and on the respirator. He disconnected the oxygen supply and waited for six to eight minutes until there was no heartbeat. Then he reconnected the oxygen supply and summoned a doctor, who pronounced Mr. Dohr dead at 6:10 P.M. Shortly after, Mr. Engel notified the Dohr family that their husband and father had died peacefully and without pain.

The nurse's surreptitious role in this case would probably have gone undetected had Mr. Engel not spoken about it. Eight months later, however, he talked of what he had done with some of his colleagues, one of whom was married to a police officer. As a result he was formally charged in a criminal complaint with practicing medicine without a license, a misdemeanor.

He pleaded guilty to this charge and received a twenty-month suspended sentence in 1984. Then on 19 March 1985, his license was revoked for a period of one year by the Wisconsin Board of Nursing. The board said that although Mr. Engel had acted with "altruism" and that his patient should have been allowed to die, his action fell outside the scope of the nursing profession. In addition, however, the board recommended that a separate disciplinary panel investigate the professional conduct of the doctors involved in the case for their refusal to withdraw treatment from the patient despite his family's request to do so. The board's recommendation implies that other doctors besides Dr. Kagen were involved.

In an interview in December 1984, Mr. Engel explained his action by describing a bedside scene with one of Mr. Dohr's daughters:

She was standing there by her father's bed stroking his arm and his cheek and crying and talking to him. He was in a coma, in a steady decline. The only thing keeping him alive was the ventilator breathing for him. "This isn't right," she said. Then she *looked across the bed at me, right in my eyes, and she said "If I could do this thing, I would."*

"Now what would you do?" Mr. Engel asked the interviewer.[33]

This case raises many of the questions discussed in this chapter. If patients or their families make a legitimate request for an action that is permitted by hospital policy, and yet an attending physician refuses to comply with it, what recourse should they have? Is it their responsibility to seek a different physician who is inclined to honor their request? Should it be the attending physician's duty to find such a physician? Should a patient representative or an Institutional Ethics Committee play a role in the situation? What should be a nurse's role in such a case? Since the Dohr family was aware of no policy for dealing with situations of this kind, they appealed to Mr. Engel, or so the quotation at the end of the case presentation would lead us to believe.

When one of the patient's daughters looked across her father's bed and said, "This isn't right. . . . If I could do this thing, I would," it could be interpreted as implying that if Mr. Engel wanted to do the right thing, and if he knew how to disconnect the ventilator, then he should do it. Mr. Engel's description of the event and his question to the interviewer, "Now what would you do?" suggests that this was, indeed, his interpretation. The question remains, however, whether Mr. Engel subsequently did the right thing.

Let us consider, first, the relationship between law and ethics. Mr. Engel probably knew that what he was doing was, strictly speaking, illegal. Hospital policy permitted the ventilator to be disconnected, but neither hospital policy nor the law permitted a nurse to do it. There would have been no problem of law had Dr. Kagen or some other physician done so. From an ethical point of view, Mr. Engel's disconnecting the ventilator was not a terribly serious offense. It was not as if what he did was absolutely forbidden. Given these circumstances, we, like the Wisconsin Board of Nursing, can understand how Mr. Engel would have been tempted, from noble motives, to perform such an action.

That Mr. Engel deceived the family and his colleagues and that his action was covert are, however, at least as troubling as the fact that his action was illegal. Would it have been better if, shortly after disconnecting the ventilator, Mr. Engel had admitted that he had done so, and then blown the whistle on Dr. Kagen as a dramatic way of trying to prevent such occurrences in the future? Questions of personal prudence aside, which is more justifiable from an ethical point of view—going public in this way or maintaining a deception? We must also ask whether more justifiable ways of trying to effect a change in policy were available to Mr. Engel. Did he exhaust regular internal channels for bringing a complaint against Dr. Kagen? Would such channels have been effective? Was there time to pursue them? Could he have threatened to call a local newspaper as a means of coercing Dr. Kagen or others to comply with the family's wishes? Would it have been likely that Dr. Kagen would have responded punitively to any overt attempts to alter his behavior? These are only some of the questions that can be raised about Mr. Engel's conduct.

Let us turn now to the other nurse involved, the one who blew the whistle on Mr. Engel. What would you do, we might ask, if you were sitting around the coffee pot and one of your colleagues revealed that eight months earlier she had done what Mr. Engel had done? In the actual case, one of the nurses apparently told her spouse and Mr. Engel was charged as a result. We do not know whether the nurse encouraged her spouse to report the case. We may still ask, however, whether a nurse should, in such circumstances, report an act of this kind, and why.

Finally, note that many of the problems raised by this case—and much more can be said about it than has been said here—cannot be resolved by individual nurses or the nursing profession alone. The issues involve matters of law and policy and of relationships among nurses, physicians, and patients and their families. Mutually satisfactory, well-grounded resolutions to these broad issues require disciplined ethical analysis and reasoning by all the parties involved. Ethical problems in health care are often public problems; they cannot be resolved by one individual or by one profession. Nurses have much to contribute to this ongoing process, and a principal aim of this book is to enable them to do so more effectively.

Notes

1. John Ladd, "The Ethics of Participation," in J. Roland Pennock and John W. Chapman, eds., *Participation in Politics* (New York: Lieber-Atherton, 1975), p. 121.
2. Amitai Etzioni, *Modern Organizations* (Englewood Cliffs, N.J.: Prentice-Hall, 1964), p. 3.
3. See Ruth Barney Fine, "New Responsibilities Call for New Relationships," *Nursing Administration Quarterly* 3 (Winter 1979):69–75. For ways of changing organizations by modifying the nurse's professional concepts, see Marlene Kramer, *Reality Shock: Why Nurses Leave Nursing* (St. Louis: C. V. Mosby, 1974), and Marlene Kramer and Claudia Schmalenberg, *Path to Biculturalism* (Wakefield, Mass.: Contemporary Publishing, 1977). For a discussion of "change" and "risk-taking" see Marlene Grissum and Carol Spengler, *Womanpower and Health Care* (Boston: Little, Brown, 1976), pp. 217–65.
4. Beatrice J. Kalisch and Philip A. Kalisch, "A Discourse on the Politics of Nursing," *Journal of Nursing Administration* 6 (March–April 1976):29–34; see guidelines for influencing public policy in Margaret Murphy Vosburgh, "Licensure, Legislation and Health Policy," in Katherine W. Vestal, ed., *Manage-*

ment Concepts for the New Nurse (Philadelphia: J. B. Lippincott, 1987), pp. 258–59.

5. The historical summary that follows is drawn from Philip A. Kalisch and Beatrice J. Kalisch, *The Advance of American Nursing* (Boston: Little, Brown, 1978), pp. 671–82; Vern L. Bullough and Bonnie Bullough, *The Care of the Sick: The Emergence of Modern Nursing* (New York: Prodist, 1978), pp. 205–12; and Catherine Ecock Connelly, Lois Kuhn, Roanne Muldoon, and Nancy Adams Wieker, "To Strike or Not to Strike: A Debate on the Ethics of Strikes by Nurses," *Supervisor Nurse* 10 (January 1979):52, 56.

6. See Kalisch and Kalisch, "A Discourse on the Politics of Nursing."

7. Robert M. Veatch, "Interns and Residents on Strike," *Hastings Center Report* 5 (December 1975):7–8.

8. William N. Nelson, "Special Rights, General Rights and Social Justice," *Philosophy and Public Affairs* 3 (Summer 1974):410–30.

9. Bonnie Steinbock, "The Removal of Mr. Herbert's Feeding Tube," *Hastings Center Report* 13 (October 1983):13–16.

10. As part of a complex decision in *Cruzan* v. *Director, Missouri Department of Public Health* (25 June 1990), the United States Supreme Court has held that artificial feeding devices, like nasogastric and gastrostomy tubes, are medical treatments and can, under certain conditions, be withheld or withdrawn from patients, including those who are no longer competent to decide for themselves. Many important and troublesome questions surrounding such decisions were, however, left unanswered by the Court's decision. For commentary on the reasoning and conclusions of *Cruzan* v. *Director, Missouri Department of Public Health*, see the series of articles collected under the heading "Cruzan: Clear and Convincing?" in the *Hastings Center Report* 20 (September/October 1990):5–11.

11. This fictitious case is based in part on a case reported by Lynell Mickelsen, "The Ordeal of Residency," *Detroit Free Press*, 5 May 1985.

12. President's Commission for the Study of Ethical Problems in Medicine and Biomedical and Behavioral Research, *Making Health Care Decisions* (U.S. Government Printing Office, 1982), and *Deciding to Forego Life-Sustaining Treatment* (U.S. Government Printing Office, 1983).

13. Ronald E. Cranford and A. Edward Doudera, eds., *Institutional Ethics Committees and Health Care Decision Making* (Ann Arbor, Mich.: Health Administration Press, 1984).

14. Joy Curtis, "Multidisciplinary Input on Institutional Ethics Committees: A Nursing Perspective," *Quality Review Bulletin* 10 (July 1984):199–202.

15. President's Commission for the Study of Ethical Problems in Medicine and Biomedical and Behavioral Research, *Deciding to Forego Life-Sustaining Treatment*, p. 77.

16. See, for example, Joanne Lynn and James F. Childress, "Must Patients Always Be Given Food and Water?" *Hastings Center Report* 13 (October 1983):17–21; Daniel Callahan, "On Feeding the Dying," *Hastings Center Report* 13 (October 1983):22; Rebecca S. Dresser and Eugene V. Boisaubin, "Ethics, Law, and Nutritional Support," *Archives of Internal Medicine* 145 (January 1985):122–24; David W. Meyer, "Legal Aspects of Withdrawing Nourishment from an Incurably Ill Patient," *Archives of Internal Medicine* 145 (January 1985):125–28; Mark Siegler and Alan J. Weisbard, "Against the Emerging Stream: Should Fluids and Nutritional Support Be Discontinued?" *Archives of Internal Medi-*

cine 145 (January 1985):129–31; and Joyce V. Zerwekh, "The Dehydration Question," *Nursing 83* (January 1983):47–49.

17. Dolly Katz, "MD Suspended from Operating Room," *Detroit Free Press*, 12 October 1984.

18. Sissela Bok, *Secrets: On the Ethics of Concealment and Revelation* (New York: Pantheon, 1982), p. 214.

19. Ibid., p. 212.

20. Ibid., p. 213.

21. George Annas, "Baby Doe Redux: Doctors as Child Abusers," *Hastings Center Report* 13 (October 1983):26.

22. Leah Curtin, "The Babies Doe: Common Sense and Common Decency," *Nursing Management* 14 (December 1983):7f.

23. The federal regulations concerning handicapped newborns have since been revised. Nurses are no longer explicitly placed in an institutionalized whistle-blowing role.

24. Bok, *Secrets*, p. 221.

25. See, for example, Patricia Murphy, "Deciding to Blow the Whistle," *American Journal of Nursing* (September 1981):1691f.

26. Myron Glazer, "Ten Whistleblowers and How They Fared," *Hastings Center Report* 13 (December 1983):33–41; Sara T. Fry, "Whistle-Blowing by Nurses: A Matter of Ethics," *Nursing Outlook* 37 (January/February 1989):56; Anonymous author, "Blowing the Whistle on Incompetence: One Nurse's Story," *Nursing 89* 19 (July 1989):47–50; Leah L. Curtin, "Sister Angelique 'Blows the Whistle' . . . ," *Nursing Management* 17 (October 1986):7–8; Irene Heywood Jones, "The Whistle Blower," *Nursing Times* 85 (8 March 1989):53–54.

27. Bok, *Secrets*, p. 227.

28. Ibid.

29. For a useful summary of relevant considerations, see Alfred G. Feliu, "Thinking of Blowing the Whistle?" *American Journal of Nursing* 83 (November 1983): 1541f.

30. This case has been adapted from one reported by Janice Olson, "To Treat or to Allow to Die: An Ethical Dilemma in Gerontological Nursing," *Journal of Gerontological Nursing* 7 (March 1981):141–47.

31. See, for example, Bruce Miller, "Autonomy and the Refusal of Lifesaving Treatment," *Hastings Center Report* 11 (August 1981):22–28; and David L. Jackson and Stuart Youngner, "Patient Autonomy and 'Death with Dignity,'" *New England Journal of Medicine* 301 (23 August 1979):404–8.

32. Arnold Relman, "Michigan's Sensible 'Living Will,'" *New England Journal of Medicine* (31 May 1979):1270f.; President's Commission for the Study of Ethical Problems in Medicine and Biomedical and Behavioral Research, *Deciding to Forego Life-Sustaining Treatment*, pp. 136–53.

33. *New York Times*, 23 September 1984 and 20 March 1985.

7

Cost Containment, Justice, and Rationing

1. Introduction

As health care costs continue to soar, nurses find themselves pulled in contrary directions. The traditional patient-centered ethic stresses the health care professional's commitment to particular patients, irrespective of their ability to pay or the cost of their care to society. At the same time, pressures to contain costs occasionally require health care professionals to limit treatment or even to turn away some patients who could benefit from their care. Consider, in this connection, the following case.

7.1 Ideals and reality

During her twenty-seven-year career in nursing, Gail Crain, RN, has earned a reputation as one of the most committed nurses in her city. She now owns and operates a home care agency. As her own boss, she is able to provide the high-quality nursing care that she thinks her clients should receive. In the face of spiraling health care costs, however, she finds herself confronted with a difficult dilemma: she can no longer continue to accept nonpaying clients if her agency is to remain financially solvent, yet she knows that if she were to declare a moratorium on accepting clients who could not themselves pay for her agency's services, they would probably not find another source of home nursing care. She knows from experience that some clients would soon be forced to leave their homes for institutionalized care. Institutionalized care, though ultimately more expensive for society and less satisfying for the clients, is publicly funded. The thought of restricting her services to those who can personally pay for them is repugnant to Gail Crain; allocating health care services based on ability to pay violates her sense of justice.

188

But how can she provide home care to anyone if providing it to some without payment will force her to close her doors?[1]

The dilemma facing Gail Crain reflects a larger problem facing the health care system and society. Deciding how to allocate access to care in the face of limited resources raises difficult questions of social justice. Should ability to pay be the principal criterion for access to care? Or should health care be rationed so as to guarantee a basic minimum of care to all? If we elect to ration, how do we determine the basic level of health care to which everyone is entitled? How do we pay for making this care available to all? And what will be the costs to the system as a whole in terms of overall quality and professional integrity and autonomy?

These questions are related to the problems of resource allocation that troubled Andrea Moore in Case 6.1. Whereas Andrea was concerned about what economists call *micro*-allocation (the allocation of particular resources at the level of the clinic or hospital), Gail Crain is concerned about matters of *macro*-allocation (determinations at the societal level about how much money should be allocated to health care—as opposed to other social needs—and exactly how this money is to be apportioned among needs for acute care, chronic care, prevention, education, and so on). Nurses, if they are to meet their social obligation to provide high-quality nursing care, must understand and address questions of macro-allocation as well as questions of micro-allocation. An obligation to provide a certain level of care to individuals entails as a corollary an obligation to do what one can to ensure that conditions exist for providing that level of care (Chapter 6, Section 1).

"Nurses who responded to an ethics survey conducted in 1985 by the Minnesota Nurses Association," writes nurse educator Mila Ann Aroskar, "identified the allocation and rationing of scarce resources as 'the most important ethical issue facing nursing today.'"[2] But, Aroskar adds, this is an issue that cannot be adequately addressed by individual nurses or by the profession of nursing by itself. It requires cooperative efforts and interdisciplinary understanding among many affected parties, as well as a new perspective on nursing ethics:

Our society is confronted directly with issues such as the allocation and rationing of resources in health care. It becomes clearer that much of the work in bioethics, and even in nursing ethics, that has focused on the intricacies of individual decision making and rights of individuals is not adequate to the challenges confronting us today—that is, making sense of how we as a society are going to use and pay for societal benefits, including nursing and health care.[3]

The aim of this chapter is, therefore, to expand the focus of nursing ethics by incorporating questions of cost containment, social justice, and the possibility of health care rationing.

We begin by identifying problems created by limited resources. The problems are deep and unavoidable. Proposals for reducing waste and inefficiency in the health care system, while softening the problems, will not, as many seem to think, eliminate them. Considerations of justice then lead to the concept of rationing—a widely used but frequently misunderstood idea. We examine a plan for rationing health care in the state of Oregon and suggest a framework for assessing the ethical justification of various rationing proposals. Finally, we show that nursing care has a special role to play in any justifiable rationing scheme.

The set of issues discussed in this chapter will frame ethical inquiry in health care for the foreseeable future. Traditional interpersonal ethical concerns like informed consent, patients' rights, allowing to die, and so on will continue to be important, but they will be inseparable from issues of macro-allocation having to do with limited resources and the justice of the health care delivery system as a whole. Debates about continued care for those in a persistent vegetative state (total and permanent loss of consciousness) must, for example, consider that there are five to ten thousand such individuals in American health care institutions at an annual cost ranging from $120 million to well over $1.2 billion.[4] Are there, one may reasonably ask, more just and effective uses for these funds in the health care system? It is therefore important that nurses understand current debates about limited resources, justice, and rationing in the health care system so that they can contribute their insights and understanding, both individually and as a profession, to the resolution of these debates.

2. Cost containment and the claims of justice

Thoughtful nurses are already aware of questions of macro-allocation as they are raised by efforts to contain health care costs:

7.2 Limiting health care

Mary Szymanski, Chairperson of the Professional Nursing Practice Committee in her two-hundred-bed community hospital, is increasingly concerned about possible limits on health care spending. She believes that nurses like herself should become involved in community grass-roots organizations to make their views known to legislators. At such a community meeting Mary met Toni Gonzales.

Mary agrees with the American Association of Retired Persons that every person of any age should have access to health care. Toni, however, advocates limiting expensive prolongation of life for persons in their eighties and nineties, and she reminds Mary that money spent on health care is money that cannot be spent on schools. She encouraged Mary to read Daniel

Callahan's Setting Limits: Medical Goals in an Aging Society, *and she emphasized the need to balance expensive high-technology care medical costs and long-term care expenses when considering health care for older groups.*

For several weeks Mary pondered Toni's position. Should she modify her own views and agree that very expensive treatments for cancers and other fatal diseases in the aged be limited? And if she modifies her position about the elderly, should she also modify her view that all newborns, no matter their size and the expense incurred, should be treated? Or can new ways be found to increase funding for health care?[5]

Mary Szymanski is asking the right questions. There are, however, no easy answers.

The increasing cost of health care in the United States is a matter of great concern. Expenditures on health care in 1989 totaled nearly $600 billion, up from $121 billion in 1980. The percentage of the nation's gross national product devoted to health care is now 11.5 percent. The United States cannot, according to most commentators, continue to spend this much on health care without neglecting other pressing societal issues such as education, housing, poverty, environmental protection, disposal of toxic wastes, and maintenance and repair of the nation's infrastructure (roads, bridges, sewers, etc.). Competitive demands of the international marketplace put additional pressures on the portion of the gross national product the United States can allocate to health care. Economist Lester Thurow reports that while cash wages of American autoworkers are only slightly higher than those of their Japanese counterparts, fringe benefits, including very costly medical insurance, render total costs for American automakers nearly double those of Japanese automakers. "If American companies cannot control their health-care costs," Thurow writes, "they cannot compete in world markets."[6] This observation is reinforced by Joseph S. Califano, currently Chair of Chrysler Corporation's committee on health care: "In 1988, Chrysler spent $700 on employee health care for each vehicle manufactured—twice as much as French and West German automakers and three times as much as the Japanese."[7]

A number of factors have contributed to the increasing cost of health care. According to one estimate, advances in, and more frequent use of, medical technology account for 30 to 40 percent of the rapid rise in health care costs.[8] Many of these new technologies, such as CAT and MRI scanning and ultrasound, provide with lesser risks greater benefits than their predecessors. But they come at a price not only for research, development, and manufacture but also for the larger number of better-trained and consequently better-paid health care professionals required to employ them.[9] The same is true of complex life-extending surgical procedures like transplantation. A second important factor is the aging of the population. The number and percentage of Americans sixty-five years of age or over is projected to rise dramatically over the next forty years. Health care costs for this part of the population are considerably higher than among other age-groups. As the ranks of the elderly continue to grow, so will their demands on the total health care budget not only for the treatment of acute illness but also for the amelioration of chronic illness and long-term, noncurative care.

It appears, therefore, that something must give. Either the society explic-itly limits or forgoes certain types of beneficial health care to all or some members of the population *or* it ignores or gives short shrift to other im-portant needs, such as education, housing, and general economic well-being (as determined by, for example, the nation's ability to compete in the world marketplace). Before coming to grips with the dilemma between either limiting health care or limiting other important societal goods, let us briefly examine two proposals for dissolving it. The first argues that there is no need for a societal decision on the matter; health care, like other goods and services, is a matter of individual decision, not public policy, and should be bought and sold according to free-market principles of supply and demand. The second proposal suggests that we can eliminate the problem by reducing waste and inefficiency in the health care system. Once the "fat" in the health care budget is cut, we will no longer be faced with having to choose between cost containment and the claims of justice. Neither of these proposals, however, nor some combination of them, can extricate us from the dilemma.

A. Health care as a consumer good

Some argue that the conflict disappears when health care is conceived as an ordinary consumer good. Like cars, television sets, music lessons, and membership in health clubs, health care should, on this view, be distributed according to general market principles to those able and willing to pay for it.[10] The government, the argument goes, has no special role in paying for or distributing health care. If those who desire and can afford to pay for expensive health care are willing to pay for it, the market will respond to their demands. Those lacking either the desire for certain forms of health care or the ability to pay for it will go without. This is the principle of distribution most compatible with individual choice and liberty and which governs the distribution of most other goods and services in the society.

The difficulty with this view is its assumption that health care is simply another consumer good or service like a stereo system or tennis lessons. Health is importantly different from ordinary consumer goods or services because, like education, it is necessary for maintaining fair equality of opportunity among members of society. Individuals can no more exercise their capacities to lead decent and meaningful lives or compete for other social goods if they are restricted, through no fault of their own, by preventable or treatable ill health than they can exercise these capacities if, due to parental poverty or neglect, they are deprived of a basic education.[11] It is for this reason, and perhaps others,[12] that we are rightly reluctant to allocate health care resources solely in accord with market principles. A commitment to preserving equal liberty, understood as equal opportunity for leading a decent and meaningful life,[13] provides the justification for a system of publicly funded, equally accessible health care, as well as for a system of publicly funded, equally accessible education; thus, for example, our deeply rooted, well-grounded reluctance to allow parental poverty or neglect to foreclose a child's access to both basic health care and basic education.

Problems remain, however, in determining the *level* or *amount* of health care to which citizens should be equally entitled. Establishing a basic minimum for health care is, for reasons examined in Section 4, more complex than establishing a similar minimum for education.

B. Reducing waste and inefficiency

A second proposal for eliminating the conflict between cost containment and the claims of justice centers on reducing waste and inefficiency in health care. According to Joseph S. Califano, "the evidence is now overwhelming that at least 25 percent of the money Americans spend on health care is wasted. And those wasted billions would be more than enough to fill the gaps and provide all the health- and long-term care our people need."[14] Among the sources of waste and inefficiency he cites are: (1) "spending $155 billion for tests and treatments that will have little or no impact on the patients involved, including at least 30 billion taxpayer dollars"; (2) inefficient hospital occupancy rates, hovering at about just over 60 percent for the years 1985–88; (3) a costly medical malpractice system that allocates vast sums to lawyers, insurers, and courts while inducing self-protective physicians to perform "millions of useless tests and procedures, at an annual cost estimated at $20 billion"; and (4) a vast, cumbersome administrative apparatus that is the world's most expensive. If we were to reduce these costly inefficiencies and, at the same time, implement various personal and institutional means of disease prevention, we could, Califano concludes, "provide higher quality health care for all our citizens at the same price we're now paying to provide a declining quality of care for only some."[15]

Although efforts to reduce cost and inefficiency in the health care system should certainly be undertaken, they will at best soften our dilemma. They cannot eliminate it. The demands for increasingly sophisticated, expensive high-technology medicine are largely inexhaustible. No matter how carefully and efficiently we use what we now have, a new set of budget-busting medical miracles will invariably appear on the horizon.

The concept of "medical need" is notoriously elastic. What counts as a medical need varies in part with the possibility of medical treatment. As new treatments become available or even conceivable, the class of "medical need" expands accordingly. And there is no natural limit to the development of medically beneficial knowledge or technology. The edge of medical progress is, as Daniel Callahan illuminatingly observes, invariably "ragged" rather than fixed or definite:

Imagine that you are trying to tear a piece of rough cloth and want to do so in a way that leaves a smooth edge. Yet no matter how carefully you tear the cloth, or where you tear it, there is always a ragged edge. It is the roughness of the material itself that guarantees the same result; a smooth edge is impossible. No matter how far we push the frontiers of medical progress we are always left with a ragged edge—poor outcomes, with cases as bad as those we have succeeded in curing, with the inexorable decline of the body however much we seem to have arrested the process. Whether it be intensive care for the premature newborn, low-birthweight baby, or bypass surgery for the very old, or AZT therapy for AIDS patients, the eventual outcome will not likely be very good; and when, eventually, those problems are solved there will then be others to take their place. That is the ragged edge of medical progress, as much a part of that progress as its success.[16]

In health care, especially if one focuses on preventing death and eliminating or mitigating pain and suffering, there will always be a ragged edge to available treatments and therapies. If we are willing to spend the money, further research and development will always promise new knowledge and technology that can forestall death and reduce pain and suffering. Success is always possible. Yet to change metaphors, no matter how many battles we may win, we can never, as long as we remain mortal, win the war. "We cannot," as Callahan puts it,

win the struggle with the ragged edge. We can only move the edge somewhere else, where it will once again tear roughly, and again and again. If this is so, and if the effort to defeat the ragged edge assures ever-rising costs (for many of the easier, cleaner tears were made earlier in history), when will we know when and how to stop? Not when and how to stop because further progress cannot be made—further progress can *always* be made; we have no reason to disbelieve that. But knowing how and when to stop because further progress entails either too great an economic or social price or too little likely improvement in the human condition, or both, is a far harder decision.[17]

Eliminating waste and inefficiency in the health care system will not, therefore, eliminate the conflict between cost containment and distributive justice. Though such efforts can do much to mitigate the problem and should certainly, where feasible, be undertaken, we will still be confronted with hard choices about limiting cost while justly distributing access to care.

3. Access to care

Should everyone have equal access to a basic level of health care regardless of ability to pay? Although when asked, most people would say yes, the fact is that not everyone in the United States has access to what everyone would agree ought to be included in a basic level of care.

7.3 Prenatal care on the critical list

June Havlicek, a nurse with eight years' experience in a maternity unit at a local community hospital, read with interest the lead article, "Prenatal Care on the Critical List," in her city newspaper. The nurse coordinator of volunteer nursing staff at the Marie Johnson Prenatal Care Clinic had announced that current limited numbers of volunteer nursing staff at the clinic would soon lead to its closing. June was well aware of the ongoing need for volunteers since she and several of her co-workers volunteered regularly at the clinic. The article reported that the late Marie Johnson, a local hospital nurse, had organized the clinic to serve women without insurance, and that during the past twenty years an all-volunteer staff had cared for a total of 2,720 women and had delivered 1,956 babies. Typical clients had been high school students whose parents' insurance had not covered their maternity care and who had needed to be on public assistance to gain Medicaid-funded care.

No additional prenatal care is currently available through other local clinics serving low-income, Medicaid-dependent women. According to the Johnson Clinic nurse coordinator, other clinics serving low-income women are filled to their collective capacity of twelve hundred women.

Simply having a Medicaid card, June knows, does not ensure access to care. In 1989 one-third of the state's eighteen thousand doctors did not accept Medicaid patients, and another third accepted only limited numbers. In the county in which the Marie Johnson Clinic is situated, only one doctor is currently willing to accept new Medicaid patients.

June knows firsthand about the value of relatively inexpensive prenatal care, which usually leads to the birth of strong, healthy babies. She also knows about expensive, high-technology care and the human tragedy associated with low-birthweight, sick babies—a number of whose mothers did not receive adequate prenatal care. June thinks it makes little sense for society not to provide access to prenatal care for everyone, regardless of ability to pay, but to be willing to spend so much on high-technology, neonatal care. We could do so much more for babies, and at less expense, she believes, by assuring access to prenatal care.[18]

June's concern reflects broad questions of justice and access to care. Despite the United States' spending a much higher percentage of its gross national product on health care than other Western industrialized nations, its overall health status is not significantly higher than that of their populations. On the contrary, among industrialized nations, the United States ranks fifteenth in male life expectancy, seventh in female life expectancy, and nineteenth in infant mortality.[19] Why, if we spend so much more on health care than other nations, is this not reflected in health care statistics? Waste and inefficiency provide part of the explanation. But there are other factors as well, including differences in access to care.[20] Despite the billions spent—much of it in the form of public funds—on state-of-the-art, high-technology health care, a disturbingly large number of Americans have little or no access to it.

About 37 million Americans—for example, the clients served by the Johnson Clinic in Case 7.3—are without medical insurance. Many of these are what are called the "working poor" and their families. Changing economic conditions in the United States, including a shift from a largely industrial economy to a service economy, have created an expanding class of Americans with little or no medical insurance. "It is unprecedented in our history," testified Joseph S. Califano before a Senate committee,

> that as unemployment goes down, fewer people than ever are covered by [medical] insurance. Jobs in service-related fields often come with no health care or inadequate health care. The number of uninsured has jumped 30 percent between 1980 and 1985. When those with inadequate insurance are added, more than 50 million Americans each year face access problems.[21]

Many of those without private medical insurance fall between the cracks of the system. Their income is too high for them to qualify for Medicaid but too low to allow them to purchase insurance. While the official poverty level for a family of four in 1990 was $12,675, the average annual premium for independently purchased health insurance for such a family was about $3,216.[22] The purchase of health insurance would thus consume nearly one-fourth the annual income of a family earning only slightly more than the officially defined poverty level.

Testifying before the same Senate committee, former Commissioner of Social Security Robert M. Ball said, "The safety net of Medicaid is full of holes. It is available to less than 50 percent of the population living below the rock-bottom level of officially defined poverty."[23] The range of those falling below the poverty level covered by Medicaid ranges from as high as 94 percent in Hawaii to as low as 16 percent in Alabama and Mississippi.

The consequences for the health of the poor are, in many respects, scandalous. "The uninsured are 33% more likely to report their health as fair or poor and spend one-third more days in bed per year than the insured do," reports the President's Commission for the Study of Ethical Problems in Medicine and Biomedical and Behavioral Research.[24] Lack of access to care, for this and other reasons, "can have serious health, economic, and social consequences for both society as a whole and for individuals. The most obvious of these is that people affected by lack of access may go without needed services and suffer the consequences."[25] According to a recent article:

Even if they are not ill, people without insurance postpone preventive care until more costly treatment is necessary—or until it's too late.

Two-thirds of all people with hypertension fail to have their disease controlled, largely because they can't afford medications. Half of those with hypertension haven't seen a doctor within the past year. A Roper poll has found that the proportion of Americans going to doctors in any one month has fallen to a 15-year low.

Women are particularly at risk. Uninsured women are much less likely than insured women to have screening tests for breast and cervical cancer or for glaucoma. If they are pregnant, they often do without prenatal care. Some five million women between the ages of 15 and 44 are covered by private health-insurance policies that don't include maternity coverage.[26]

In testimony before the Senate committee mentioned above, David Smith, Medical Director of the Brownsville Community Health Center in Texas, reported the following:

Pregnant women have been turned away after being unable to pay a $3,500 deposit and fearing the debt that would be incurred in a family of four and a combined income of $5,800 per year. One woman turned to a midwife for a complicated delivery rather than paying the $2,500 deposit at the hospital for "prenatal management," and went on to deliver a one and a half pound baby. The child was transferred via cab in a plastic bag to the emergency room, where it died three days later.[27]

Children, it should be noted, currently make up about 32 percent of the uninsured.[28]

To remedy this situation, many—including nurses like June Havlicek in Case 7.3—see the need for providing access to health care for all with certain medical needs, regardless of their ability to pay. Yet intense, widespread resistance to increasing taxes together with pressures to contain health care costs make it unlikely that the problem can be solved simply by additional infusions of public funds. Moreover, the inexhaustible demand for increased medical technology—what Callahan characterizes as the "ragged edge" of medical progress—limits what may be gained by reducing waste and inefficiency. If, therefore, the claims of justice require that society provide everyone with equal access to a certain level of health care, regardless of ability to pay, we must face up to the prospect of rationing.

4. The concept of rationing

Rationing implies a just and efficient allocation of limited goods or services. The paradigm is, perhaps, allocating food among soldiers at a battlefront.

When food supplies are limited, every soldier is entitled to a certain fixed amount. The allotments of food are in this context dubbed "rations," as in C rations, K rations, and so on. Other items may, in wartime, be rationed as well. During World War II gasoline, sugar, coffee, and so on were rationed among the civilian population both to conserve supplies and to assure that what was available was distributed equally.

An illuminating, frequently overlooked feature of the term *rationing* is its Latin root. *Ration*ing is (or should be) an essentially *ration*al undertaking, the Latin word *ratio* having to do with reason and rationality.[29] Rationing, therefore, is something undertaken deliberately and in the name of reason or rationality. This is not to say that all existing or proposed rationing schemes are in fact justified or the most rational, but rather that rationing policies are explicitly adopted and defended for the sake of reasons having to do with justice or fairness. Strictly speaking, then, it is a misnomer to talk of "tacit," "invisible," or "unintentional" rationing or of "rationing by default" (in contrast with "rationing by design"). Not all processes that allocate a limited supply of goods or services can be said, strictly speaking, to ration them. Medical economist Victor Fuchs therefore obscures an important distinction when he writes:

> The United States has always rationed medical care, just as every country always has and always will ration care. No nation is wealthy enough to supply all the care that is technically feasible and desirable; no nation can provide "presidential medicine" for all its citizens. Moreover, medical care is hardly unique in this respect. The United States "rations" automobiles, houses, restaurant meals—all the goods and services that make up our standard of living.[30]

What Fuchs calls "rationing" is more accurately described as allocation by supply and demand. To allocate automobiles, houses, and restaurant meals in accord with market principles is not thereby to ration them. To ration health care is, as in rationing food among soldiers, to apportion or allot a fixed amount of a limited resource *for reasons* of fairness or overall efficiency or both.

Access to a certain level of health care is necessary for maintaining fair equality of opportunity, which is in turn necessary for everyone's having more or less equal liberty to lead a decent and meaningful life in a society that repeatedly affirms this liberty as an important defining value. Yet health care is a set of goods and services for which supply falls, and will always fall, short of demand. Money alone, even if, contrary to fact, the society were willing to raise taxes so as to increase access for the poor, cannot itself solve the problem. There is, therefore, a strong prima facie case for rationing health care. (Indeed, most nurses are already familiar with rationing within their own caseloads or assignments, given the extensive demands on their time and energy.) The question is whether we can determine what ought to count as an appropriate portion or allotment of health care to which everyone ought to have access. Where, in other words, are we going to draw the line in determining a basic minimum level of health care?

This is a vexing question. Health care differs from the customary objects of rationing, such as food or gasoline, in a number of important ways. First, health care needs, unlike nutritional needs, vary widely among individuals. Some, through good fortune, live entire lives requiring very little in the way of health care. Others, through decidedly ill fortune, consume health care resources totaling hundreds of thousands of dollars. It is, therefore, difficult to specify an equal allotment, perhaps in terms of number of dollars worth of care, to which each person should be entitled over a lifetime. Second, it is more difficult to distinguish needs from wants in rationing health care than it is, say in rationing food or clothing. One's craving for caviar carries no weight in determining a basic level of nutritional need; nor does a longing for a mink coat determine what counts as sufficient clothing. But whether the basic level of health care provided by a system of rationing should include, for example, liver transplants, attractive wigs or hairpieces for chemotherapy patients, or infertility treatment for childless couples is harder to say. Third, the very complexity of health care—including tensions between extending the quantity of life and improving its quality, or competing claims for the benefits of basic research, health promotion, prevention, palliation, rehabilitation, supportive care, or acute care—places added burdens on determining a coherent rationing scheme. Finally, health care's open-endedness—the shifting sands of medical progress and resulting changes in what medicine can provide—makes it difficult to determine, once and for all, what counts as a basic level of health care to which everyone ought to have access.

5. The Oregon proposal

The state of Oregon was the first unit of government to publicly address the problem of justly distributing limited health care resources. In 1986, 400,000 Oregonians were without any health insurance—one person out of six under age 65.[31] Of these, 120,000 were employed but earning below the federal poverty level; 260,000 were adults and families earning above the federal poverty level; and 20,000 were high-risk individuals who were denied insurance and others. Acknowledging that optimal health care for all—that is, providing everyone with everything that may benefit him or her—is not a genuine possibility, Oregon began developing a plan for distributing some of its health care resources as fairly as possible. The aim is to set a floor in terms of access to health care below which no Oregonian will fall.

In 1983 a prescient organization called Oregon Health Decisions initiated a statewide series of "town meetings" to inform Oregonians of ethical and economic issues in health care and to elicit informed citizen opinion on these issues.[32] Similar groups have subsequently developed similar programs in other states.[33] Then in 1987, faced with a very tight budget, those administering Oregon's Medicaid program decided the program should, for reasons of justice and efficiency, no longer fund heart, liver, bone marrow, and pancreas transplantation. Funds that had previously been spent on these very expensive transplant operations for no more than thirty Medicaid recipients would now be shifted to prenatal care. If, for example, the Johnson Clinic in Case 7.3, "Prenatal care on the critical list," had been in Oregon, the shifted funds would fully cover care for its clients. The *ratio*nale was that the same sum of money would purchase more in the way of effective health care for the Medicaid population as a whole if devoted to fifteen hundred pregnant women—thereby reducing the number of low-birthweight and disabled infants—than if spent on a very small number of expensive transplant operations of limited effectiveness.

This first instance of governmental rationing attracted national attention when seven-year-old Medicaid recipient Coby Howard died of leukemia. His last weeks were spent helping family and friends desperately try to raise one hundred thousand dollars to pay for a bone marrow transplant that would have had some chance of saving his life. They had managed to collect seventy thousand dollars when Coby died. A year earlier the state of Oregon would have paid for this operation without question. Coby Howard and his family were the first identifiable individuals to feel negative effects of Oregon's decision to ration Medicaid benefits.

In 1988, despite heated criticism, the Oregon legislature reaffirmed the Medicaid program's controversial decision to limit funding for transplants. The next year the legislature, led by senate president (and emergency room physician) John Kitzhaber, extended and systematized this decision by passing a three-part Basic Health Care Act seeking to do the following:

1. Expand Medicaid to cover everyone at or below the federal poverty level. (Like many states, Oregon had been containing its Medicaid budget by the politically expedient but ethically questionable practice of raising eligibility standards. As standards rose, one had to be more and more desperately poor to qualify for Medicaid. This meant the state provided the full range of benefits but made them available to a declining portion of the poor. Thus, in 1988, Oregon Medicaid benefits were available to only slightly more than half of those falling below the official federal poverty level.)
2. Require nearly all employers who do not now provide health insurance to their employees to do so.
3. Establish a state-sponsored insurance pool to provide coverage for all who, because of preexisting severe illness, are presently uninsurable.

The Basic Health Care Act would thus require the state to assume broad responsibility for providing a basic minimum of health care to all falling below the federal poverty level, and the private sector would be required to cover nearly all who were employed. Extending Medicaid coverage to all falling below the poverty level would, however, involve an explicit trade-off. Instead of extending a fairly generous level of benefits to slightly more than half of this population, the Medicaid program would subsequently provide a more limited basic minimum of health care benefits to *all* falling below the federal poverty level. The next step in the process was to determine this basic minimum. Once specified, it would provide the standard for coverage in all three categories.

Implementation of Oregon's Basic Health Care Act called for the creation of an eleven-member Health Services Commission (HSC) to develop a priority list ranking health care services in terms of cost-effectiveness and the extent to which they are valued or deemed important by the community. The HSC would do this by collecting data on the effectiveness of various medical procedures and their costs. It would also collect data on values and what citizens regarded as important as revealed through town meetings and surveys. Putting these kinds of data together, the HSC would rank order medical services in terms of their costs, benefits, and perceived value. The most cost-effective, highly valued services would be at the top of the list, the least cost-effective, least-valued services at the bottom. This list would then be given to the legislature, which would use it to define the basic level of health care. The legislature would not be obligated to follow the list mechanically (for example, take a fixed amount previously budgeted for health care and go as far down the list as this amount would cover and then simply draw a line) but could use the list to inform its judgment. It is conceivable, though perhaps unlikely, that legislators could, in the light of where the line would be drawn, elect to increase the Medicaid budget even if this required raising taxes. Wherever and however the legislature draws the line in determining the basic minimum, it would then have the opportunity to redraw it every two years (Oregon's legislature meets biennially), taking into account changes in the health of the state's economy, the size of the state budget, the development of new technology, new knowledge about the cost-effectiveness of various procedures, competing claims on the state treasury, and so on.

Currently the Oregon plan is unfolding. An initial ranking of priorities issued by the HSC in the spring of 1990 encountered heavy criticism and is being revised. The timetable now calls for the revised priority list to be presented to the legislature; the legislature will then determine the basic level of health care and put the Medicaid component into place. Before the proposal can actually be implemented, however, Oregon's Medicaid program must apply to the Health Care Financing Administration (HCFA) for a waiver from current federal Medicaid mandates. Assuming that the waiver is granted, the Medicaid component of the Oregon proposal could be implemented in July 1992. The provisions requiring all employers to provide health care benefits for all employees and their dependents and establishing the high-risk pool for those currently uninsurable are scheduled to go into effect in 1994.

The ultimate fate of the Oregon proposal is uncertain. What is important for our purposes, however, is the example that Oregon has set. The Oregon legislature is the first significant unit of American government to actually come to grips with the dilemmas of rationing health care, and there is much to be learned from its efforts even if they are, in their present form, subject to criticism.

Those responsible for the Oregon proposal should be commended for directly confronting a deep and important problem that most Americans still deny exists.[34] They should be commended, too, for conducting their deliberations in full view and striving to involve the citizenry through the Oregon Health Decisions project. In making its work public, those developing the proposal have received a great deal of criticism. But much of the criticism has been helpful and has resulted in a number of refinements in the overall proposal. This sort of improvement is a significant benefit of a public process.

At the same time, many of the criticisms point to deep difficulties.[35] First, in developing its priority list, the HSC had to have accurate information about the effectiveness and real costs of various procedures. Yet much of the necessary data do not yet exist. Studies determining the long-term outcomes of various procedures and types of care together with their real costs (as opposed to physician- and hospital-determined charges) have not, for the most part, been undertaken. The Oregon proposal may serve as a useful spur to needed research along these lines, but it is, as an implementable proposal, somewhat ahead of its time. Second, participation in the statewide series of meetings aimed at determining community values on these matters was not adequately representative of the population as a whole. For example, nearly 70 percent of the 1,048 individuals who met to determine community values in the later stages of the program were employed either in the health care system or in the field of mental health. This is a group that is likely to enjoy excellent medical insurance coverage and, given their middle- and upper-middle-class status, to embrace health care values different in certain respects than those of many poorer people. They would, for example, be more likely to place a higher premium on prevention and providing for their old age than those whose precarious medical and financial status emphasized more immediate needs for acute care. Third, there are limits as to what single states can do about these issues. When, for example, Oregon Medicaid stopped paying for heart, liver, pancreas, and bone marrow

transplantation, a number of Oregon Medicaid patients needing such operations went to the neighboring state of Washington, placing new burdens on
that state's Medicaid system. A just and stable policy for rationing health
care is ultimately the responsibility of the federal government, not the
individual states. Fourth, for political reasons, supporters of the Oregon
proposal have exempted the elderly, the blind, and the disabled from its
provisions. These populations currently receive 70 percent of Medicaid
dollars while comprising only 30 percent of the Medicaid population in
Oregon. Consequently the elderly, the blind, and the disabled will, under the
Oregon proposal, continue to receive the same (comparatively high) level of
benefits they currently receive. The brunt of the cost cutting will therefore
fall on the remainder of Medicaid recipients, for the most part women and
children. Related to this is a concern of overall justice. Why, one might ask,
should efforts to ration health care in the United States be restricted, at least
initially, to the Medicaid population? By operating within the constraints of
the Medicaid budget, these initial efforts at rationing seem to require
robbing poor Peter to pay even poorer Paul. A more comprehensive effort,
involving the entire population, would spread the burdens more equitably.
Finally, the proposal seems to take the health care system as it is, making
little effort to reduce waste, improve efficiency, and cut administrative costs
(currently over 20 percent for the American health system as a whole).

These and other criticisms can be plausibly raised against the Oregon
proposal. Yet its proponents are right to demand that critics accompany
their objections with better, more workable alternatives. Finding fault with
aspects of the Oregon proposal is, at this point, fairly easy; supporting the
present system or providing more adequate resolutions to the conflict between cost containment and the claims of justice is, however, much more
difficult.

Despite its present shortcomings and eventual fate, the Oregon proposal
is likely to play a vital role in what is surely to be a long, difficult process of
developing a more just and rational system of health care delivery in the
United States. We should, therefore, regard the Oregon proposal not as the
last word on the matter but rather as a useful starting point.

6. Toward ethical rationing

Debates over health care rationing are likely to continue for a number of
years. The informed participation of nurses in these debates will prove
important both for the public and for the profession of nursing. In what
follows we provide an ethical framework for developing and assessing
specific policies for rationing health care.

A realistic, ethically justifiable rationing system must, in the first place,
acknowledge that we will occasionally have to deny patients types of care

that could possibly benefit them, despite our best efforts to eliminate waste and inefficiency in health care. The combination of an aging population, advances in medical knowledge and technology (with emphasis on what Callahan calls its "ragged edge"), competing claims on the health care dollar for research, prevention, and public health, other pressing social needs like education, housing, maintaining the infrastructure, and so on, makes this inescapable. The question is not whether we can avoid having to limit possibly beneficial health care—a realistic understanding of limited resources and the unlimited possibilities of medical benefits makes this inevitable—but whether, when we are forced to do so, we can do so fairly and without violating the integrity of health care professionals.

A rationing scheme threatens the integrity of health care professionals when it forces them to sacrifice or betray their traditional commitment to the health or welfare of particular patients for the sake of some overall social good. This is part of what troubles nurse Gail Crain in Case 7.1, "Ideals and reality," as she considers the ethics of restricting her services to those who can pay for them. How, then, can the traditional patient-centered ethic of nursing and medicine be reconciled with the aims of justly and efficiently allocating limited health care resources?

A. Fairness in allocation

It is useful in responding to this important question to distinguish a result's being unfortunate from its being unfair. Suppose, to take a comparatively straightforward example, we have what everyone agrees is a fair system of allocating a limited supply of transplantable hearts among a large number of potential recipients:

7.4 Unfortunate but not unfair?

Three patients—Mr. Smith, Ms. Chang, and Mr. Herrera—of roughly the same size, age, and blood type are each in desperate need of a new heart. As the rules of the allocation system (perhaps some variant of "first-come, first-served") are scrupulously followed, the first heart to become available goes to Mr. Smith. A week later a second donor heart becomes available and is successfully transplanted into Ms. Chang. Then, while awaiting a donor heart for himself, Mr. Herrera dies of heart failure. Has the system treated Mr. Herrera unfairly?[36]

Assuming that the scarcity of donor hearts in this case was unavoidable and that the system of allocation was more just than any alternative, we conclude that Mr. Herrera's dying before receiving a life-extending heart transplant was not unfair, though certainly unfortunate.[37] The question now is whether this distinction can be extended to a rationing scheme for the entire health care system. That a patient who could benefit from one or another type of medical treatment does not receive it is always unfortunate. But it is not necessarily unfair. Although there may be little we can do to eliminate scarcity and the need to ration health care, we can try to ensure that the principles guiding our rationing policies are just or fair.

The best criterion of the justness or fairness of such a rationing scheme may be that all to whom it applies have at some earlier point agreed to abide by its results or would have so agreed if given the opportunity. This agreement is similar in some respects to the consent one gives in buying a raffle ticket. If a person fully understands the rules of the raffle and voluntarily engages in it, and the rules are scrupulously followed, the person can hardly claim to be a victim of injustice if he or she loses. That the person loses is perhaps unfortunate—he or she has been unlucky—but it is not, under these conditions, unjust or unfair. A guiding thought, therefore, as we evaluate proposals for rationing health care should be whether we can reasonably expect a particular rationing scheme to be agreed upon by those to whom it applies, especially those who would, on its terms, be denied access to possibly beneficial care.

B. Contractualist justification

We already have a model for contractually justified rationing in cases in which members of a voluntary, cooperative prepaid health plan must jointly determine whether coverage should be extended to an expensive, modestly successful treatment for a disease affecting a small number of participants. Paul T. Menzel presents an example, based on an actual situation, involving adult liver transplantation:

After surveying the membership and a variety of discussions at different levels, the plan decided not to cover them. At a cost of nearly $300,000 per transplanted patient in first-year care and $6,000 to $7,000 per year per patient for follow-up costs, and with a five-year survival rate of 65 percent, in effect this is a decision that $600,000 could be better spent on other things than five- to twenty-year additional life spans. The decision is publicized to the plan's current and prospective members and some other plans that cover this procedure are available in the community. Under these circumstances, who would really want to argue that the plan's doctors and nurses are violating their moral oath to patients if they subsequently cooperate with this decision?[38]

Justifications of this sort place a premium on prior informed agreement and are, accordingly, called *contractualist*.

As formulated by T. M. Scanlon, the contractualist criterion of moral justification states that an act can be justified if it follows from a system of rules that, on reflection, cannot reasonably be rejected by anyone seeking informed, unforced, general agreement about the matter in question.[39] That agreement be *informed* presupposes that the contracting parties are aware of their circumstances. In the present context, this would include full knowledge of the increasing costs of health care, Callahan's "ragged edge" of technology, competing social needs, and so on. *Unforced* agreement rules out coercion as well as being forced to accept an agreement by being in a weak bargaining position; for example, in this context by being forced by one's desperate medical condition to settle for a particularly low minimal level of care on threat of otherwise receiving none at all. To say that the system of rules to which one agrees *cannot, on reflection, be reasonably rejected* presupposes the need or desirability of finding principles or a policy that could be the basis of informed, unforced general agreement. It is not reasonable, on reflection, to reject a principle or policy simply because its application has some untoward or unfortunate results if the consequences of any alternative principle or policy or of having no applicable principle or policy at all would be worse. We must in the present context compare the unfortunate consequences of a sound rationing policy with the unjust consequences of the status quo, as identified above in Section 3. Finally, in placing a premium on prior *agreement*, contractualists hope that even when principles or policies so chosen turn out to work against the interests or desires of some individuals, these same individuals will nonetheless acknowledge the justification of what is being done.

Applied to health care rationing, contractualism directs us to develop a set of criteria that, given unavoidably limited resources and the need for general prior agreement, cannot reasonably be rejected by anyone *seeking a fair, efficient, and workable system* for allocating access to care. Foremost in our mind should be patients who are likely to be denied possibly beneficial care under the proposed rationing scheme. Assuming they acknowledge the facts (for example, limited resources, the "ragged edge" of medical technology, other pressing social needs, and so on) and the need for general agreement on a fair and efficient rationing policy, we must ask whether we can reasonably expect them, at a point optimal for this kind of decision-making, to have endorsed the specific criteria by which they lose out.

C. *Respect for persons*

The previous example involving payment for liver transplantation shows that a contractualist justification of health care rationing can resolve the integrity-threatening conflict between a health care professional's commitment to individual patients and his or her role as agent of a more impersonal rationing scheme. Nurses who, as directed by a contractually justifiable rationing policy, withhold possibly beneficial health care from patients would, in effect, be doing it *at the direction of these very patients*. The point has been well expressed by Menzel, whose contractualist conception of health care rationing is the most fully developed to date:

If individual patients beforehand would have granted consent to the rationing policies and procedures in question (or more clearly yet, if they actually have consented to them), then the appeal of those policies and procedures will rest not merely on attachment to the morally controversial goal of aggregate welfare, "efficiency"; such policies will gain their moral force from respecting individual patients' own will.[40]

A health care professional who, in the name of a rationing policy to which all members of society have given their informed agreement, withholds a possibly beneficial type of treatment would not, therefore, be betraying the patient's trust. On the contrary, such a health care professional would be doing exactly what this patient and all other potential patients have, at some earlier time, optimal from the standpoint of policy-making, directed him or her to do. The health care professional would, in this respect, be an agent of the patient's autonomy. That the policy directs that the patient not receive the treatment would be, to recall the distinction illustrated by Case 7.4, unfortunate but not unfair.

One may, at this point, raise an objection. Granted, the patient may have agreed, well before he or she became sick, that treatment for this comparatively rare, very expensive illness should be limited to competent, compassionate palliative care, but include no system-supported efforts to cure. But that was then; this is now. Having contracted the illness, the patient at this point desperately wants the treatment, and for health care professionals to withhold it is to betray and deny the autonomy of the actual, flesh-and-blood person before them.

The response to this objection provides further illumination of contractualist justification. If we are concerned with cost containment, we will have to place some restrictions on access to care; if we are concerned with fairness, we will have to do so without discriminating against identifiable individuals. These considerations, together with the fact that health care needs vary among individuals and within an individual's life, require that the standpoint from which we seek the sort of unforced, informed, general agreement characteristic of contractualism be either prior to or abstracted from that of a concrete individual suffering from a particular illness.[41]

The reason health care professionals would not be violating their commitments to particular patients in the foregoing case involving liver transplantation is that they would, in withholding access, be respecting the patients' prior informed, unforced agreement to the policy requiring them to do so. In so doing they are, Menzel suggests, actually respecting the autonomy of these patients if we construe this as respecting the informed, unforced decisions of the whole person and if "whole person" is understood to include informed, unforced decisions made at an earlier time in a person's life and intended to apply to later times as well.[42] This, by the way, is the sense of respecting a person's autonomy to which we appeal in overriding, on parentalistic grounds, the actual, here-and-now, suicidal request of one who is temporarily aggrieved, depressed, or insane (Chapter 3, Section 2). Before undergoing the grief, depression, or loss of sanity, we presume, the person wanted to continue to live—even during the period in which he or she is expressing suicidal desires—and it is this prior decision, not the present one, that we must honor if we are to respect the whole person's capacity for rational choice.

D. Expanding the model

The question now is whether the contractualist model represented by Menzel's example of informed choice by members of a voluntary, cooperative, prepaid health plan can be extended to the nation and its health care system as a whole. This is an enormous undertaking, beset with numerous obstacles. The implementation of a contractually justified system of rationing will, for example, require major changes and restructuring in the health care system. Funding for the level of care to which everyone has access would have to be centralized and prospectively budgeted in a "closed" system—one in which funds withheld or withdrawn from one type of care could, with assurance, be allocated to another type of care that is, from the standpoint of justice and efficiency, more important.[43] The transition to such a system will assuredly encounter significant opposition and resistance from powerful, deeply entrenched elements of the medical establishment and industries and institutions profiting heavily from present arrangements. There will be problems of design as well as implementation. Defining the basic level of health care remains a great difficulty. Given vast differences in individual circumstances, it will be difficult to draw the line simply in terms of categories of treatment. Cost-benefit ratios for various therapies differ widely from patient to patient, and developing guidelines taking account of all relevant variables is a formidable task.[44] Moreover, although Menzel has made a useful beginning, the notion of prior consent as applied to health care rationing needs to be developed in much more detail, and on a larger scale taking account of additional complexities.[45] Yet, despite these and other difficulties, there is no more promising model for devising a realistically just and effective health care system than that based on contractualism and prior consent. It must, as we proceed, serve both as an ideal and as a benchmark for assessing the adequacy of various steps toward its realization.

7. Rationing and the importance of nursing care

We cannot forecast the details of the long period of contentious national debates and experiments that will, we hope, eventually lead to a contractually justified system of health care rationing, one providing access to decent minimum health care for all, regardless of ability to pay.[46] The first steps along this path are, however, now being taken. A number of states are initiating the sorts of community consciousness-raising educational forums that were instrumental in leading to the Oregon proposal.[47] The participation of informed health care professionals—including nurses—in such forums is an indispensable part of the process. Citizens need to understand the realities of health care—the limitations as well as the promises, the values of palliation as well as of attempts to cure. They must also come to grips, as must health care professionals themselves, with what is perhaps the greatest barrier to devising a contractually justified rationing system—a denial, rooted deeply in our culture, of limits imposed by the human condition.

"There is," Daniel Callahan points out in his challenging account of the limits of medical progress, "a hard philosophical truth at which we have avoided looking, one that must be radically disquieting for any hopeful beliefs about the possibility of some ultimate efficiency. It is simply the burden of mortality: *Illness, decline, aging, and death can only be forestalled, kept at bay, never permanently vanquished.*"[48] Until the culture, and those shaping and shaped by it, acknowledge limits to what health care can achieve, the network of problems, to which a contractually justified system of rationing provides the most plausible answer, will continue to be ignored. Health care professionals are well placed to bring this "hard truth" to the attention of the public and will, in this capacity, make a vital contribution to the eventual development of a more just and efficient health care system.

Nursing plays a special role in this connection. To withhold further efforts to cure certain patients, in the name of a contractually justified system of health care rationing, would not justify abandoning them. Patients denied expensive, marginally effective curative treatments would nonetheless be likely to require various forms of palliative care and emotional support that *must* be included as part of an ethically justified basic minimum to which everyone would have access. "At the center of caring," writes Callahan,

should be a commitment never to avert its eyes from, or wash its hands of, someone who is in pain or is suffering, who is disabled or incompetent, who is retarded or demented; that is the most fundamental demand made upon us. It is also the one commitment a health care system can almost always make to everyone, *the one need that it can reasonably meet*. Where the individual need for cure is infinite in its possibilities, the need for caring is much more finite—there is always something we can do for each other. The possibilities of caring are, in that respect, far more self-contained than the possibilities of curing. That is why their absence is inexcusable.[49] (emphasis added)

The need for caring enters debates over rationing in two ways. First, the need for caring is increasingly sacrificed by the present system as the quest for cure, regardless of cost or likelihood of success, consumes an increasing percentage of the health care budget. One motivation, then, for seeking a justifiable rationing policy is to assure that the resources for meeting this vital need for caring are adequate and fairly distributed. Second, in designing such a policy we must see to it that the sort of caring under consideration is available to all, regardless of ability to pay.

No other health professionals know as much about, or are as skilled in, meeting the patient's round-the-clock, combined needs for physical, emotional, and spiritual care as nurses. Given the central role of such caring in any rationing scheme and the fact that withholding expensive, marginally effective efforts to cure may require redoubled efforts at caring, nurses assume a correspondingly central role in debates over and experiments in health care rationing. As Barbara Redman, Executive Director of the American Nurses' Association, maintains:

Nurses see who needs care, who is getting care and who is not. We see it every day and all through the night; in our emergency departments and trauma centers; in our hospital wards and ICUs; in nursing homes and mental health centers; in the streets, schools and workplaces of our communities.

Nurses have something important to say about health care reform and *now* is the time to say it. It is not only our right, but our obligation to speak out. We must speak out forcefully and with one voice about the terrible inequities and inconsistencies in our nation's health policy; about the nearly 37 million Americans without adequate health insurance, prevented from access to appropriate and affordable care; about the barriers that discriminate and disenfranchise our most vulnerable populations— the unborn and very young, the very old, those with chronic illnesses, the working poor, and those whose skin color, ethnic or life-style backgrounds are different from the majority; and about what we believe must be done to correct this growing national travesty.[50]

The special knowledge and expertise of nurses are thus indispensable to the enormously complex, but unavoidable, social and political task of turning the ideal of an ethically justified system of health care rationing into a just and caring reality.

8. The expanding scope of nursing ethics

We conclude with a case that dramatically illustrates the expanding scope of ethics in health care.

7.5 Ending life support against the family's wishes

One year ago eighty-six-year-old Helga Wanglie tripped on a scatter rug in her hallway and fractured her right hip. A month after undergoing surgery for her hip, she developed breathing problems and was placed on a respirator. For five months she remained fully conscious and alert, writing notes to her doctors and her husband, since the respirator prevented her from speaking. A week after being weaned from the respirator and transferred to a long-term care institution, her heartbeat and respiration suddenly stopped. By the time she could be resuscitated, she had undergone severe brain damage and was subsequently determined to be in a persistent vegetative state. She had, in other words, suffered a total and permanent loss of consciousness.

Eight months later, the question is whether, and if so how long, treatment should be continued. Led by its medical director, the hospital wants to terminate Mrs. Wanglie's life support. Yet the family vehemently objects. Mrs. Wanglie, her husband said in an interview, is the daughter of a Lutheran minister "and she has strong religious convictions. We talked about this a year ago. If anything happened to her, she said, she wants everything done. She told me, 'Only He who gave life has the right to take life.' It seems to me they're trying to play God. Who are they to determine who's to die and who's to live? I take the position that as long as her heart is beating there's life there."[51]

This case, as the newspaper reports emphasize, places a new twist on a now-familiar problem. Often, it is the family that wants treatment withdrawn in cases like this and the nurses, physicians, and hospital who object. Here, however, the roles are reversed. The family wants treatment continued, and it is the caretakers who want to terminate treatment. It is not difficult to imagine why health care professionals would find such treatment medically futile and ethically questionable.

Before long, however, in this case or in similar cases another factor will have to be taken into account—the cost of such a patient's care and whether this cost is borne by a larger social group. Given limited resources and escalating demand, is providing continued nursing and medical care, at a cost ranging from three thousand to over ten thousand dollars a month, a just or prudent use of the health care dollar? Should private insurance companies or Medicaid or Medicare continue to underwrite such forms of life-extending treatment while the sort of basic needs identified in Section 3 are routinely denied to large portions of the population? These questions will soon become unavoidable, if they are not already.

This chapter outlines a framework for thinking about such matters—a framework based upon fairness, contractualist justification, and respect for persons. It directs us to ask the following kinds of questions: What are the competing, unmet health care needs of the relevant population (members of a prepaid health plan or those covered by a private insurance plan, Medicaid, or Medicare)? How important are these needs to the relevant population when compared with sustaining patients in a persistent vegetative state for as long as they or their families wish? Are health care resources genuinely limited? If so, would members of the population be likely to give informed, unforced general agreement to a policy that would pay for the care of patients in a persistent vegetative state but not, for example, provide access to prenatal care to all members of the relevant population who could benefit from it?

Our concern in this chapter is not to settle these complex questions but rather to show that matters of overall cost, efficiency, and justice can no longer be separated from more individualized ethical considerations. As payment for health care becomes increasingly shared or social, conceptions of nursing ethics that focus entirely on individual clients will, as Leonard M. Fleck has cogently argued, prove to be much too narrow:

If the demands of justice are to be taken seriously, if we are to have just health care policies and a just health care system, then nurses will have to be advocates of such policies. They will have to participate intelligently and vigorously in the broad moral and political conversations that will shape future health care policy. This is not an optional aspect of the nurse's role.[52]

With this we heartily agree, and it has been the aim of this chapter to provide a foundation for such an expanded conception of nursing ethics.

Notes

1. This case is based upon an editorial by Lucie S. Kelly, "When Nurses Ration Patient Care," *Nursing Outlook* 33 (May/June 1985):123.
2. Mila Ann Aroskar, "The Interface of Ethics and Politics in Nursing," *Nursing Outlook* 35 (November/December 1987):269.
3. Ibid.
4. Ronald E. Cranford, "The Persistent Vegetative State: The Medical Reality (Getting the Facts Straight)," *Hastings Center Report* 18 (February/March 1988):27–32. According to the Council on Scientific Affairs and Council on Ethical and Judicial Affairs of the American Medical Association, "if one includes patients totally demented from Alzheimer's disease and similar disorders, an estimate of the number of persistently vegetative patients in this country is approximately 15,000 to 25,000. How to deal with this emotionally painful, financially costly, and generally unwanted outcome of modern medical treatment is an increasing problem." See "Persistent Vegetative State and the Decision to Withdraw or Withhold Life Support," *Journal of the American Medical Association* 263 (19 January 1990):427.
5. This case is based on Donald Robinson, "Who Should Receive Medical Aid?" *Parade Magazine*, 28 May 1989, pp. 4–5. Robinson mentions the organization to

write if one is interested in forming or joining a grass-roots health care organization: American Health Decisions, Dept. P, 1200 Larimer St. Campus Box 133, Denver CO 80204.

6. Lester Carl Thurow, "Learning to Say 'No,'" *New England Journal of Medicine* 311 (13 December 1984):1569-72.

7. Joseph S. Califano, "Billions Blown on Health," *New York Times*, 12 April 1989.

8. B. Jennett, *High Technology Medicine* (Oxford: Oxford University Press, 1986).

9. Reinhard Priester and Arthur L. Caplan, "Ethics, Cost Containment, and the Allocation of Scarce Resources," *Investigative Radiology* 24 (November 1989): 919.

10. Robert M. Sade, "Is There a Right to Health Care?" *New England Journal of Medicine* 285 (2 December 1971):1288-92.

11. Norman Daniels, *Just Health Care* (New York: Cambridge University Press, 1985), pp. 36-58.

12. Other reasons for our reluctance to allow health care to be distributed solely through market mechanisms include the fact that those who purchase health care are, as a rule, unable to make knowledgeable choices among the alternatives. The buyer (the patient) is often in the position of having to rely on the seller (usually the physician) to tell the buyer what he or she must purchase and at what price. In many cases limits of time as well as limits on knowledge foreclose the possibility of "comparison shopping." Moreover, we are, as a society, reluctant to force those who have been imprudent in deciding to seek medical attention or purchase medical insurance to live with the consequences of their decisions when they are felled by ill health. It is one thing to turn one's back on a lazy or imprudent person who, as a result, has to go without television or a radio, and quite another to ignore that same person's need for emergency medical care.

13. For the relationship between the capacity for leading a decent and meaningful life and having access to a certain minimum of health care, see John Arras, "Utility, Rights, and the Right to Health Care," in James M. Humber and Robert F. Almeder, eds., *Biomedical Ethics Reviews 1984* (Clifton, N.J.: Humana Press, 1984), pp. 23-45.

14. Califano, "Billions Blown on Health."

15. Ibid.

16. Daniel Callahan, *What Kind of Life: The Limits of Medical Progress* (New York: Simon and Schuster, 1990), p. 63.

17. Ibid., p. 64f.

18. This case is based on a front-page story in the *Lansing State Journal*, 6 December 1990.

19. Priester and Caplan, "Ethics, Cost Containment, and the Allocation of Scarce Resources," p. 918.

20. Among the other factors contributing to lowered overall health care status in the United States are poverty, lack of housing, and poor education, all of which must compete for funding with the burgeoning national health care budget.

21. *New York Times*, 13 January 1987.

22. The figure for the federal poverty line is attributable to the United States Bureau of the Census, Statistical Abstract 1990. The insurance figure was obtained by telephone from the Health Insurance Association of America,

Washington, D.C. It is for typical Blue Cross/Blue Shield coverage for a fee-for-service type plan and is based on an employer survey collected by the Health Insurance Association.

23. *New York Times*, 13 January 1987. Ball is referring to the 1985 federal poverty level, $10,989 for a family of four.

24. President's Commission for the Study of Ethical Problems in Medicine and Biomedical and Behavioral Research, *Securing Access to Health Care*, vol. 1 (Washington, D.C.: U.S. Government Printing Office, 1983), p. 111.

25. Ibid., p. 20.

26. "The Crisis in Health Insurance," *Consumer Reports*, August 1990, p. 533.

27. *New York Times*, 13 January 1987.

28. Office of Technology Assessment, *Healthy Children: Investing in the Future* (U.S. Government Printing Office, 1976), pp. 41–44.

29. We are grateful to Carl Cohen for having called this to our attention.

30. Victor R. Fuchs, "The 'Rationing' of Medical Care," *New England Journal of Medicine* 311 (13 December 1984):1572.

31. Committee for Counting the Medically Indigent, "1986 Health Insurance Coverage Survey," Description of Findings (Portland, Oreg., 1986).

32. Ralph Crawshaw et al., "Oregon Health Decisions: An Experiment with Informed Community Consent," *Journal of the American Medical Association* 254 (13 December 1985):3213–16.

33. Bruce Jennings, "A Grassroots Movement in Bioethics," *Hastings Center Report* 18 (June/July 1988):special supplement. See also the collection of articles assembled by Jennings under the heading "Grassroots Bioethics Revisited: Health Care Priorities and Community Values," *Hastings Center Report* 20 (September/October 1990):16–23.

34. This paragraph draws, in part, on an analysis of the Oregon proposal presented by Reinhard Priester of the University of Minnesota at a symposium, "Rationing Medical Services: The Oregon Plan," sponsored by the Greater Detroit Area Health Council, 30 October 1990.

35. This paragraph draws, in part, on an assessment of the Oregon proposal presented by Arthur Caplan of the University of Minnesota at a conference, "Drawing the Line: Defining a Basic Level of Health Care," at the University of Minnesota, 19 October 1990.

36. This oversimplified case has been constructed especially for this book.

37. The distinction between something's being unfortunate and its being unfair is cogently drawn by H. Tristram Engelhardt, Jr., "Allocating Scarce Medical Resources and the Availability of Organ Transplantation," *New England Journal of Medicine* 311 (5 July 1984):66–71.

38. Paul T. Menzel, *Strong Medicine: The Ethical Rationing of Health Care* (New York: Oxford University Press, 1990), p. 10. "In something very close to the detail hypothesized here," Menzel adds in an endnote, "Group Health Cooperative of Puget Sound considered heart and liver transplants in 1985–86. The outcome of their long and complex process was board of trustees approval of coverage for heart transplants and for liver transplants in children with biliary atresia but not coverage of liver transplants for adults."

39. Thomas Scanlon, "Contractualism and Utilitarianism," in Amartya Sen and Bernard Williams, eds., *Utilitarianism and Beyond* (Cambridge: Cambridge University Press, 1982), p. 110.

40. Menzel, *Strong Medicine*, p. 10.

41. See Norman Daniels, *Am I My Parents' Keeper?* (New York: Oxford University Press, 1988), for an argument to the effect that in choosing among rationing systems we must consider how each will affect us over the course of an entire life span.

42. Ibid.

43. Norman Daniels, "Why Saying No to Patients in the United States is So Hard: Cost Containment, Justice, and Provider Autonomy," *New England Journal of Medicine* 314 (22 May 1986):1380–83.

44. William B. Schwartz and Henry J. Aaron, "The Achilles Heel of Health Care Rationing," *New York Times*, 9 July 1990.

45. Menzel, *Strong Medicine*. See also Daniels, *Just Health Care*, and, especially, Daniels, *Am I My Parents' Keeper?*

46. There is nothing about such a system, we should note, that precludes the availability of higher levels of health care for those with the desire and financial resources to pay for them. The similarity with access to education is again instructive. That the system aspires to provide access to a decent minimum of education for all, regardless of ability to pay, does not preclude access to higher levels of education for those who value and can pay for them.

47. Jennings, "A Grassroots Movement in Bioethics."

48. Callahan, *What Kind of Life*, p. 100.

49. Ibid., p. 145.

50. Barbara Redman, "Mobilizing Nurses for Health Care Reform," *The American Nurse* (January 1991):4.

51. *New York Times*, 10 January 1991.

52. Leonard Fleck, "Decisions of Justice and Health Care," *Journal of Gerontological Nursing* 13 (March 1987):45.

Appendix A

International Council of Nurses
Code for Nurses
ETHICAL CONCEPTS APPLIED TO NURSING
1973

The fundamental responsibility of the nurse is fourfold: to promote health, to prevent illness, to restore health and to alleviate suffering.

The need for nursing is universal. Inherent in nursing is respect for life, dignity and rights of man. It is unrestricted by considerations of nationality, race, creed, colour, age, sex, politics or social status.

Nurses render health services to the individual, the family and the community and coordinate their services with those of related groups.

Nurses and people

The nurse's primary responsibility is to those people who require nursing care.

The nurse, in providing care, promotes an environment in which the values, customs and spiritual beliefs of the individual are respected.

The nurse holds in confidence personal information and uses judgement in sharing this information.

Nurses and practice

The nurse carries personal responsibility for nursing practice and for maintaining competence by continual learning.

The nurse maintains the highest standards of nursing care possible within the reality of a specific situation.

Adopted by the ICN Council of National Representatives in Mexico City in May 1973; reprinted by permission.

The nurse uses judgement in relation to individual competence when accepting and delegating responsibilities.

The nurse when acting in a professional capacity should at all times maintain standards of personal conduct which reflect credit upon the profession.

Nurses and society

The nurse shares with other citizens the responsibility for initiating and supporting action to meet the health and social needs of the public.

Nurses and co-workers

The nurse sustains a cooperative relationship with co-workers in nursing and other fields.

The nurse takes appropriate action to safeguard the individual when his care is endangered by a co-worker or any other person.

Nurses and the profession

The nurse plays the major role in determining and implementing desirable standards of nursing practice and nursing education.

The nurse is active in developing a core of professional knowledge.

The nurse, acting through the professional organization, participates in establishing and maintaining equitable social and economic working conditions in nursing.

Appendix B

American Nurses' Association Code for Nurses

Preamble

A code of ethics makes explicit the primary goals and values of the profession. When individuals become nurses, they make a moral commitment to uphold the values and special moral obligations expressed in their code. The Code for Nurses is based on a belief about the nature of individuals, nursing, health, and society. Nursing encompasses the protection, promotion, and restoration of health; the prevention of illness; and the alleviation of suffering in the care of clients, including individuals, families, groups, and communities. In the context of these functions, nursing is defined as the diagnosis and treatment of human responses to actual or potential health problems.

Since clients themselves are the primary decision makers in matters concerning their own health, treatment, and well-being, the goal of nursing actions is to support and enhance the client's responsibility and self-determination to the greatest extent possible. In this context, health is not necessarily an end in itself, but rather a means to a life that is meaningful from the client's perspective.

When making clinical judgments, nurses base their decisions on consideration of consequences and of universal moral principles, both of which prescribe and justify nursing actions. The most fundamental of these principles is respect for persons. Other principles stemming from this basic princi-

Reprinted with the permission of the American Nurses' Association, copyright 1976, 1985. *The Code for Nurses with Interpretive Statements* is published by the American Nurses' Association.

ple are autonomy (self-determination), beneficence (doing good), nonmaleficence (avoiding harm), veracity (truth-telling), confidentiality (respecting privileged information), fidelity (keeping promises), and justice (treating people fairly).

In brief, then, the statements of the code and their interpretation provide guidance for conduct and relationships in carrying out nursing responsibilities consistent with the ethical obligations of the profession and with high quality in nursing care.

Introduction

A code of ethics indicates a profession's acceptance of the responsibility and trust with which it has been invested by society. Under the terms of the implicit contract between society and the nursing profession, society grants the profession considerable autonomy and authority to function in the conduct of its affairs. The development of a code of ethics is an essential activity of a profession and provides one means for the exercise of professional self-regulation.

Upon entering the profession, each nurse inherits a measure of both the responsibility and the trust that have accrued to nursing over the years, as well as the corresponding obligation to adhere to the profession's code of conduct and relationships for ethical practice. The *Code for Nurses with Interpretive Statements* is thus more a collective expression of nursing conscience and philosophy than a set of external rules imposed upon an individual practitioner of nursing. Personal and professional integrity can be assured only if an individual is committed to the profession's code of conduct.

A code of ethical conduct offers general principles to guide and evaluate nursing actions. It does not assure the virtues required for professional practice within the character of each nurse. In particular situations, the justification of behavior as ethical must satisfy not only the individual nurse acting as a moral agent but also the standards for professional peer review.

The Code for Nurses was adopted by the American Nurses' Association in 1950 and has been revised periodically. It serves to inform both the nurse and society of the profession's expectations and requirements in ethical matters. The code and the interpretive statements together provide a framework within which nurses can make ethical decisions and discharge their responsibilities to the public, to other members of the health team, and to the profession.

Although a particular situation by its nature may determine the use of specific moral principles, the basic philosophical values, directives, and suggestions provided here are widely applicable to situations encountered in clinical practice. The Code for Nurses is not open to negotiation in employment settings, nor is it permissible for individuals or groups of nurses to adapt or change the language of this code.

The requirements of the code may often exceed those of the law. Violations of the law may subject the nurse to civil or criminal liability. The state nurses' associations, in fulfilling the profession's duty to society, may discipline their members for violations of the code. Loss of the respect and confidence of society and of one's colleagues is a serious sanction resulting from violation of the code. In addition, every nurse has a personal obligation to uphold and adhere to the code and to ensure that nursing colleagues do likewise.

Guidance and assistance in applying the code to local situations may be obtained from the American Nurses' Association and the constituent state nurses' associations.

Code for nurses

1. The nurse provides services with respect for human dignity and the uniqueness of the client unrestricted by considerations of social or economic status, personal attributes, or the nature of health problems.
2. The nurse safeguards the client's right to privacy by judiciously protecting information of a confidential nature.
3. The nurse acts to safeguard the client and the public when health care and safety are affected by the incompetent, unethical, or illegal practice of any person.
4. The nurse assumes responsibility and accountability for individual nursing judgments and actions.
5. The nurse maintains competence in nursing.
6. The nurse exercises informed judgment and uses individual competence and qualifications as criteria in seeking consultation, accepting responsibilities, and delegating nursing activities to others.
7. The nurse participates in activities that contribute to the ongoing development of the profession's body of knowledge.
8. The nurse participates in the profession's efforts to implement and improve standards of nursing.
9. The nurse participates in the profession's efforts to establish and maintain conditions of employment conducive to high quality nursing care.
10. The nurse participates in the profession's effort to protect the public from misinformation and misrepresentation and to maintain the integrity of nursing.
11. The nurse collaborates with members of the health professions and other citizens in promoting community and national efforts to meet the health needs of the public.

Appendix C

**American Hospital Association:
A Patient's Bill of Rights**

The American Hospital Association presents a Patient's Bill of Rights with the expectation that observance of these rights will contribute to more effective patient care and greater satisfaction for the patient, his physician, and the hospital organization. Further, the Association presents these rights in the expectation that they will be supported by the hospital on behalf of its patients, as an integral part of the healing process. It is recognized that a personal relationship between the physician and the patient is essential for the provision of proper medical care. The traditional physician-patient relationship takes on a new dimension when care is rendered within an organizational structure. Legal precedent has established that the institution itself also has a responsibility to the patient. It is in recognition of these factors that these rights are affirmed.

1. The patient has the right to considerate and respectful care.
2. The patient has the right to obtain from his physician complete current information concerning his diagnosis, treatment, and prognosis in terms the patient can be reasonably expected to understand. When it is not medically advisable to give such information to the patient, the information should be made available to an appropriate person in his behalf. He has the right to know, by name, the physician responsible for coordinating his care.
3. The patient has the right to receive from his physician information necessary to give informed consent prior to the start of any procedure and/or treatment. Except in emergencies, such information for in-

formed consent should include but not necessarily be limited to the specific procedure and/or treatment, the medically significant risks involved, and the probable duration of incapacitation. Where medically significant alternatives for care or treatment exist, or when the patient requests information concerning medical alternatives, the patient has the right to such information. The patient also has the right to know the name of the person responsible for the procedures and/or treatment.

4. The patient has the right to refuse treatment to the extent permitted by law and to be informed of the medical consequences of his action.

5. The patient has the right to every consideration of his privacy concerning his own medical care program. Case discussion, consultation, examination, and treatment are confidential and should be conducted discreetly. Those not directly involved in his care must have the permission of the patient to be present.

6. The patient has the right to expect that all communications and records pertaining to his care should be treated as confidential.

7. The patient has the right to expect that within its capacity a hospital must make reasonable response to the request of a patient for services. The hospital must provide evaluation, service, and/or referral as indicated by the urgency of the case. When medically permissible, a patient may be transferred to another facility only after he has received complete information and explanation concerning the needs for and alternatives to such a transfer. The institution to which the patient is to be transferred must first have accepted the patient for transfer.

8. The patient has the right to obtain information as to any relationship of his hospital to other health care and educational institutions insofar as his care is concerned. The patient has the right to obtain information as to the existence of any professional relationships among individuals, by name, who are treating him.

9. The patient has the right to be advised if the hospital proposes to engage in or perform human experimentation affecting his care or treatment. The patient has the right to refuse to participate in such research projects.

10. The patient has the right to expect reasonable continuity of care. He has the right to know in advance what appointment times and physicians are available and where. The patient has the right to expect that the hospital will provide a mechanism whereby he is informed by his physician or a delegate of the physician of the patient's continuing health care requirements following discharge.

11. The patient has the right to examine and receive an explanation of his bill regardless of source of payment.

12. The patient has the right to know what hospital rules and regulations apply to his conduct as a patient.

No catalog of rights can guarantee for the patient the kind of treatment he has a right to expect. A hospital has many functions to perform, including the prevention and treatment of disease, the education of both health professionals and patients, and the conduct of clinical research. All these activities must be conducted with an overriding concern for the patient, and, above all, the recognition of his dignity as a human being. Success in achieving this recognition assures success in the defense of the rights of the patient.

Appendix D
Cases for Analysis

A.1 Refusing the researcher

Matt Burns, head nurse at a large university medical center, was not certain that Dr. Hemphill's oncology research was best for the patients involved. Mr. Burns tried to consider the research from Dr. Hemphill's point of view, which, he reasoned, included concern for the overall results, Hemphill's reputation as an oncologist and researcher, and funding. When Mr. Burns examined the research from his own point of view, he focused on the sufferings of individual patients. He questioned whether the patients should have consented to spend their last months undergoing experimental chemotherapy since the treatments did not seem to help and often made patients sicker. He could support the research and the patients' participation only because he knew there was no cure for them and because he believed that oncology research was vital.

According to Mr. Burns, "Dr. Hemphill insisted on having things his way. The staff nurses on the oncology unit were not paid by him and did not work for him, but he asked us to do many things that I could not okay. For instance, he wrote orders for the nurses to give a certain medication straight IV push, an order that overall hospital policy forbids nurses to carry out. I had to consider what would happen to any of the nurses if they went against the policy, which was designed, I think, to protect them. I also had to be supportive of nursing administration policy in order to remain head nurse." Mr. Burns believed, as well, that his staff wanted him to tell them to follow hospital policy rather than Dr. Hemphill's orders.

When he told the doctor that the nurses could not give the medication straight IV, the doctor asked him to deviate from the policy and not to tell anyone he was doing so. Mr. Burns refused. Dr. Hemphill's solution was to hire his own nurse to give the medication, which created problems for the staff nurses. Adding to the general tension was Mr. Burns' belief that Dr. Hemphill was trying to make his life miserable so that he would quit and the doctor might be able to work with someone he could manipulate. Nevertheless, the doctor's efforts to make Mr. Burns uncomfortable by embarrassing him on rounds in front of physicians, nurses, and patients failed to cause him to resign, and both Dr. Hemphill and Mr. Burns worked to the end of the research period.

A.2 Summer job

Sarah, a junior nursing student, has recently started a summer job in a rural area near her parents' house. She is working at Restwood Nursing Home. The staff for the 3-to-11 shift consists of only nurse aides. Sarah does not know of any RN or LPN on duty during her shift. Sarah also learns that the nurse aides are trained with a short instruction from day staff LPNs on how to pass medications.

Sarah questions this procedure. After a little research, she finds out that state law does not allow nurse aides to pass medications. Sarah also wonders if the doctors are aware of the level of staff carrying out their orders.

She asks Becky, another staff member from her shift, why the aides are passing medications to the clients. Becky explains, "We cannot get any RNs to work the 3-to-11 shift here. That leaves no one to pass medication on this shift, so an aide ends up doing this." Sarah also questions Becky to see if the doctors are aware of this procedure. "Yes," Becky answers, "the doctors are aware of who is passing the medication, and they agree with our ways. Because if we did not do this, we would not have a nursing home for all these old people. Where would all these older people live, since most of their families either cannot take care of them or else they don't want to." (This case has been adapted from one prepared for our Ethical Issues in Nursing course by Beth Carrington.).

A.3 Too many medicines

Connie Delinger, community health nurse for six years, knew that Grace Weiss, a seventy-eight-year-old widow who lived alone, preferred to handle her own affairs. On a previous visit, Connie had encouraged Mrs. Weiss to speak to her doctor about the large number of prescription medications she took routinely. Later, Mrs. Weiss told Connie that the doctor had said she was doing the right thing—she was taking her medicine. Connie was not convinced that Mrs. Weiss had told her doctor clearly that she was taking at least ten different medications. Connie could see, as she had seen before, that the numerous drug containers filled a small cake pan. Connie carefully examined each container and immediately recognized "two different heart medications that did essentially the same thing." Connie now realized that Mrs. Weiss was totally confused about the purpose of her various medications. "It was probable," Connie reasoned, "that Mrs. Weiss was being abused by medication and her doctor didn't really know what was happening to her." However, when Connie said that she would like to check the medicines with the pharmacy, Mrs. Weiss balked; the physician had very recently said that she was doing the right thing. Connie thought that Mrs. Weiss probably did not want her to do anything that might call attention to the fact that she needed help. Nevertheless, Connie chose to ignore Mrs. Weiss' protests, called the pharmacist, obtained a review of the medications, and then called Mrs. Weiss' doctor. The office nurse could hardly believe that such an array of medications had been ordered, but at Connie's insistence she arranged for Mrs. Weiss to show the doctor all her medications. Mrs. Weiss was perturbed at Connie for setting up the appointment, but she agreed to go since the doctor was expecting her.

A.4 Birth control pills

Aretha Washington is a public health nurse in an urban county health department. Among her caseload of fifteen to twenty families are high-risk infants and children and potential or actual child abuse and neglect families. During a home visit, Aretha learned that Sheila Long was having leg pains and had been getting refills on her birth control prescriptions without seeing her doctor. Given Sheila's medical history and possible side effects from birth control pills, Aretha thought that Sheila should contact her doctor for evaluation. Aretha also thought that the physician would take Sheila off the pill and substitute a less effective form of birth control. Knowing Sheila, Aretha expected that Sheila would like nothing so well as the pill.

Aretha thought, "This woman has to take the pill; I really don't want her to have any more kids. I don't think it's right for children to be born when they are not wanted. Also, Sheila has the right not to have to bear children she doesn't want. But what are the consequences of that? Should she stay on the pill and possibly endanger her life? Should she try something that isn't as effective and possibly have an unwanted child?"

Aretha could see advantages and disadvantages both with Sheila's continuing on the pill and changing to another form of contraception which, though possibly safer, would also be likely to be less effective. Aretha had to decide whether to discuss this problem with Sheila and, if so, whether she should encourage her to opt for one alternative rather than another.

A.5 Sit-down strike

Ronna Smith is one of two registered nurse team leaders in the Pinecrest Care Center north wing, which serves one hundred geriatric patients who require skilled nursing care. Adequate staffing requires thirteen aides on the north wing, but on Sunday Ms. Smith arrived at 6:30 to find she was short-staffed again. For the past four months, she had had an adequate staff fewer than ten days. Lights were blinking, breakfast trays were arriving, and the seven aides scheduled to work announced that they were not staying. To prove their point, they sat in the staff lounge.

The aides were at the breaking point; they were infuriated by minimum wages and the task of caring for one hundred people with only seven or even fewer aides. Aware that they could not do an adequate job and tired of everyone's complaints, they had met repeatedly with the administration but had made no progress.

Ms. Smith called her director, who told her to "try to be a motivating leader," but Ms. Smith thought, "How am I going to motivate anyone when I feel pretty unmotivated myself?" She knew the patients needed help from more aides than the administration had hired, and she felt sorry for the patients, the aides, and herself. Even while on the phone, she could hear the patients calling impatiently for help. She quickly told the director she must come to the center and, with the other team leader, attempted to answer the blinking lights and calls for help from the patients.

The director came, and, after failing to convince the aides to return to work, she called the departmental administrator, who finally arrived after almost an hour's delay. After three hours the sit-down strike ended with a promise of time-and-a-half for the day and with another meeting between the aides and administration scheduled for Monday. At that meeting all the aides received a ten-cent hourly raise and the promise that when the north wing was short-staffed in the future, each would receive a five-dollar bonus for the day.

Ms. Smith was not satisfied because she believed that paying more for the same inadequate level of service would not help the patients or the nursing staff. After work on Monday, she contemplated resigning. After Ms. Smith married four months ago, she took the job at the nursing home because she could get day work and no shift rotation. However, she was offered $1.50 less per hour than at the hospital and was told that the nursing home did not pay differentials for weekends or shifts because nurses were hired for the shift they selected. On the other hand, she believes that she has developed professionally in this, her first nursing home job; she has learned much about older people, finds her care of geriatric patients rewarding, likes the responsibility, and works well with the doctors, especially the man who *cares for most of the patients. She has learned, however, that few nurses stay for more than a year and that many aides stay less than a week. The nursing director repeatedly hires people as aides who have no prior experience or training, so that consequently the team leaders must teach them. Ms. Smith resents the lost time she has spent on those who have quit after the first day or two of orientation and training. She has talked repeatedly to the nursing director and administrator about the low pay scale for aides and nurses, hiring poorly qualified people, consequent high turnover rates, and detrimental effects on the patients' welfare, only to be told that because the center is new and takes a while to grow, they are sorry but, at present, nurses' wages can not be raised.*

Ms. Smith seriously doubts that the short-staffing problem will be resolved merely because the administration made some concessions to the aides. After seeing how drastically the many helpless patients were affected by even a three-hour sit-down strike (no one was fed until after 9:30), she does not believe that she and the other registered nurse should use a strike in trying to change pay scales and hiring policies. Yet talking has been useless, and if she leaves, some other nurse will take the job and the cycle will only continue. Ms. Smith now wonders whether she would be ethically justified if she joined the aides to exert pressure on an administration that has refused to respond to the nurses' suggestions and complaints but has responded promptly to the aides' sit-down strike.

A.6 Failure to comply

Joan Horner, staff nurse on a general medical unit in a large urban private hospital, and Mrs. Barton, a seventy-three-year-old retired schoolteacher hospitalized with a diagnosis of congestive heart failure, look upon Mrs. Barton's fluid restrictions differently. Joan sees that Mrs. Barton must stay within restricted amounts of fluid intake, and she tries to control the amount of fluid available to her. Mrs. Barton, who is oriented and talkative, agrees with Joan's explanations, but she drinks fluids indiscriminately, especially when her friends visit. In describing Mrs. Barton, Joan says that "The restrictions are just not important to her, or she doesn't see what fluids do to her. Maybe she doesn't care." After attempting to reason with Mrs. Barton and to understand the reasons for her failure to comply with the fluid restrictions, Joan tried teasing and finally scolding her to gain her cooperation, but without success. Finally, Joan explained to Mrs. Barton's friends the reasons for the fluid restrictions and gained their cooperation in keeping her bedside intake record accurate so that Mrs. Barton could be kept within the fluid restrictions. Nonetheless, Joan wondered whether she was morally justified in acting behind Mrs. Barton's back.

A.7 Removal of tracheostomy tubes

At 7:55 A.M. Mary Kowalski was about to give report when she heard patients yelling, "Nurse, Nurse." She and two other nurses rushed to the room and saw Mrs. Audrey Johnson turning blue. Her tracheostomy tubes, in place a few minutes earlier, were on the table, and she had a large new dressing with an Ace bandage around her neck. After they quickly cut everything off and reinserted the tubes, the other nurses stayed with Mrs. Johnson, who was extremely upset, while Mary left to get another set of tubes and ties. As she passed the nurses' station and saw the two physicians who, without informing the nurses, had removed Mrs. Johnson's tracheostomy tubes and applied the dressings, she said, "We're putting the tube back in; she can't breathe." Ms. Kowalski remembers that neither moved and one said, "Oh, she obstructed, huh." When she returned to the room, a very frightened Mrs. Johnson would not let the nurses leave her to attend report until someone else could sit with her.

According to Ms. Kowalski, "After the crisis was over, the two physicians proceeded to chew us out because we didn't know where the obturator was for the trach tube. They missed the point of the whole incident. They didn't tell us they were doing it, and they picked a very bad time because there were only three of us working that night. When we went to report, there was nobody left."

Ms. Kowalski does not want to be someone the physicians can "walk right over," keep ignorant of information important for safe nursing care, or blame when things don't go right. To her, the doctors had just "yanked out the tube" and walked out, expecting that the nurses—being women—"would clean up their mess." When the situation developed into a crisis, they found fault with the nurses over the obturator.

The nurses first told the physicians how they felt and discussed the incident with the assistant head nurse, who was coming on duty at the time, and who is also the otology clinician. A few days later, however, the same doctors did essentially the same thing. In that situation, however, a nurse observed them and informed the rest of the nursing staff. Ms. Kowalski thinks that the incident concerning Mrs. Johnson should be prevented from happening repeatedly. She has talked with her co-workers, "trying to figure out what to do, and the answer keeps coming up as zero."

A.8 A nurse's suggestion is rejected

As charge nurse of a thirty-two-bed orthopedic unit, Ms. Connie Bowles is used to working with nurse discretion medical orders, to asking physicians for particular medications, and to questioning treatments. She thinks her interdisciplinary relationships with physicians are generally good, especially with some of the surgeons who, as she describes them, "are very open to hearing your points." But her relationship with Dr. Olsen is different.

Dr. Olsen was treating Mr. Floyd Trapp for an orthopedic problem when Ms. Bowles asked him to arrange a medical consultation. The doctor who came was Mr. Trapp's general practitioner. He had discontinued Mr. Trapp's hypertension medication earlier, and after seeing him in the hospital, had not reordered the medication. Ms. Bowles continued to be concerned, however, because "Mr. Trapp was still running a fairly high blood pressure plus having some other symptoms." She told Dr. Olsen about Mr. Trapp's continuing problems and asked if he would consider another medical consultant who was associated with the hospital. In response, Dr. Olsen asserted that he was the doctor, that he would take care of the consults, and that Ms. Bowles should take care of nursing matters.

After he left, Ms. Bowles wondered, "Was there another way that I could have said it but didn't? Could I have done it differently?" She had tried, as she usually did with all doctors, "to phrase questions so they would be nonthreatening." Should she try to find another way to get a medical consult for Mr. Trapp?

A.9 A request to be excused

Rita Marcos, a newly immigrated Filipino surgical scrub nurse, has told her supervisor, Sue Taylor, that she absolutely cannot participate in sterilization procedures. The previous week she had been caught by surprise when, immediately after a caesarean delivery, the physician had proceeded to ligate the fallopian tubes of the young mother. Even though the mother had requested the operation, this did not satisfy Rita since she is strongly opposed to sterilization on religious grounds.

Sue Taylor is unsure how to deal with Rita's request to be excused from future participation in such procedures. On the one hand, she would like to respect and accommodate Rita's religious views. On the other hand, she thinks that doing so would involve a number of problems; juggling staff assignments would be time-consuming and take away from other duties; other nurses would probably resent what they would perceive as special treatment; and, given the hospital's emphasis on cost containment, accommodating Rita would require some additional costs without appreciably improving services. (This case was prepared especially for this text.)

A.10 Refusal to begin a research procedure

An eighty-two-year-old woman is referred to the hospital research unit for consideration in a therapeutic research protocol that may improve her physical condition. The research physician discusses the study with the woman and her husband and, as she is interested in participating, she reads over the informed consent document and questions the patient afterward to assess her comprehension of the material. The physician is satisfied that the patient understands, and she schedules her for the study.

Two days later the patient arrives on the research unit to begin the study but is confused and unable to remember why she is there or any of the information provided in the informed consent which she had agreed to and signed previously.

After talking with the patient, the nurse refuses to begin the infusion and contacts the research physician. She arrives and orders that the procedures begin according to the study schedule, stating she will take the responsibility for the decision. (This case was prepared by Katherine McGrath-Miller, M.A., Research Volunteer Services Coordinator, Bronson Clinical Investigation Unit, Kalamazoo, Michigan.)

A.11 Confidentiality and an attempted suicide

In a particular metropolitan area, public health nurses employed by the county health department are organized in teams of four nurses. In the field the nurses practice independently, but they arrange meetings to collaborate on difficult cases, such as that of the Cass family. LeeAnn Cass, pregnant at age sixteen, planned to keep her baby after delivery. Her father believed that he could not afford a separate apartment for LeeAnn and that she must, therefore, stay with the family. Mrs. Cass, age thirty-eight, feared that LeeAnn's presence in the home—and the baby's—would upset the family, especially LeeAnn's three younger sisters. Mrs. Cass had been having anxiety with each of her menstrual periods and recurrent urinary tract infections.

Susan Statler, a public health nurse and one of several professionals involved with the Cass family, learned that Mrs. Cass had attempted suicide by taking an overdose of Valium within the month that the various professionals had been working with the family. During a meeting of the nursing team, one team member strongly questioned Susan's decision not to report to the physician that Mrs. Cass had attempted suicide with the Valium and pointed out that Susan was not legally prohibited from passing such information on to the physician. Susan did not want to risk alienating Mrs. Cass by breaking her confidentiality unless it was absolutely necessary. She knew that Mrs. Cass' psychotherapist, a psychiatric social worker, was aware of her suicide attempt. Susan had not discussed with Mrs. Cass whether all the professionals involved with her, including the physician, knew of her suicide attempt. One of her colleagues argued that if the physician knew about it he would probably then prescribe fewer tranquilizers as a limited form of protection for Mrs. Cass.

Within a few days, Susan discussed with Mrs. Cass the question of informing the physician about Mrs. Cass' attempted suicide, but Mrs. Cass rejected the suggestion that she herself inform him or that Susan tell him. Mrs. Cass saw no value in doing so and did not want to discuss personal problems with the physician since she was already doing so with her therapist.

Susan and her nursing team never agreed as to the correct course of action, and Susan did not tell the physician.

A.12 Candor and hope

Wendy Barrett, a senior-level nursing student, sees her clients—mainly elderly persons with chronic or terminal illnesses—in their own homes. Over the course of the last month sixty-one-year-old Sam Richardson has become one of Wendy's favorite people. Mr. Richardson suffers from prostate cancer which has metastasized to his spine. Weak and in pain, he is nonetheless alert and able to move about in his home with the aid of a walker. He is very conscientious about taking medications and complying with Wendy's suggestions. His wife is equally conscientious and provides his twenty-four-hour care (e.g., fixing meals, bathing and dressing him, and so on).

On her last visit, just as Wendy was leaving, Mrs. Richardson had asked when Sam would start getting better. The couple knew that Mr. Richardson had cancer, but Wendy's suspicions were now confirmed: They did not fully understand that his condition was irreversible and that death was impending. She strongly believes that if the couple were to face up to Mr. Richardson's prognosis, they would give up hope and his care would quickly deteriorate, and this would result in an earlier death.

Wendy did not have time to discuss Mr. Richardson's prognosis with his wife on her last visit. Her next visit is scheduled for tomorrow. Although she has tried to put the question out of her mind, she can no longer do so. How candid should she be, she wonders, about Mr. Richardson's prognosis? (*This case is based on a situation reported by Andrea Taylor when she was a student at Michigan State University's College of Nursing.*)

A.13 Who should pay?

Vicki LaPorte, a Visiting Nurses' Services supervisor, is concerned about nursing care costs. Vicki has assigned Sue Brown, a nurse with two years' experience, to Grace Ely, a fifty-eight-year-old woman who was discharged from the local hospital the previous day. To prepare for her visit to Grace, Sue has collected from the VNS supply room some medical supplies, including some nonstick dressings and a 500-ml bottle of normal saline, that she plans to use in Grace's care. Sue knew from previous experience that the hospital probably has not sent home adequate medical supplies to cover Grace's first week at home.

Sue also knows that Grace's care was reimbursed by Medicaid. In addition, she believed that the supplies she selected were routinely reimbursed so she did not waste her time reading the posted computer printout that listed which supplies are reimbursed by Medicaid without prior authorization.

After the visit Sue learned that neither the particular type of nonstick dressings she selected nor the 500ml size bottle of normal saline was covered by Medicaid. Had she substituted a different type of dressing and chosen a 1000ml size bottle (knowing that she would waste half), Medicaid would have reimbursed VNS for the supplies. Being aware of these restrictions, Sue initiated a prior authorization process to cover medical supplies she would need in Grace's future care.

Vicki is concerned about Sue's failure to check which supplies were covered, but she is also concerned about the amount of time nurses like Sue must spend in learning the special nuances of reimbursement. Vicki wonders who should pay for VNS supplies not routinely reimbursed. Should Sue be charged for the cost (or some of the cost) of the unauthorized supplies she used? Should the hospital, which routinely does not send an adequate first week of medical supplies, be charged? Should VNS increase its charges to all patients to cover nonreimbursed medical supplies? (Case provided by Lois Hauver, RN, Visiting Nurses' Services of Greater Lansing.)

A.14 Strike vote

Joan Hames is debating whether to vote in support of a nursing strike in seventeen hospitals in her metropolitan area. The two major issues over which the union would strike are:

1. *A layoff clause in the contract proposed by the hospitals. The union maintains that if layoffs are needed, staff reductions should proceed according to seniority; that is, the least senior registered nurse is to be laid off first, then those with somewhat more seniority, and so on. The hospitals want to reduce staff by cutting the hours of specific nurses, with each hospital free to determine which nurse and the extent of his or her reduction in hours on the basis of total nursing hours needed for various services of the hospital. The union is concerned that the hospitals may take advantage of this to lay off more-experienced (and expensive) nurses and to replace them with less-experienced (and less expensive) nurses.*

2. *The duration of training across specialty areas. Such training is designed to allow nurses trained in one specialty (e.g., pediatrics) to function in another (e.g., intensive care). The union wants a four-week training period. The hospitals want a two-week training period. The union main-*

tains that two weeks is too little time for even a senior nurse to safely make the transition from one specialty to another.

Joan Hames wonders what she should do. Is a vote for going on strike justified? And, if not, what should she do if the majority, in fact, votes to go on strike? (This case was prepared especially for this text.)

A.15 Who gets a transplant?

Diane Alff, forty-year-old nurse manager of an intensive care unit, has been a member of the team caring for Lana Oberstar during the final days of her life. Seventeen-year-old Lana was a victim of an auto accident caused by an intoxicated driver. In the hours immediately following admission, Marge Oberstar, Lana's mother, discussed with the physician and her minister her decision to donate Lana's organs for transplant should Lana die. Soon thereafter, Lana's physician told Marge that Lana had died. A few minutes later, as Diane sat holding Marge's hand, Marge told Diane about Lana's short life. She ended by saying that at least with modern technology some other young person could be saved with Lana's organs. Then she faced Diane and asked, "They wouldn't take anything to save a drunk, would they?"

Diane knows that the state transplant committee has discussed recently whether persons whose alcoholism has destroyed their livers ought to receive liver transplants. The local paper has carried statements by national experts in bioethics and summaries of research that support making liver transplants available to such persons. Further, the paper has reported that former alcoholics have received liver transplants in the state. What should Diane say? (Case created for this text.)

Suggestions for Further Reading

(This list is designed to supplement sources identified in the text. Therefore footnoted works have been omitted.)

1. Philosophical analysis and reasoning

Bandman, Elsie L., and Bandman, Bertram. *Critical Thinking in Nursing*. Norwalk, Conn.: Appleton and Lange, 1989.

Conway, David A., and Munson, Ronald. *The Elements of Reasoning*. Belmont, Calif.: Wadsworth, 1990.

Moore, Brooke Noel, and Parker, Richard. *Critical Thinking: Evaluating Claims and Arguments in Everyday Life*. Palo Alto, Calif.: Mayfield, 1986.

Russow, Lilly-Marlene, and Curd, Martin. *Principles of Reasoning*. New York: St. Martin's, 1988.

Weston, Anthony. *A Rulebook for Arguments*. Indianapolis: Hackett, 1987.

2. Ethical theory

Beauchamp, Tom L., and Childress, James F. *Principles of Biomedical Ethics*. 3rd ed. New York: Oxford University Press, 1989.

DeMarco, Joseph P., and Fox, Richard M., eds. *New Directions in Ethics: The Challenge of Applied Ethics*. New York and London: Routledge and Kegan Paul, 1986.

Gert, Bernard. *Morality: A New Justification for the Moral Rules*. New York: Oxford University Press, 1988.

Glover, Jonathan, ed. *Utilitarianism and Its Critics*. New York: Macmillan, 1990.

Kant, Immanuel. *Grounding for the Metaphysics of Morals*. Indianapolis: Hackett, 1981.

Kittay, Eva Feder, and Myers, Diana T., eds. *Women and Moral Theory*. Savage, Md.: Rowman and Littlefield, 1987.

MacIntyre, Alasdair. *A Short History of Ethics*. New York: Macmillan, 1966.

Mill, John Stuart. *Utilitarianism*. Indianapolis: Hackett, 1980.

Pincoffs, Edmund L. *Quandaries and Virtues: Against Reductivism in Ethics*. Lawrence, Kans.: University Press of Kansas, 1986.

Rachels, James. *The Elements of Moral Philosophy*. New York: Random House, 1986.

Singer, Peter. *Practical Ethics*. Cambridge: Cambridge University Press, 1979.

Smart, J. J. C., and Williams, Bernard. *Utilitarianism: For and Against*. Cambridge: Cambridge University Press, 1973.

3. General and reference works

Ackerman, Terence F., and Strong, Carson. *A Casebook of Medical Ethics*. New York: Oxford University Press, 1989.

Arras, John, and Rhoden, Nancy, eds. *Ethical Issues in Modern Medicine*. 3rd ed. Mountain View, Calif.: Mayfield, 1989.

Battin, Margaret Pabst. *Ethical Issues in Suicide*. Englewood Cliffs, N.J.: Prentice-Hall, 1982.

Beauchamp, Tom L., and Walters, Leroy, eds. *Contemporary Issues in Bioethics*. 3rd ed. Belmont, Calif.: Wadsworth, 1989.

Becker, Lawrence C., and Becker, Charlotte B., eds. *Encyclopedia of Ethics*. New York: Garland, 1991.

Brody, Baruch. *Life and Death Decision Making*. New York: Oxford University Press, 1988.

Brody, Howard. *Stories of Sickness*. New Haven: Yale University Press, 1987.

Buchanan, Allen E., and Brock, Dan W. *Deciding for Others: The Ethics of Surrogate Decision Making*. Cambridge: Cambridge University Press, 1989.

Callahan, Joan C., ed. *Ethical Issues in Professional Life*. New York: Oxford University Press, 1988.

Cohen, Cynthia B. *Casebook on the Termination of Life-Sustaining Treatment and the Care of the Dying*. Bloomington: Indiana University Press, 1988.

Dougherty, Charles J. *American Health Care: Realities, Rights, and Reform*. New York: Oxford University Press, 1988.

Freeman, John M., and McDonnell, Kevin. *Tough Decisions: A Casebook in Medical Ethics*. New York: Oxford University Press, 1987.

Hastings Center. *Guidelines on the Termination of Life-Sustaining Treatment and the Care of the Dying*. Bloomington: Indiana University Press, 1987.

Hull, Richard T., ed. *Ethical Issues in the New Reproductive Technologies*. Belmont, Calif.: Wadsworth, 1990.

Katz, Jay. *The Silent World of Doctor and Patient*. New York: Free Press, 1984.

Lynn, Joanne, ed. *By No Extraordinary Means: The Choice to Forgo Life-Sustaining Food and Water*. Bloomington: Indiana University Press, 1986.

Macklin, Ruth. *Mortal Choices: Bioethics in Today's World*. New York: Pantheon, 1987.

Mappes, Thomas A., and Zembaty, Jane S., eds. *Biomedical Ethics*. 2nd ed. New York: McGraw-Hill, 1986.

Momeyer, Richard W. *Confronting Death*. Bloomington: Indiana University Press, 1988.

Munson, Ronald, ed. *Intervention and Reflection: Basic Issues in Medical Ethics*. 3rd ed. Belmont, Calif.: Wadsworth, 1988.

Pence, Gregory E. *Classic Cases in Medical Ethics.* New York: McGraw-Hill, 1990.

President's Commission for the Study of Ethical Problems in Medicine and Biomedical and Behavioral Research. *Making Health Care Decisions.* Washington, D.C.: U.S. Government Printing Office, 1982.

Reich, Warren T., ed. *Encyclopedia of Bioethics.* New York: Macmillan and Free Press, 1978.

Van De Veer, Donald. *Paternalistic Interference.* Princeton: Princeton University Press, 1986.

Veatch, Robert M., ed. *Medical Ethics.* Boston: Jones and Bartlett, 1989.

Weil, William B., and Benjamin, Martin, eds. *Ethical Issues at the Outset of Life.* Boston: Blackwell Scientific Publications, 1987.

Weir, Robert F., ed. *Ethical Issues in Death and Dying.* 2nd ed. New York: Columbia University Press, 1986.

Wright, Richard A. *Human Values in Health Care.* New York: McGraw-Hill, 1987.

4. The nursing context

Advances in Nursing Science 11 (April 1989). Issue devoted to ethical issues.

Aiken, Linda H., and Mullinix, Connie Flynt. "Special Report—The Nurse Shortage: Myth or Reality?" *New England Journal of Medicine* 317 (3 September 1987):644–46.

American Nurses' Association. *Education for Nursing Practice in the Context of the 1980s.* Kansas City, Mo.: American Nurses' Association, 1983.

——— . *Ethics in Nursing: Position Statements and Guidelines.* Kansas City, Mo.: American Nurses' Association, 1988.

——— . *Ethics References for Nurses.* Kansas City, Mo.: American Nurses' Association, 1982

——— . *Human Rights Guidelines for Nurses in Clinical and Other Research.* Kansas City, Mo.: American Nurses' Association, 1985.

——— . *Issues in Professional Nursing Practice.* Kansas City, Mo.: American Nurses' Association, 1984–85.

——— . *Nursing: A Social Policy Statement.* Kansas City, Mo.: American Nurses' Association, 1980.

——— . *The Nursing Shortage: A Briefing Paper, 2.* Kansas City, Mo.: American Nurses' Association, 1987.

Amnesty International. *Ethical Codes and Declarations Relevant to the Health Professions.* London: Amnesty International, 1985.

Anderson, Elizabeth T. "Community Focus in Public Health Nursing: Whose Responsibility?" *Nursing Outlook* 31 (January/February 1983):44–48.

Aroskar, Mila A. "Anatomy of an Ethical Dilemma: The Theory and the Practice." *American Journal of Nursing* 80 (April 1980):658–63.

Bandman, Elsié L., and Bandman, Bertram. *Nursing Ethics through the Life Span.* 2nd ed. Norwalk, Conn.: Appleton-Century Crofts, 1990.

Beardshaw, Virginia. *Conscientious Objectors at Work: Mental Hospital Nurses—A Case Study.* London: Social Audit Ltd., 1981.

Benjamin, Martin. "Nursing Ethics." In Becker, Lawrence, and Becker, Charlotte, eds. *Encyclopedia of Ethics.* New York: Garland, 1991.

Benjamin, Martin, and Curtis, Joy. "Ethical Autonomy in Nursing." In Regan, Tom, and VanDeVeer, Donald, eds. *Health Care Ethics*. Philadelphia: Temple University, 1987.

――― . "Nursing." In 1986 *Medical and Health Annual*. Chicago: Encyclopaedia Britannica, 1985.

――― . "Virtue and the Practice of Nursing." In Shelp, Earl E., ed. *Virtue in Medicine*. Dordrecht: D. Reidel, 1985.

Bernal, Ellen. "The Nurse's Appeal to Conscience." *Hastings Center Report* 17 (April 1987):25–26.

Bishop, Anne H., and Scudder, John R., Jr., eds. *Caring, Curing, Coping: Nurse Physician Patient Relationships*. University, Ala.: University of Alabama Press, 1985.

――― . *The Practical, Moral, and Personal Sense of Nursing: A Phenomenological Philosophy of Practice.* Albany, N.Y.: State University of New York Press, 1990.

Carni, Amnon, and Schneider, Stanley, eds. *Nursing Law and Ethics*. New York: Springer-Verlag, 1985.

Chaska, Norma L., ed. *The Nursing Profession: Turning Points*. St. Louis: C. V. Mosby, 1990.

Curtin, Leah, and Flaherty, M. Josephine. *Nursing Ethics: Theories and Pragmatics*. Bowie, Md.: Robert J. Brady, 1982.

Curtis, Joy. "Recent Developments in the World of Nursing." In *1987 Medical and Health Annual*. Chicago: Encyclopaedia Britannica, 1986.

Davis, Anne J., and Aroskar, Mila A. *Ethical Dilemmas and Nursing Practice*. 2nd ed. Norwalk, Conn.: Appleton-Century-Crofts, 1983.

Department of Health and Human Services. *Secretary's Commission on Nursing Report*. Washington, D.C.: Department of Health and Human Services, 1988.

Donley, Rosemary, and Flaherty, Mary Jean. "Strategies for Changing Nursing's Image." In McCloskey, Joanne Comi, and Grace, Helen Kennedy, eds. *Current Issues in Nursing*. 3rd ed. St. Louis: C. V. Mosby, 1990, pp. 431–39.

Erde, Edmund L. "Notions of Teams and Team Talk in Health Care: Implications for Responsibilities." *Law, Medicine and Health Care* 9 (October 1981): 26–28.

Fairbairn, Gavin, and Fairbairn, Susan. *Ethical Issues in Caring*. Brookfield, Vt.: Gower, 1988.

Fitzpatrick, F. J. *Ethics in Nursing Practice: Basic Principles and Their Application*. London: Linacre Center, 1988.

Fowler, Marsha, and Fry, Sara. "Ethical Inquiry." In Sarter, Barbara, ed. *Paths to Knowledge: Innovative Research Methods for Nursing*. New York: National League for Nursing, 1988, pp. 145–63.

Fowler, Marsha D. M., and Levine-Ariff, June, eds. *Ethics at the Bedside: A Source Book for the Critical Care Nurse*. Philadelphia: J. B. Lippincott, 1987.

Hoeffer, Beverly. "The Private Practice Model: An Ethical Perspective." *Journal of Psycho-Social Nursing* 21 (July 1983):31–37.

Hull, Richard T. "Responsibility and Accountability, Analyzed." *Nursing Outlook* 29 (December 1981):707–12.

Jameton, Andrew. *Nursing Practice: The Ethical Issues*. Englewood Cliffs, N.J.: Prentice-Hall, 1984.

Johnstone, Megan-Jane. "Law, Professional Ethics and the Problem of Conflict with Personal Values." *International Journal of Nursing Studies* 25 (1988): 147–57.

Kane, Rosalie A., and Caplan, Arthur L., eds. *Everyday Ethics: Resolving Dilemmas in Nursing Home Life.* New York: Springer, 1990.

Kluge, Eike-Henner W. "The Profession of Nursing and the Right to Strike." *Westminster Institute Review* 2 (Fall 1982):3–6.

Kuhse, Helga, and Singer, Peter. "The Quality/Quantity-of-Life Distinction and Its Moral Importance for Nurses." *International Journal of Nursing Studies* 26 (1989):203–12.

Mappes, E. Joy Kroeger. "Ethical Dilemmas for Nurses: Physicians' Order vs. Patients' Rights." In Mappes, Thomas A., and Zembaty, Jane S., eds. *Biomedical Ethics.* 2nd ed. New York: McGraw-Hill, 1986, pp. 127–34.

Mitchell, Christine. "Integrity in Interprofessional Relationships." In Agich, George J., ed. *Responsibility in Health Care.* Dordrecht: D. Reidel, 1982, pp. 163–84.

Miya, Pamela A. "Do Not Resuscitate: When Nurses' Duties Conflict with Patients' Rights." *Dimensions of Critical Care Nursing* 3 (September–October 1984): 293–98.

Murphy, Catherine P. "The Changing Role of Nurses in Making Ethical Decisions." *Law, Medicine and Health Care* 12 (September 1984):173–75, 184.

Muyskens, James L. *Moral Problems in Nursing: A Philosophical Investigation.* Totowa, N.J.: Rowman and Littlefield, 1982.

———. "Nurses' Collective Responsibility and the Strike Weapon." *Journal of Medicine and Philosophy* 7 (1982):101–12.

National Commission on Nursing. *Summary Report and Recommendations.* Chicago: The Hospital Research and Education Trust, April 1983.

National Commission on Nursing Implementation Project. *Nursing's Vital Signs: Shaping the Profession for the 1990s.* Battle Creek, Mich.: W. K. Kellogg Foundation, 1989.

National League for Nursing. *The Emergence of Nursing as a Political Force.* New York: National League for Nursing, 1979.

———. *Ethical Issues in Nursing and Nursing Education.* New York: National League for Nursing, 1980.

Nelson, Hilde Lindemann. "Against Caring." *Journal of Clinical Ethics* 2 (Fall 1991), in press.

Nursing Clinics of North America 24 (June 1989):461–577. Devoted to ethics—issues in nursing.

Nursing Clinics of North America 24 (December 1989):951–1057. Devoted to ethics—applications in nursing.

Pence, Terry. *Ethics in Nursing: An Annotated Bibliography.* 2nd ed. New York: National League for Nursing, 1986.

Pence, Terry, and Cantrall, Janet, eds. *Ethics in Nursing: An Anthology.* New York: National League for Nursing, 1990.

Purtilo, Ruth, and Cassell, Christine K. *Ethical Dimensions in the Health Professions.* Philadelphia: W. B. Saunders, 1981.

Quinn, Carroll A., and Smith, Michael D. *The Professional Commitment: Issues and Ethics in Nursing.* Philadelphia: W. B. Saunders, 1987.

Sawyer, Linda M. "Nursing Codes of Ethics: An International Comparison. *International Nursing Review* 36 (September/October 1989):145–48.

Silva, Mary C., ed. *Ethical Decision Making in Nursing Administration*. Norwalk, Conn.: Appleton and Lange, 1990.

Spicker, Stuart F., and Gadow, Sally, eds. *Nursing: Images and Ideals*. New York: Springer, 1980.

Veatch, Robert M., and Fry, Sara T. *Case Studies in Nursing Ethics*. New York: J. B. Lippincott, 1987.

Viens, Diane C. "A History of Nursing's Code of Ethics." *Nursing Outlook* 37 (January/February 1989):45–49.

Winslow, Gerald R. "From Loyalty to Advocacy: A New Metaphor for Nursing." *Hastings Center Report* 14 (June 1984):32–40.

Yarling, Roland R., and McElmurry, Beverly J. "The Moral Foundation of Nursing." *Advances in Nursing Science* 8 (January 1986):63–73.

Index

Printed in the United States
1294800002B/62